MECHANICS
AND
PROPERTIES OF MATTER

BOOKS BY M. NELKON

Published by Heinemann
LIGHT AND SOUND
ADVANCED LEVEL PHYSICS (*with P. Parker*)
MECHANICS AND PROPERTIES OF MATTER
A MODERN ELECTRICITY
ADVANCED LEVEL PRACTICAL PHYSICS (*with J. Ogborn*)
AN INTRODUCTION TO THE MATHEMATICS OF PHYSICS
(*with J. H. Avery*)
ELEMENTARY PHYSICS, Books I and II (*with A. F. Abbott*)
GENERAL SCIENCE PHYSICS
GRADED EXERCISES IN PHYSICS
TEST PAPERS IN PHYSICS
EXERCISES IN PRACTICAL PHYSICS
NOTES ON ORDINARY LEVEL PHYSICS
REVISION NOTES IN PHYSICS
———— Book I. Heat, Light, Sound
Book II. Magnetism, Electricity, Mechanics & Properties of Matter
SOLUTIONS TO ORDINARY LEVEL PHYSICS QUESTIONS
SOLUTIONS TO ADVANCED LEVEL PHYSICS QUESTIONS

Published by Arnold
ELECTRICITY AND MAGNETISM
PHYSICS AND RADIO

Published by Blackie
PRINCIPLES OF TECHNICAL ELECTRICITY
HEAT

Published by Christophers
PRINCIPLES OF PHYSICS

A1⁰

SOUTHAMPTON ITCHEN GRAMMAR SCHOOL

EN AVANT

This Book is loaned to	Form	Date of Issue	Issued by
1 M. EBERT	U1A	9. 9. 76	
2			
3			
4			
5			
6			

N.B.—This Book is the property of the Education Committee.

Rule 1. No alteration of any kind is to be made on this label.

Rule 2. The person to whom this book is issued is held responsible for the same until it is returned.

Rule 3. This book is to be returned at the end of the Summer Term to the person by whom it was issued.

Rule 4. When leaving all books must be returned at the end of the Term to the Form Teacher.

MECHANICS
AND
PROPERTIES OF MATTER

by

M. NELKON, M.Sc. (Lond.), A.Inst.P. A.K.C.

Head of the Science Department, William Ellis School, London
Formerly Lecturer, Northampton College of Advanced Technology, London.

THIRD EDITION

HEINEMANN
EDUCATIONAL BOOKS LIMITED

LONDON

Heinemann Educational Books Ltd
LONDON MELBOURNE TORONTO
CAPE TOWN SINGAPORE
AUCKLAND IBADAN

First published 1952
Second edition 1955
Reprinted 1955, 1956, 1957
Third edition 1958
Reprinted 1959, 1960, 1961, 1963

Published by
Heinemann Educational Books Ltd
15–16 Queen Street, Mayfair, London W.1
Printed in Great Britain by
Bookprint Limited, Kingswood, Surrey

PREFACE

THIS text-book is written for General Certificate (Advanced) and Intermediate students, and covers, to that standard, Dynamics, Statics, Hydrostatics, Surface Tension, Elasticity, Friction in Solids, Viscosity, Osmosis, and Diffusion. The book is based on the lessons and lectures given to sixth-form and intermediate students at schools and polytechnics, and in the treatment a knowledge of Physics to the General Certificate Ordinary level, or matriculation standard, has been assumed.

I have begun Mechanics with dynamics, circular and simple harmonic motion, and moments of inertia, as these topics have more applications in Physics than statics; the theory of dimensions has been utilised where the mathematics is too difficult, as in the subject of viscosity for example; the "excess pressure" formula has been extensively used in the treatment of surface tension; and worked examples have been added to the text to assist the student. The exercises at the end of chapters are graded, and there are appendices containing basic definitions and formulæ to help revision. Accounts of the history of mechanics have been omitted as this is usually treated at length in text-books of Ordinary level, and the kinetic theory of gases is discussed in another volume on Heat. I have endeavoured to explain clearly the physical principles of the subjects, and it is hoped that the book will prove a useful introduction and stepping-stone to the many existing text-books of Scholarship standard in *Mechanics and Properties of Matter*.

I acknowledge with thanks the generous assistance with the work given to me by P. Parker, M.Sc., Senior Lecturer, Northampton Polytechnic, London, A. W. K. Ingram, M.A., Senior Science Master, Lawrence Sheriff School, Rugby, C. R. Ensor, M.A., Senior Physics Master, Downside School, Bath, and D. W. Stops, B.Sc., Ph.D., Senior Lecturer, Northampton Polytechnic, London, who kindly read the proofs and made suggestions. I also acknowledge with thanks the permission to reprint questions set in past Advanced-level examinations by the following Examining Boards:

Matriculation and School Examinations, London University	(*L.*)
Northern Universities Joint Matriculation Board	(*N.*)
Cambridge Local Examinations Syndicate	(*C.*)
Oxford and Cambridge Joint Board	(*O. & C.*)
Welsh Joint Education Committee	(*W.*)

M. N.

PREFACE TO THE SECOND EDITION

In this edition I have included an Appendix on Scholarship-level topics. A number of corrections and additions have been made in the text, and I am indebted to many correspondents for their helpful suggestions.

M.N.

NOTE ON REPRINT OF SECOND EDITION, 1956

In this reprint an additional section (no. 8) has been added to the Appendix.

M.N.

PREFACE TO THE THIRD EDITION

In this edition a further section (no. 9) has been added to the Appendix.

February 1958.   M.N.

CONTENTS

MECHANICS

CHAPTER I

DYNAMICS

1. Motion in a Straight Line. Velocity.

The "velocity" of a moving object is defined as "the distance moved in a constant direction in unit time". If a car travels steadily in a constant direction and covers a distance s in a time t, then its velocity $= s/t$. If the car does not travel steadily, then s/t is its average velocity, and

the distance, s, $=$ average velocity $\times t$.

Velocity can be expressed in "centimetres per second" or "kilometres per hours"; or in "ft. per sec." or "miles per hour". By calculation, 60 m.p.h. $=$ 88 ft. per sec. It should be noted here that "velocity" is a quantity which has direction as well as magnitude (p. 6).

If an object moving in a straight line travels equal distances in equal times, no matter how small these distances may be, the object is said to be moving with *uniform* velocity. The velocity of a falling stone increases continuously, and so is a *non-uniform* velocity.

Suppose an object moving with a non-uniform velocity has travelled a distance s in a time t. If δs is the further small distance travelled in a small time δt, the velocity, v, over the small distance $= \delta s/\delta t$. Thus, in the limit, the velocity v at the time t is given by

$$v = \frac{ds}{dt},$$

using the calculus notation.

When a stone is released from a height it falls a distance s in feet given by the equation $s = 16t^2$, where t is the time of fall (p. 3). Thus, by differentiation, the velocity of the stone is given by

$$v = \frac{ds}{dt} = 2 \times 16t = 32t.$$

Hence at the end of 2 secs., when $t = 2$, the velocity is 64 ft. per sec.

2. Acceleration.

The *acceleration* of a moving object at an instant is defined as the *rate of change of its velocity* (i.e., the velocity change per sec.) at that

1

instant. In the case of a train accelerating steadily from 30 m.p.h. (44 ft. per sec.) to 45 m.p.h. (66 ft. per sec.) in 10 secs., the acceleration

$$= (45 - 30) \text{ m.p.h.}/10 \text{ secs.} = 1 \cdot 5 \text{ m.p.h. per sec.},$$

or

$$(66 - 44) \text{ ft. per sec.}/10 \text{ sec.} = 2 \cdot 2 \text{ ft. per sec. per sec.}$$

Since the time element (second) is repeated twice in the latter case, the acceleration is usually given as $2 \cdot 2$ ft. per sec.[2] Another unit of acceleration is "cm. per sec.[2]" In terms of the calculus, the acceleration f of a moving object is given by

$$f = \frac{dv}{dt},$$

where dv/dt is the velocity change per sec.

If the velocity changes by equal amounts in equal times, no matter how small the time-intervals may be, the acceleration is said to be *uniform*. Suppose that the velocity of an object moving in a straight line with uniform acceleration f increases from a value u to a value v in a time t. Then, from the definition of acceleration,

$$f = \frac{v - u}{t},$$

from which $\mathbf{v = u + ft}$.   .   .   .   (1).

3. Distance Travelled with Uniform Acceleration. Equations of Motion.

Suppose an object with a velocity u accelerates with a uniform acceleration f for a time t and attains a velocity v. The distance s travelled by the object in the time t is given by

$$s = \text{average velocity} \times t$$
$$= \tfrac{1}{2}(u + v) \times t$$

But $v = u + ft$

$$\therefore s = \tfrac{1}{2}(u + u + ft)t$$
$$\therefore \mathbf{s = ut + \tfrac{1}{2}ft^2} \quad . \quad . \quad . \quad (2).$$

If we eliminate t by substituting $t = (v - u)/f$ from (1) in (2), we obtain, on simplifying,

$$\mathbf{v^2 = u^2 + 2fs} \quad . \quad . \quad . \quad . \quad (3).$$

Equations (1), (2), (3) are the equations of motion of an object moving in a straight line with uniform acceleration. When an object undergoes a uniform *retardation*, for example when brakes are applied to a car, f has a *negative* value.

EXAMPLES

1. A car moving with a velocity of 30 m.p.h. accelerates uniformly at the rate of 2 yd. per sec.^{2}. Calculate the distance travelled from the place where acceleration began to that where the velocity reaches 45 m.p.h., and the time taken to cover this distance.

(i) 30 m.p.h. = 44 ft. per sec., 45 m.p.h. = 66 ft. per sec., acceleration f = 6 ft. per sec.^{2}

Using
$$v^2 = u^2 + 2fs,$$
$$\therefore 66^2 = 44^2 + 2 \times 6 \times s$$
$$\therefore s = \frac{66^2 - 44^2}{2 \times 6} = 201\tfrac{2}{3} \text{ ft.}$$

(ii) Using
$$v = u + ft.$$
$$\therefore 66 = 44 + 6t$$
$$\therefore t = \frac{66 - 44}{6} = 3\tfrac{2}{3} \text{ secs.}$$

2. A train travelling at 60 m.p.h. undergoes a uniform retardation of 4 ft. per sec.^{2} when brakes are applied. Find the time taken to come to rest and the distance travelled from the place where the brakes were applied.

(i) 60 m.p.h. = 88 ft. per sec., and f = − 4 ft. per sec.^{2}, v = 0.

Using
$$v = u + ft.$$
$$\therefore 0 = 88 - 4t$$
$$\therefore t = 22 \text{ secs.}$$

(ii) The distance, s, = $ut + \tfrac{1}{2}ft^2$
$$= 88 \times 22 - \tfrac{1}{2} \times 4 \times 22^2 = 968 \text{ ft.}$$

4. Motion Under Gravity.

When an object falls to the ground under the action of gravity experiment shows that the object has a constant or uniform acceleration of about 32 ft. per sec.^{2}, or 980 cm. per sec.^{2}, while it is falling (see p. 43). The numerical value of this acceleration is usually denoted by the symbol g. Suppose that an object is dropped from a height of 100 ft. above the ground. Then the initial velocity u = 0, and the acceleration f = g = 32, in this case. Substituting in $s = ut + \tfrac{1}{2}ft^2$, the distance s fallen is calculated from

$$s = \tfrac{1}{2}gt^2 = 16t^2.$$

When the object reaches the ground, s = 100 ft.

$$\therefore 100 = 16t^2, \text{ or } t = \frac{10}{4} = 2\tfrac{1}{2} \text{ secs.}$$

Thus the object takes $2\tfrac{1}{2}$ secs. to reach the ground.

If a cricket-ball is thrown vertically upwards, it slows down owing to the attraction of the earth. The ball is thus retarded, and the magnitude of the retardation is 32 ft. per sec.^{2}, or g. Mathematically, a retardation can be regarded as a negative acceleration in the direction along which the object is moving; and hence $f = -32$ ft. per sec.^{2} in this case.

Suppose the ball was thrown straight up with an initial velocity, u, of 80 ft. per sec. The time taken to reach the top of its motion can be obtained from the equation $v = u + ft$. The velocity, v, at the top is zero; and since $u = 80$ and $f = -32$ numerically, we have

$$0 = 80 - 32t.$$

$$\therefore t = \frac{80}{32} = 2\tfrac{1}{2} \text{ secs.}$$

The highest distance reached is thus given by

$$s = ut + \tfrac{1}{2}ft^2$$
$$= 80 \times 2\tfrac{1}{2} - 16 \times 2\tfrac{1}{2}^2 = 100 \text{ ft.}$$

5. Distance-Time Curve.

When the distance s of a moving car from some fixed point is plotted against the time t, a *distance-time* ($s - t$) *curve* of the motion is obtained. The velocity of the car at any instant is given by the change in distance per second at that instant; i.e., by the *gradient* to the curve at the instant considered. If the distance-time curve is a straight line CD,

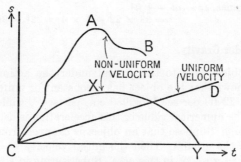

FIG. 1. Distance-time curves.

the gradient is constant at all points; it therefore follows that the car is moving with a *uniform* velocity, Fig. 1. If the distance-time curve is a curve CAB, the gradient varies at different points. The car then

moves with non-uniform velocity, and we can deduce that the velocity
is zero at the instant corresponding to A, since the gradient at A to the
curve CAB is zero.

When a ball is thrown upwards, the height s reached at any instant
t is given by $s = ut - \frac{1}{2}gt^2 = ut - 16t^2$, where u is the initial velocity.
The graph of s against t is represented by the parabolic curve CXY in
Fig.1; the gradient at X is zero, showing that the velocity of the ball at
its maximum height is zero.

6. Velocity-Time Curves.

When the velocity of a moving train is plotted against the time, a
"velocity-time curve" is obtained. Useful information can be deduced
from this curve, as we shall see shortly. If the velocity is uniform, the
velocity-time graph is a straight line parallel to the time-axis, as shown
by line (1) in Fig. 2. If the train accelerates uniformly from rest, the
velocity-time graph is a straight line, line (2), inclined to the time-axis.

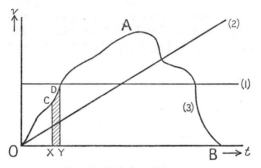

Fig. 2.   Velocity-time curves.

If the acceleration is not uniform, the velocity-time graph is curved.
In Fig. 2, the velocity-time graph OAB represents the velocity of a
train starting from rest which reaches a maximum velocity at A, and
then comes to rest at the time corresponding to B; the acceleration and
retardation are both not uniform in this case.

Since acceleration is the change of velocity per second, i.e., the rate of
change of the velocity, *the acceleration of the train at any instant is given
by the gradient to the velocity-time graph* at that instant. At the peak
point A of the curve OAB the gradient is zero, i.e., the acceleration is
then zero. At any point between A, B the gradient to the curve is
negative, i.e., the train undergoes a retardation.

7. Area Between Velocity-Time Graph and Time-Axis.

Consider again the velocity-time graph OAB, and suppose the velocity
increases in a very small time-interval XY from a value represented by

XC to a value represented by YD, Fig. 2. Since the small distance travelled = average velocity × time XY, the distance travelled is represented by the *area* between the curve CD and the time-axis, shown shaded in Fig. 2. By considering every small time-interval between OB in the same way, it follows that *the total distance travelled by the train in the time OB is given by the area between the velocity-time graph and the time-axis*. This result applies to any velocity-time graph, whatever its shape. In calculus notation, the distance s travelled from an instant t_1 to an instant t_2 is given by

$$s = \int_{t_1}^{t_2} v \, . \, dt.$$

8. Vector and Scalar Quantities.

Cambridge is 50 miles from London in a direction 20° E. of N. We can therefore represent the distance between the cities in magnitude and direction by a straight line LC 2·5 cm. long 20° E. of N., where 1 cm. represents 20 miles, Fig. 3 (i). Similarly, we can represent the

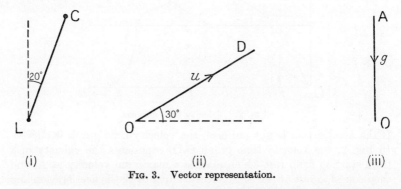

(i)   (ii)   (iii)

FIG. 3.   Vector representation.

velocity u of a ball initially thrown at an angle of 30° to the horizontal by a straight line OD drawn to scale in the direction of the velocity u, the arrow on the line showing the direction, Fig. 3 (ii). The acceleration due to gravity, g, is always represented by a straight line OA to scale drawn vertically downwards, since this is the direction of the acceleration, Fig. 3 (iii).

A physical quantity which can be represented in magnitude and direction by a straight line is known as a *vector* quantity; acceleration and velocity are examples of vector quantities. The tension in a rope can be represented in magnitude and direction by a straight line, and thus "force" is a vector quantity. The mass of an object, its volume, and its temperature have magnitude but no direction, and they are known as *scalar* quantities

9. Resultant. Components.

If a boy is running along the deck of a ship in a direction OA, and the ship is moving in a different direction OB, the boy will move relatively to the sea along a direction OC, between OA and OB, Fig. 4 (i). Now in one second the boat moves from O to A, where OA represents the velocity of the boat in magnitude and direction, and the boy moves from A to C in the same time, where AC represents the velocity of the boat in magnitude and direction. Thus in one second the net effect relative to the sea is that the boy moves from O to C. It can now be seen that if lines OA, OB are drawn to represent in magnitude and direction the respective velocities of the boy and the ship, the magnitude and direction of the **resultant** velocity of the boy is represented by the diagonal OC of the completed parallelogram having OA, OB as two of its sides; OACB is known as a *parallelogram of velocities*. Conversely, a velocity represented completely by OC can be regarded as having an "effective part", or *component* represented by OA, and another component represented by OB.

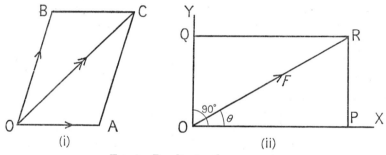

Fig. 4. Resultant and component.

In practice, we often require to find the component of a vector quantity in a certain direction. Suppose OR represents the vector F, and OX is the direction, Fig. 4 (ii). If we complete the parallelogram OQRP by drawing a perpendicular RP from R to OX, and a perpendicular RQ from R to OY, where OY is perpendicular to OX, we can see that OP, OQ represent the components of F along OX, OY respectively. Now the component OQ has no effect in a perpendicular direction; consequently OP represents the total effect of F along the direction OX. OP is called the "resolved component" in this direction. If θ is the angle ROX, then, since triangle OPR has a right angle at P,

$$OP = OR \cos \theta = F \cos \theta \qquad . \qquad . \qquad . \qquad (4).$$

The component of the acceleration g due to gravity in a direction inclined at 60° to it is thus given by $g \cos 60°$, or $32 \cos 60°$ ft. per sec.^{2}, which is 16 ft. per sec.^{2}.

10. Projectiles.

Suppose a cricket-ball is thrown with a velocity u in a direction making an angle a with the horizontal, Fig. 5. The component of the velocity in a horizontal direction is $u \cos a$. The component in a vertical direction $= u \cos (90° - a) = u \sin a$. Now the acceleration in a vertical direction $= -g$. Thus, from $v = u + ft$ and $s = ut + \frac{1}{2}ft^2$ respectively, the vertical velocity v at the end of a time t is given by

$$v = u \sin a - gt \qquad . \qquad . \qquad . \qquad \text{(i).}$$

and the vertical distance s at the end of the time is given by

$$s = u \sin a . t - \frac{1}{2}gt^2 \qquad . \qquad . \qquad . \qquad \text{(ii).}$$

The graph of s vs. t is thus a parabola OAB, as shown in Fig. 5. The horizontal component, $u \cos a$, remains constant in magnitude, since there is no component of gravity in a horizontal direction.

The vertical velocity of the ball at the *maximum* height A is zero.

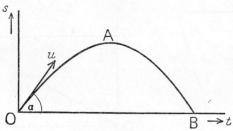

Fig. 5.   Projectile.

Now $\qquad\qquad\qquad v = u + ft$ (p. 2).

$$\therefore 0 = u \sin a - gt,$$

where t is the time to reach A.

$$\therefore t = \frac{u \sin a}{g} \qquad . \qquad . \qquad . \qquad . \qquad . \qquad \text{(iii).}$$

When the ball reaches the ground again at a time corresponding to OB, the vertical distance s travelled is zero. Thus, from (ii),

$$0 = u \sin a . t - \frac{1}{2}gt^2.$$

$$\therefore t = \frac{2u \sin a}{g}$$

∴ horizontal distance travelled = range of ball

$$= \text{horizontal velocity} \times \text{time}$$

$$= u \cos a \times \frac{2u \sin a}{g}$$

$$= \frac{u^2}{g} \sin 2a \quad . \quad . \quad . \quad . \quad \text{(iv)}.$$

Since the maximum magnitude of $\sin 2a$ is 1, the angle $2a = 90°$ for a maximum range. Thus, for a given velocity of throw, a ball should be thrown at an angle of 45° to the horizontal to achieve a maximum range.

11. Addition of Vectors.

Suppose a ship is travelling due east at 30 m.p.h. and a boy runs across the deck in a north-west direction at 6 m.p.h., Fig. 6 (i). We can find the velocity and direction of the boy relative to the sea by adding the two velocities. Since velocity is a vector quantity, we draw a line OA to represent 30 m.p.h. in magnitude and direction, and then, from

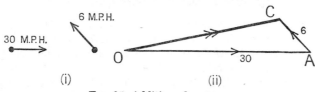

6 M.P.H.

30 M.P.H.

C

6

O

30

A

(i)   (ii)

Fig. 6.   Addition of vectors.

the end of A, draw a line AC to represent 6 m.p.h. in magnitude and direction, Fig. 6 (ii). The sum, or resultant, of the velocities is now represented by the line OC in magnitude and direction, because a distance moved in one second by the ship (represented by OA) together with a distance moved in one second by the boy (represented by AC) is equivalent to a movement of the boy from O to C relative to the sea.

12. Subtraction of Vectors.

The sum of two vectors X, Y is thus represented by one side of a triangle whose other two sides are drawn to represent X, Y in magnitude and direction. By adopting a similar method we can *subtract* two vectors, P, Q say, a process required in finding relative velocity for example (p. 10), Fig. 7 (i). The subtraction can be represented by $\overrightarrow{P} - \overrightarrow{Q}$, the arrows above the letters indicating that P and Q are vector quantities and not scalar quantities. Now

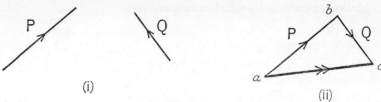

FIG. 7.   Subtraction of vectors.

$$\vec{P} - \vec{Q} = \vec{P} + (- \vec{Q}).$$

In words, the difference between the vectors $\vec{P}$, $\vec{Q}$ is the *sum* of the vectors $\vec{P}$ and $(- \vec{Q})$. Now $(- \vec{Q})$ is a vector drawn exactly equal and opposite to the vector $\vec{Q}$. We therefore draw ab to represent $\vec{P}$ completely, and then draw bc to represent $(- \vec{Q})$ completely, Fig. 7 (ii). Then $\vec{P} + (- \vec{Q})$ = the vector represented by $ac = \vec{P} - \vec{Q}$.

13. Relative Velocity and Relative Acceleration.

If a car A travelling at 30 m.p.h. is moving in the same direction as another car B travelling at 32 m.p.h., the *relative velocity* of B to A = 32 - 30 = 2 m.p.h. If, however, the cars are travelling in opposite directions, the relative velocity of B to A = 32 - (- 30) = 62 m.p.h.

Suppose that a car X is travelling with a velocity v along a road 30° east of north, and a car Y is travelling with a velocity u along a road

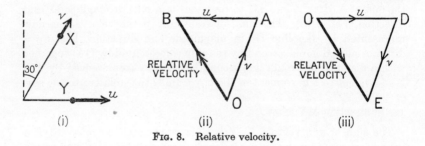

FIG. 8.   Relative velocity.

due east, Fig. 8 (i). Since "velocity" has direction as well as magnitude, i.e., "velocity" is a vector quantity (p. 6), we cannot subtract u and v numerically to find the relative velocity. We must adopt a method which takes into account the direction as well as the magnitude of the velocities, i.e., a vector subtraction is required.

The velocity of X relative to Y $= \vec{v} - \vec{u} = \vec{v} + (-\vec{u})$. Suppose OA represents the velocity, v, of X in magnitude and direction, Fig. 8 (ii). Since Y is travelling due east, a velocity AB numerically equal to u but in the due *west* direction represents the vector $(-\vec{u})$. The vector sum of OA and AB is OB from p. 9, which therefore represents in magnitude and direction the velocity of X relative to Y. By drawing an accurate diagram of the two velocities, OB can be found.

The velocity of Y relative to X $= \vec{u} - \vec{v} = \vec{u} + (-\vec{v})$, and can be found by a similar method. In this case, OD represents the velocity, u, of Y in magnitude and direction, while DE represents the vector $\left(-\vec{v}\right)$, which it is drawn numerically equal to v but in the *opposite* direction, Fig. 8 (iii). The vector sum of OD and DE is OE, which therefore represents the velocity of Y relative to X in magnitude and direction.

When two objects P, Q are each accelerating, the acceleration of P relative to Q = acceleration of P – acceleration of Q. Since "acceleration" is a vector quantity, the relative acceleration must be found by vector subtraction, as for the case of relative velocity.

EXAMPLE

Explain the difference between a scalar and a vector quantity.

What is meant by the relative velocity of one body with respect to another? Two ships are 10 sea-miles apart on a line running S. to N. The one farther north is steaming W. at 20 knots. The other is steaming N. at 20 knots. What is their distance of closest approach and how long do they take to reach it?   (*C.*)

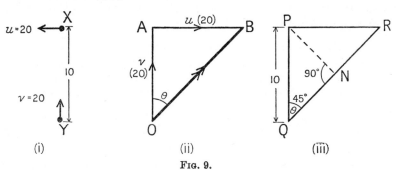

(i)   (ii)   (iii)

FIG. 9.

First part.   See text.

Second part.   Suppose the two ships are at X, Y, moving with velocities u, v respectively, each 20 knots, Fig. 9 (i). The velocity of Y relative to X $= \vec{v} - \vec{u} = \vec{v} + (-\vec{u})$. We therefore draw OA to represent $\vec{v}$ (20) and add to it AB, which represents $(-\vec{u})$, Fig. 9 (ii). The relative velocity is then represented by OB.

Since OAB is a right-angled triangle,

$$OB = \sqrt{OA^2 + AB^2} = \sqrt{20^2 + 20^2} = 28\cdot28 \text{ knots} \qquad \text{(i).}$$

Also, $\tan \theta = \dfrac{AB}{OA} = \dfrac{20}{20} = 1$, i.e., $\theta = 45°$ . . . (ii).

Thus the ship Y will move along a direction QR relative to the ship X, where QR is at 45° to PQ, the north-south direction, Fig. 9 (iii). If PQ = 10 sea miles, the distance of closest approach is PN, where PN is the perpendicular from P to QR.

$$\therefore PN = PQ \sin 45° = 10 \sin 45° = 7\cdot07 \text{ sea-miles.}$$

The distance QN = 10 cos 45° = 7·07 sea-miles. Since, from (i), the relative velocity is 28·28 knots, it follows that

$$\text{time to reach N} = \frac{7\cdot07}{28\cdot28} = \tfrac{1}{4} \text{ hour.}$$

LAWS OF MOTION. ENERGY AND MOMENTUM

14. Newton's Laws of Motion.

In 1686 SIR ISAAC NEWTON published a work called *Principia*, in which he expounded the Laws of Mechanics. He formulated in the book three "laws of motion" which paved the way for the later development of machines in motion:

Law I. *Every body continues in its state of rest or uniform motion in a straight line, unless impressed forces act on it.*

Law II. *The change of momentum per unit time is proportional to the impressed force, and takes place in the direction of the straight line along which the force acts.*

Law III. *Action and reaction are always equal and opposite.*

These laws cannot be proved in a formal way; we believe they are true because all the theoretical results obtained by assuming them agree with the experimental observations, as for example in astronomy (p. 51).

Newton's first law expresses the idea of **inertia**. The inertia of a body is its reluctance to start moving, and its reluctance to stop once it has begun moving. Thus an object at rest begins to move only when it is pushed or pulled, i.e., when a *force* acts on it; an object moving in a straight line with constant velocity changes its direction or moves faster only if a new force acts on it. Passengers in a bus or car appear to be jerked forward when the vehicle stops suddenly, as they continue in their state of motion until brought to rest by friction or collision.

15. Mass. Momentum. Force.

Observation shows that a given force produces a greater acceleration in a light object A than in a heavy object B. We say that the *mass* of A is less than the mass of B. The mass of an object is constant all over the world; it is measured in pounds in this country, and in grams in the scientific (c.g.s.) system.

When an object X is moving it is said to have an amount of *momentum* given, by definition, by

$$momentum = mass\ of\ X \times velocity \qquad . \qquad (5).$$

Thus an object of mass 200 lb. moving with a velocity of 30 ft. per sec. has a momentum of 6,000 units. If another object collides with X its velocity alters, and thus the momentum of X alters. The *force* of the collision, from Newton's Law II, is proportional to the change of momentum per second. Thus if P is the magnitude of a force acting on a constant mass m,

$$P \propto m \times \text{change of velocity per second}$$

$$\therefore P \propto mf,$$

where f is the *acceleration* produced by the force, by definition of f.

$$\therefore P = kmf \qquad . \qquad . \qquad . \qquad . \qquad . \qquad (i).$$

where k is a constant.

The **poundal** is a unit of force which is defined as the force acting on a mass of 1 lb. which gives it an acceleration of 1 ft. per sec.^{2}. Substituting $P = 1$ poundal, $m = 1$ lb., and $f = 1$ ft. per sec.^{2} in (i), we obtain $k = 1$; thus

$$\mathbf{P = mf,} \qquad . \qquad . \qquad . \qquad . \qquad . \qquad (6)$$

a standard equation in Dynamics.

The **dyne** is the unit of force in the centimetre-gram-second system; it is defined as the force acting on a mass of 1 gram which gives it an acceleration of 1 cm. per sec.^{2}. The equation $P = mf$ also applies when m is in grams, f is in cm. per sec.^{2}, and P is in dynes.

16. Weight. Relation between poundal and lb. wt., dyne and gm. wt.

The *weight* of an object is defined as the *force* acting on it due to gravity; the weight of an object can hence be measured by attaching it to a spring-balance and noting the extension, as the latter is proportional to the force acting on it (p. 137).

Suppose the weight of an object of mass m is denoted by W. If the object is released so that it falls to the ground, its acceleration is g.

Now $P = mf$. Consequently the force acting on it, i.e., its weight, is given by

$$W = mg \qquad . \quad . \quad . \quad . \quad . \quad (7).$$

If the mass m is 1 lb., then, since $g = 32$ ft. per sec.[2], the weight $W = 1 \times 32 = 32$ poundals. We call the force due to gravity on a mass of 1 lb. a *pound-weight* (*lb. wt.*), and hence it follows that

1 lb. wt. = 32 poundals.

At this stage the reader should note carefully the difference between the "pound" and the "pound-weight"; the former is a *mass* and is therefore constant all over the earth, whereas the pound-weight is a *force* whose magnitude depends on the value of g. The acceleration due to gravity, g, depends on the distance of the place considered from the centre of the earth; it is slightly greater at the poles than at the equator, since the earth is not perfectly spherical (see p. 43). It therefore follows that the weight of an object differs in different parts of the world.

The weight of a mass of 1 gram is called a *gram-weight* (*gm. wt.*). From $P = mf$, it follows that

1 gm. wt. = 1 × 980 = 980 dynes,

since $g = 980$ cm. per sec.[2] (approx.). The relations between 1 gm. wt. and 1 dyne, and between 1 lb. wt. and 1 poundal, are used extensively in later sections, and should be memorised by the reader.

17. Verification of P = mf. Fletcher's Trolley.

The relation between the force P and the acceleration f can be investigated with the aid of *Fletcher's trolley*, Fig. 10. This consists of a heavy trolley H, with holes in the side in which various masses can

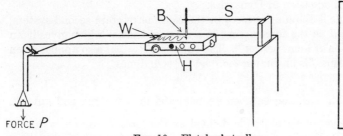

Fɪɢ. 10.   Fletcher's trolley.

be inserted. The trolley is connected to a scale pan by a light string passing over a grooved wheel, and the force acting on the trolley is varied by placing different weights on the scale-pan. The total mass moved is that of the trolley plus the scale-pan and masses on it; but as the latter is negligible compared with the mass of the trolley, the mass moved is practically constant and equal to the mass of the trolley.

The time of movement of the trolley is measured by means of a springy strip of metal S fixed to one end, with an inked pen B attached to the other end. S is drawn back and released so that it vibrates, the trolley is then allowed to accelerate from rest, and the pen B marks a wavy trace W on a sheet of paper on the trolley as a result of the vibrations of S. The time to make one complete wave is constant and equal to the period of vibration of the spring, which is sometimes marked on the spring.

In order to verify that the acceleration of an object is proportional to the force acting on it, a weight is placed on the scale-pan and a wavy trace is obtained when the trolley is released from rest. Now the acceleration f is given by $s = ut + \frac{1}{2}ft^2 = \frac{1}{2}ft^2$, since $u = 0$. Hence $f = 2s/t^2$. The distance s moved by the trolley at the end of the fourth trace, for example, is measured, and the corresponding time t is 4 units, where one unit is the period of vibration of the spring. Thus f is known. The experiment is now repeated with different weights in the scale-pan, i.e., P is varied, and the corresponding acceleration f is measured. *Experiment shows that P/f is a constant*; and hence $P \propto f$ for a given mass. By placing different masses in the holes of the trolley the mass m can be varied; and if the force P is kept constant and the acceleration f is measured each time, experiment shows that $f \propto 1/m$.

18. Action and Reaction are Equal and Opposite.

When a brick is resting on the ground, the brick exerts a downward force on the ground and the ground exerts an upward force on the brick. The downward force may be termed the "action" of the brick on the ground and the upward force the "reaction" of the ground on the brick. As the brick is in equilibrium, the reaction is equal to the weight of the brick, and from Newton's third law (p. 12), it follows that the action of the brick on the ground is equal to the weight of the brick. From Newton's third law, the force on the molecules of gas ejected from a jet aeroplane is equal and opposite to the force on the aeroplane.

Newton's third law applies to all branches of Physics. Thus if a magnet attracts a piece of iron with a force of 100 dynes, the iron attracts the magnet with a force of 100 dynes acting in the opposite direction. If an electric current in a wire produces a force of 10 dynes on a magnet near it, the wire is subjected to a force of 10 dynes in the opposite direction.

EXAMPLES

1. An object of mass 200 gm. is attached to the hook of a spring-balance, and the latter is suspended vertically from the roof of a lift. What is the reading on the spring-balance when the lift is (i) ascending with an acceleration of 20 cm. per sec.^{2} (ii) descending with an acceleration of 10 cm. per sec.^{2} (iii) ascending with a uniform velocity of 15 cm. per sec.

Suppose T is the tension (force) in the spring-balance in dynes.

(i) The object is acted upon two forces: (a) The tension T dynes in the spring-balance, which acts upwards, (b) its weight, 200 × 980 dynes, which acts downwards. Since the object moves upwards, T is greater than 200 × 980 dynes, and hence the net force, P, acting on the object = $(T - 200 \times 980)$ dynes.

But $P = mf$,

where f is the acceleration.

$$\therefore T - 200 \times 980 = 200 \times 20$$
$$\therefore T = 200 \times 20 + 200 \times 980 \text{ dynes}$$
$$\therefore T = \frac{200 \times 20 + 200 \times 980}{980} \text{ gm. wt.}$$
$$= 204 \text{ gm. wt.}$$

Thus 204 gm. wt. is the reading on the spring-balance.

(ii) Since the lift is descending, the weight is greater than the tension T_1 in the spring. Hence the net force $P = (200 \times 980 - T_1)$ dynes.

But $P = mf$

$$\therefore 200 \times 980 - T_1 = 200 \times 10$$
$$\therefore T_1 = 200 \times 980 - 200 \times 10 \text{ dynes}$$
$$\therefore T_1 = \frac{200 \times 980 - 200 \times 10}{980} \text{ gm .wt.}$$
$$= 198 \text{ gm. wt.}$$

Thus 198 gm. wt. is the reading on the spring-balance.

(iii) If the velocity is uniform, the net force $P = 0$. Thus the tension is now equal to the weight, and hence

$$\text{reading on spring-balance} = 200 \text{ gm. wt.}$$

2. An object of mass 10 lb. rests on a smooth table, and is attached by an inextensible string passing over a grooved wheel to a 20 lb. object hanging over the table. Assuming friction is negligible, calculate the acceleration of the objects when they are allowed to move.

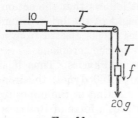

Fig. 11.

Suppose T is the tension in poundals in the string, Fig. 11. The acceleration f of the two objects is the same since they are connected together. For the object of mass 20 lb., the net force acting downwards = $(20g - T)$ poundals, where $g = 32$, since the weight = 20 lb. wt. = $20g$ poundals. From $P = mf$, we have

$$20g - T = 20f \quad . \quad . \quad . \quad . \quad . \quad . \quad \text{(i).}$$

The force T is the only force acting on the object in a horizontal direction .

$$\therefore T = 10f \quad . \quad . \quad . \quad . \quad . \quad . \quad \text{(ii)}.$$

Adding (i) and (ii) to eliminate T,

$$\therefore 20g = 30f.$$

$$\therefore f = \frac{20g}{30} = \frac{20 \times 32}{30} = 21\tfrac{1}{3} \text{ ft. per sec.}^2$$

3. A hose ejects 80 c.c. of water per second through a hole 2 mm. in diameter. Find the backward force on the person holding the hose.

The area of the hole $= \pi r^2 = \pi \times (0 \cdot 1)^2$ sq. cm.

$$\therefore \text{ velocity, } v, \text{ of water } = \frac{80}{\pi \times (0 \cdot 1)^2} \text{ cm. per sec.}$$

If the initial velocity of water is zero, the change of momentum per second produced

$$= mv = 80 \times \frac{80}{\pi \times (0 \cdot 1)^2}$$

But force is defined as the "change of momentum per second" (p. 12).

$$\therefore \text{ force on water } = 80 \times \frac{80}{\pi \times (0 \cdot 1)^2} = 20 \cdot 4 \times 10^4 \text{ dynes.}$$

$$\therefore \text{ backward force on person } = 20 \cdot 4 \times 10^4 \text{ dynes.}$$

19. Work.

When an engine pulls a train with a constant force of 50 units through a distance of 20 units, the engine is said by definition to do an amount of *work* equal to 50 × 20 or 1,000 units, the product of the force and the distance. Thus if W is the amount of work,

$$W = force \times distance \quad . \quad . \quad . \quad \text{(8)}.$$

Since the unit of a force is a "poundal" or a "lb. wt.", the work done is expressed in *ft. poundals* or *ft. lb. wt.* (the latter is often written as "ft. lb." but "ft. lb. wt." is intended). Suppose a force of 640 poundals pulls an object 20 ft. in its direction. The work done is then 640 × 20 or 12,800 ft. poundals. Since 640 poundals = 640/32 lb. wt. (p. 14) = 20 lb. wt., the work done is also given by 20 × 20 or 400 ft. lb. wt.

The c.g.s. unit of work is the **erg**, which is defined as the work done when a force of 1 dyne moves a distance 1 centimetre in its direction. If a force of 5 gm. wt. pulls an object 10 cm. in its direction, then, since 1 gm. wt. = 980 dynes,

$$\text{work done} = 5 \times 980 \times 10 = 49,000 \text{ ergs.}$$

In practice the erg is so small (it is approximately equal to the work done in raising a milligram one centimetre) that a larger unit is adopted.

This is the **joule**, named after the famous scientist J. P. JOULE. By definition,

$$1\ joule = 10\ million\ ergs = 10^7\ ergs.$$

Before leaving the topic of "work", the reader should note carefully that we have assumed the force to move an object in its own direction. Suppose, however, that a force P pulls an object a distance s along a line OA acting at an angle θ to it, Fig. 12. The component of P along

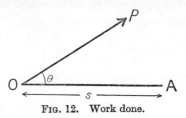

FIG. 12.   Work done.

OA is $P \cos \theta$ (p. 7), and this is the effective part of P pulling along the direction OA. The component of P along a direction perpendicular to OA has no effect along OA. Consequently

$$\text{work done} = P \cos \theta \times s.$$

In general, the work done by a force is equal to the product of the force and the displacement of its point of application in the direction of the force.

20. Power.

When an engine does work quickly, it is said to be operating at a high *power*; if it does work slowly it is said to be operating at a low power. "Power" is defined as the *work done per second*, i.e.,

$$\text{power} = \frac{\text{work done}}{\text{time taken}} \qquad . \qquad . \qquad . \qquad (9).$$

The c.g.s. unit of power is thus "erg per sec.", or "joule per sec." The **watt** is defined as **one joule per second** rate of working, or 10^7 ergs *per second*. The f.p.s. unit of power is "ft. lb. wt. per sec.", and by definition

$$1\ horse\ power\ (h.p.) = 550\ ft.\ lb.\ wt.\ per\ sec.$$

By changing the units, it can be shown that

$$1\ h.p. = 746\ watts.$$

21. Kinetic Energy.

An object is said to possess *energy* if it can do work. When an object possesses energy because it is moving, the energy is said to be *kinetic*, e.g., a flying stone can disrupt a window. Suppose that an object of mass m is moving with a velocity u, and is gradually brought to rest in a distance s by a constant force P acting against it. The kinetic energy originally possessed by the object is equal to the work done against P, and hence

$$\text{kinetic energy} = P \times s.$$

But $P = mf$, where f is the retardation of the object. Hence $P \times s = mfs$. From $v^2 = u^2 + 2fs$ (see p. 2), we have, since $v = 0$ and f is negative in this case,

$$0 = u^2 - 2fs, \text{ i.e., } fs = \frac{u^2}{2}.$$

$$\therefore \text{ kinetic energy} = mfs = \tfrac{1}{2} mu^2 \quad . \quad . \quad . \quad (10).$$

When m is in grams and the velocity u is in cm. per sec., then $\tfrac{1}{2} mu^2$ is in *ergs*; when m is in pounds and u is in ft. per sec., then $\tfrac{1}{2}mu^2$ is in *ft. poundals*.

A car of 15 cwt. moving with a velocity of 30 m.p.h. has thus an amount W of kinetic energy given by

$$W = \tfrac{1}{2}mu^2 = \tfrac{1}{2} \times 15 \times 112 \times 44^2 \text{ ft. poundals,}$$

since 15 cwt. $= 15 \times 112$ lb. and 30 m.p.h. $= 44$ ft. per sec.

$$\therefore W = 1626240 \text{ ft. poundals.}$$

$$= \frac{1626240}{32} \text{ ft. lb. wt.} = 50{,}820 \text{ ft. lb. wt.}$$

A bullet of 40 grams moving with a velocity of 300 cm. per sec. has an amount W of kinetic energy given by

$$W = \tfrac{1}{2}mu^2 = \tfrac{1}{2} \times 40 \times 300^2 = 1{,}800{,}00 \text{ ergs,}$$

$$= \frac{1{,}800{,}000}{10^7} \text{ joules} = 0{\cdot}18 \text{ joules.}$$

22. Potential Energy.

A weight held stationary above the ground has energy, because, when released, it can raise another object attached to it by a rope passing over a pulley, for example. A coiled spring also has energy, which is released gradually as the spring uncoils. The energy of the weight or spring is called *potential energy*, because it arises from the position or arrangement of the body, and not from its motion.

If the mass of an object is m, and the object is held stationary at a height h above the ground, the energy released when the object falls to the ground

$$= \text{force} \times \text{distance}$$

$$= \text{weight of object} \times h.$$

When m is in grams, its weight is m gm. wt. or mg dynes, where $g = 980$ numerically. In this case, at a height of h cm.,

$$potential\ energy = mgh\ ergs \qquad . \qquad . \qquad . \qquad (11A).$$

if m is in $lb.$, its weight is m lb. wt.; and hence, if h is in feet,

$$potential\ energy = mh\ \text{ft. lb. wt.} \qquad . \qquad . \qquad (11B).$$

Thus if an object of mass 4 kilograms is 2 metres above the ground, its potential energy, W, $= 4000 \times 980 \times 200 = 784{,}000{,}000$ ergs. If an object of mass 50 lb. is 12 ft. above the ground, its potential energy $= 50 \times 12 = 600$ ft. lb. wt.

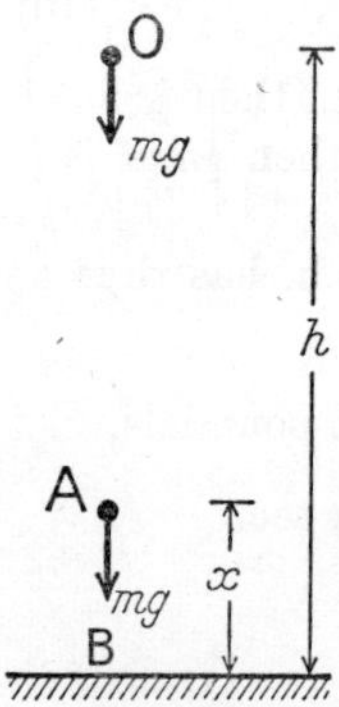

23. Conservation of Energy.

One of the fundamental principles in Science is the Principle of the Conservation of Energy, which states that the total energy in a given system is constant although energy may change from one form to another. As a simple illustration of the principle in Mechanics, consider an object of mass m held at O at a height h above the ground, Fig. 13.

The energy of the stationary object = the potential energy at O. Suppose the object is released and falls to a point A at a height x above the ground. The velocity, v, at A is given by

FIG. 13.
Conservation of energy.

$$v^2 = u^2 + 2fs = 0 + 2g(h - x) = 2g(h - x).$$

$\therefore$ kinetic energy at A $= \frac{1}{2}mv^2 = \frac{1}{2}m \times 2g(h - x) = mg(h - x).$

Also, potential energy at A $= mgx.$

$\therefore$ total energy at A $\quad = $ potential energy $+$ kinetic energy

$$= mgx \qquad\qquad + mg(h - x)$$

$$= mgh.$$

But the energy at O $= mgh$. Consequently the energy is conserved.

When the object just reaches the ground at B the whole of its energy is kinetic and equal to $\frac{1}{2}mv_1^2$, where v_1 is the velocity at B.

But $\qquad\qquad v_1^2 = u^2 + 2fs = 0 + 2gh = 2gh,$

$\therefore$ kinetic energy at B $= \frac{1}{2}mv_1^2 = mgh = $ energy at A or O.

The resistance of the air has been omitted from these calculations. If the resistance is taken into account, some work is done against it as the object falls and some mechanical energy is therefore lost; the energy reappears, however, as *heat*.

24. Mass.

Newton said that the "mass" of an object was the "quantity of matter" in it, which is a very vague definition of "mass". In 1905, however, EINSTEIN proved from his Theory of Relativity that the energy W released from an object when its mass decreases by an amount m is given by

$$W = mc^2 , \qquad . \quad . \quad . \quad . \quad (i)$$

where c is the numerical value of the velocity of light. When m is in grams and c is in cm. per sec., then W is in ergs. Experiments in Radioactivity on objects emitting radiation showed that Einstein's law was true. Now, from (i), $m = W/c^2$. Einstein therefore declared that *the mass of an object is a measure of the total energy obtainable from its atoms*. Thus, since $c = 3 \times 10^{10}$ in cm. per sec., an object can be said to have a mass of 1 gram if 9×10^{20} ergs of energy can be obtained from all its atoms.

Before Einstein proved that the mass of an object was a measure of the energy of its atoms, two recognised laws of science were:

(1) *The Principle of the Conservation of Mass* (the total mass of a given system of objects is constant even though collisions or other actions took place between them);

(2) *The Principle of the Conservation of Energy* (the total energy of a given system is constant). From Einstein's relation, however, the two laws can be combined into one, namely, the Principle of the Conservation of Energy.

On p. 88 we shall see that the masses of objects can be compared by a common balance. Thus if we define a mass of 1 pound as the mass of a certain piece of platinum, we can measure the masses of objects as so many "pounds".

The summary on page 22 may assist the reader; it refers to the units of some of the quantities encountered, and their relations.

25. Conservation of Linear Momentum.

Newton defined the force acting on an object as the rate of change of its momentum, the momentum being the product of its mass and velocity (p. 12). Momentum is thus a vector quantity. Suppose that the mass of an object is m, its initial velocity is u, and its final velocity due to a force P acting on it for a time t is v. Then

Quantity	c.g.s. Unit	f.p.s. Unit	Relations
Force	Dyne or gm. wt.	Poundal or lb. wt.	980 dynes = 1 gm. wt. 32 poundals = 1 lb. wt.
Mass	Gram	Pound (lb.)	
Energy	Ergs or joules	Ft. lb. wt.	10^7 ergs = 1 joule
Power	Watt	Ft. lb. wt./sec. or horse-power	1 watt = 1 joule/sec. 1 h.p. = 550 ft. lb. wt. per sec. = 746 watts.

$$\text{change of momentum} = mv - mu,$$

and hence
$$P = \frac{mv - mu}{t}$$

$$\therefore Pt = mv - mu = momentum\ change \qquad . \qquad . \qquad (13).$$

The quantity Pt (force × time) is known as the *impulse* of the force on the object, and from (13) it follows that the units of momentum are the same as those of Pt, i.e., *dyne-sec.* or *poundal-sec.*

Suppose that a moving object A, of mass m_1 and velocity u_1, collides with another object B, of mass m_2 and velocity u_2, moving in the same direction, Fig. 14. By Newton's law of action and reaction, the force P

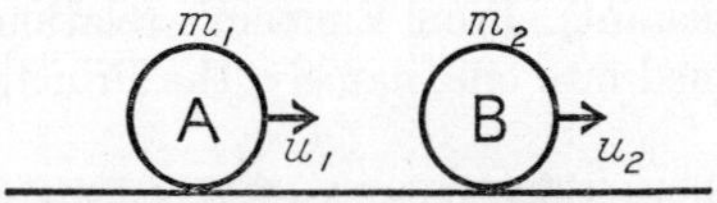

FIG. 14.   Collision of bodies.

exerted by A on B is equal and opposite to that exerted by B on A. Moreover, the time t during which the force acted on B is equal to the time during which the force of reaction acted on A. Thus the magnitude of the impulse, Pt, on B is equal and opposite to the magnitude of the impulse on A. Now from equation (13), the impulse is equal to the change of momentum. It therefore follows that the change in the total momentum of the two objects is *zero*, i.e., the total momentum of the two objects is constant although a collision had occurred. Thus if A moves with a reduced velocity v_1 after collision, and B then moves with an increased velocity v_2,

$$m_1u_1 + m_2u_2 = m_1v_1 + m_2v_2.$$

The *principle of the conservation of momentum* states that, *if no external forces act on a system of colliding objects, the total momentum of the objects remains constant.*

Example. Suppose that the sphere A has a mass of 15 lb., the sphere B has a mass of 10 lb., and that their respective velocities prior to collision are 6 ft. per sec. and 4 ft. per sec. in the same direction. Their total momentum in this direction

$$= 15 \times 6 + 10 \times 4 = 130 \text{ poundal-sec.}$$

If the two spheres are inelastic, they collide and move with a common velocity u. The new total momentum in the same direction as before $= 15u + 10u = 25u$. From the principle of the conservation of momentum, it follows that

$$25u = 130$$

$$\therefore \quad u = \frac{130}{25} = 5 \cdot 2 \text{ ft. per sec.}$$

26. Verification of Principle of Conservation of Momentum.

The Principle of the Conservation of Momentum can be verified by HICKS' ballistic balance, Fig. 15. Two masses A, B are placed on light wooden blocks or scale pans, each suspended by four strings, and the

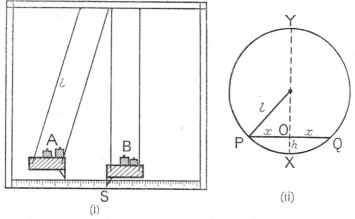

Fig. 15.   Ballistic balance.

horizontal displacement of each mass is measured on the scale S with the aid of a pointer attached to each block. The mass A is first displaced as shown in Fig. 15 (i), and collides with B after it is released. The horizontal displacements of A and B before and after collision are then noted.

Suppose A is initially at P on the arc of a circle of radius l, Fig. 15 (ii). Its velocity is then zero. When it collides with B it passes through its lowest position X with a velocity u given by $mgh = \frac{1}{2}mu^2$, by the principle of conservation of energy, where h is the vertical distance, OX, traversed by A, Fig. 15 (ii). Thus

$$u^2 = 2gh.$$

Now XO . OY $=$ PO . OQ, from the geometry of the circle, where XY is a diameter. Suppose $2l$ is the diameter, and x is the horizontal distance PO.

$$\therefore h(2l - h) = x . x = x^2$$

$$\therefore h = \frac{x^2}{2l},$$

if h is small compared with l, which is true in practice.

$$\therefore u^2 = 2gh = 2g \times \frac{x^2}{2l} = \frac{gx^2}{l}$$

$$\therefore u \propto x,$$

since g, l are constants. *Thus the velocity of A as it collides with B is proportional to the horizontal displacement of A.* It can be shown by a similar treatment that the velocities of A and B after the collision are also proportional to their respective horizontal displacements, which may be read on the scale S. From a table of measurements of the masses m_1, m_2 of A, B, the velocity u of A just before it collides with B, and the velocities u_1, v_1 of A, B respectively after collision, it can be verified by calculation that

$$m_1u = m_1u_1 + m_2v_1.$$

The total momentum of A, B before collision is thus equal to the total momentum of A, B after collision, the momentum of B being initially zero since B was stationary.

27. Dimensions.

By the *dimensions* of a physical quantity we mean the way it is related to the fundamental quantities mass, length, and time; these are usually denoted by [M], [L], and [T] respectively. An area, length $\times$ breadth, has dimensions [L] $\times$ [L] or [L]^2; a volume has dimensions [L]^3; density, which is mass/volume, has dimensions [M]/[L]^3 or [M] [L]$^{-3}$; specific gravity has no dimensions, since it is the ratio of similar quantities, in this case two weights (p. 95); an angle has no dimensions, since it is the ratio of two lengths.

The following are the dimensions of some quantities in Mechanics:

Velocity. Since velocity $= \dfrac{\text{distance,}}{\text{time}}$ its dimensions are $\dfrac{[L]}{[T]}$ or [L] [T]$^{-1}$.

Acceleration. The dimensions are those of velocity/time, i.e., $\dfrac{[L]}{[T]^2}$ or $[L] [T]^{-2}$.

Force. Since force $=$ mass $\times$ acceleration, its dimensions are $[M] [L] [T]^{-2}$.

Work or Energy. Since work $=$ force $\times$ distance, its dimensions are $[M] [L]^2 [T]^{-2}$.

28. Application of Dimensions.

Simple pendulum. If a small mass is suspended from a long thread so as to form a simple pendulum, we may reasonably suppose that the period, T, of the oscillations depends only on the mass m, the length l of the thread, and the acceleration, g, due to gravity at the place concerned. Suppose then that

$$T = km^x l^y g^z \qquad \cdots \qquad \text{(i)}$$

where x, y, z, k are unknown numbers. The dimensions of g are $[L] [T]^{-2}$ from above. Now the dimensions of both sides of (i) must be the same.

$$\therefore [T] = [M]^x [L]^y [L]^z [T]^{-2z}$$

Equating the indices of M, L, T on both sides, we have

$$x = 0,$$
$$y + z = 0,$$

and $\qquad\qquad -2z = 1.$

$$\therefore z = -\tfrac{1}{2},\, y = \tfrac{1}{2},\, x = 0.$$

Thus, from (i), the period T is given by

$$T = kl^{\frac{1}{2}} g^{-\frac{1}{2}},$$

or $\qquad\qquad T = k\sqrt{\dfrac{l}{g}}.$

We cannot find the magnitude of k by the method of dimensions, since it is a number. A complete mathematical investigation shows that $k = 2\pi$ in this case, and hence $T = 2\pi \sqrt{l/g}$. (See also p. 42.)

29. Velocity of Transverse Wave in a String.

As another illustration of the use of dimensions, consider a wave set up in a stretched string by plucking it. The velocity, V, of the wave depends on the tension, F, in the string, its length l, and its mass m, and we can therefore suppose that

B

$$V = kF^x l^y m^z, \qquad . \quad . \quad . \quad . \quad . \quad \text{(i)}$$

where x, y, z are numbers we hope to find by dimensions and k is a constant.

The dimensions of velocity, V, are $[L]$ $[T]^{-1}$, the dimensions of tension, F, are $[M]$ $[L]$ $[T]^{-2}$, the dimension of length, l, is $[L]$, and the dimension of mass, m, is $[M]$. From (i), it follows that

$$[L]\,[T]^{-1} = [M]^x\,[L]^x\,[T]^{-2x} \times [L]^y \times [M]^z.$$

Equating power of $[M]$, $[L]$, and $[T]$ on both sides,

$$\therefore 0 = x + z\ , \qquad . \quad . \quad . \quad . \quad . \quad . \quad \text{(i)}$$

$$1 = x + y\ , \qquad . \quad . \quad . \quad . \quad . \quad \text{(ii)}$$

and $\qquad\qquad -1 = -2x \qquad . \quad . \quad . \quad . \quad . \quad . \quad \text{(iii)}$

$$\therefore x = \tfrac{1}{2}, z = -\tfrac{1}{2}, y = \tfrac{1}{2}.$$

$$\therefore V = k\,.\,F^{\frac{1}{2}}\,l^{\frac{1}{2}}\,m^{-\frac{1}{2}},$$

$$\text{or } V = k\sqrt{\frac{Fl}{m}} = k\sqrt{\frac{F}{m/l}} = k\sqrt{\frac{\text{Tension}}{\text{mass per unit length}}}$$

A complete mathematical investigation shows that $k = 1$.

The method of dimensions can thus be used to find the relation between quantities when the mathematics is too difficult. It has been extensively used in hydrodynamics, for example. See also pp. 160, 165.

EXAMPLES

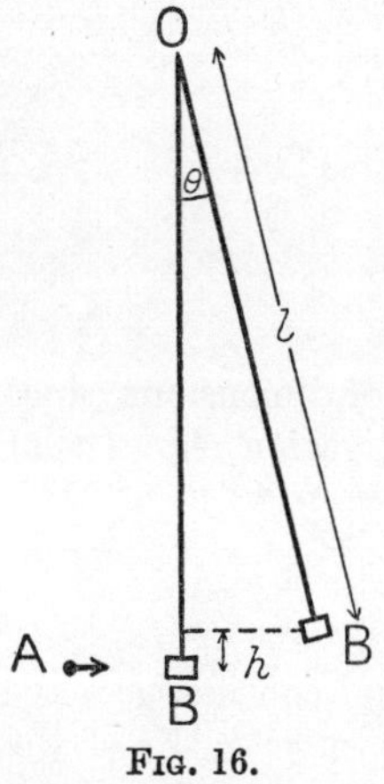

FIG. 16.

$$(1000 + 20)\,v = 20 \times 10,000$$

1. What is understood by (a) the principle of the *conservation of energy*, (b) the principle of the *conservation of momentum*?

A bullet of mass 20 gm., travelling horizontally at 100 metres per sec., embeds itself in the centre of a block of wood of mass 1 kgm. which is suspended by light vertical strings 1 metre in length. Calculate the maximum inclination of the strings to the vertical.

Describe in detail how the experiment might be carried out and used to determine the velocity of the bullet just before the impact of the block. (*N.*)

First part. See text.

Second part. Suppose A is the bullet, B is the block suspended from a point O, and θ is the maximum inclination to the vertical, Fig. 16. If v cm. per sec. is the common velocity of block and bullet when the latter is brought to rest relative to the block, then, from the principle of the conservation of momentum,

$$\therefore v = \frac{10,000}{51} \text{ cm. per sec.}$$

The vertical height h risen by block and bullet is given by

$$v^2 = 2gh.$$

But
$$h = l - l \cos \theta = l(1 - \cos \theta)$$

$$\therefore v^2 = 2gl(1 - \cos \theta)$$

$$\therefore \left(\frac{10,000}{51}\right)^2 = 2 \times 980 \times 100 \ (1 - \cos \theta)$$

$$\therefore 1 - \cos \theta = \left(\frac{10,000}{51}\right)^2 \times \frac{1}{2 \times 980 \times 100} = 0.1962$$

$$\therefore \cos \theta = 0.8038$$

$$\therefore \theta = 36.5°$$

The velocity, v, of the bullet can be determined by means of the apparatus described on p. 23, applying the conservation of momentum principle.

Thus $mv = (m + M)V$, where m is the mass of the bullet, M is the mass of the block, and V is the common velocity. Then $v = (m + M)V/m$. The quantities m and M can be found by weighing, and V is calculated from the displacement h of the block.

2. State and explain what is meant by the law of conservation of momentum and describe an experiment to illustrate it.

A wooden pendulum bob is moving east with a velocity of 2m./sec. and is hit by a bullet travelling north-west with a velocity of 100 m./sec. If the mass of the pendulum bob is 1 kg. and that of the bullet 100 gm., and if the bullet remains embedded in the bob, find the velocity after impact. (*C.*)

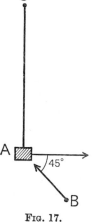

FIG. 17.

First part. For the law and the experiment, see text.

Second part. Suppose A is the pendulum bob moving eastward, B is the bullet moving north-west, and u is the velocity after impact in metres/sec. in a direction $\theta°$ N. of W., Fig. 17. Applying the conservation of momentum in a west direction,

$$\therefore (1000 + 100)u \cos \theta = 100 \times 100 \cos 45° - 1000 \times 2$$

$$\therefore 1100u \cos \theta = 5070 \quad . \quad . \quad . \quad . \quad \text{(i)}$$

Applying the conservation of momentum in a north direction,

$$\therefore (1000 + 100)u \sin \theta = 100 \times 100 \sin 45°$$

$$\therefore 1100u \sin \theta = 7070 \quad . \quad . \quad . \quad . \quad . \quad \text{(ii)}$$

Squaring (i) and (ii), and then adding,

$$\therefore 1100^2 u^2 (\cos {}^2\theta + \sin {}^2\theta) = 5070^2 + 7070^2$$

$$\therefore 1100^2 u^2 = 5070^2 + 7070^2$$

$$\therefore u = \sqrt{\frac{5070^2 + 7070^2}{1100^2}} = 7 \cdot 9 \text{ metres/sec.}$$

Also, dividing (ii) by (i),

$$\therefore \tan \theta = \frac{7070}{5070} = 1 \cdot 394$$

$$\therefore \theta = 54° 21'$$

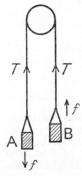

FIG. 18.

3. Derive the principle of the conservation of momentum from two of Newton's laws of motion. Two buckets, each of mass 15 lb., joined by a weightless string which passes over a frictionless pulley. If a 2-lb. lump of putty falls from a height of 4 ft. into one of the buckets, find (a) the velocity of the system immediately after the impact, (b) its subsequent acceleration. (L.)

First part. Newton's law of action and reaction, and his law relating to force, are used in deriving the principle of the conservation of momentum. See text.

Second part. (a) The velocity v of the putty as it falls into the bucket A is given by

$$v^2 = u^2 + 2fs = 0 + 2 \times 32 \times 4. \quad \text{(Fig. 18.)}$$

$$\therefore v = \sqrt{2 \times 32 \times 4} = 16 \text{ ft./sec.}$$

Suppose v is the velocity of the system immediately after the impact. Then, from the conservation of momentum,

$$2 \times 16 = (2 + 15 + 15)v.$$

$$\therefore v = 1 \text{ ft. per sec.}$$

(b) Let $f =$ the subsequent acceleration, and $T =$ the tension in poundals in the string. The net force downwards on the bucket A $= (17g - T)$ poundals, where g is numerically 32. Hence, from $P = mf$,

$$17g - T = 17f \quad \cdot \quad \cdot \quad \cdot \quad \cdot \quad \cdot \quad \text{(i)}$$

The net force upwards on the bucket B $= (T - 15g)$ pounds.

$$\therefore T - 15g = 15f \quad \cdot \quad \cdot \quad \cdot \quad \cdot \quad \text{(ii)}$$

Adding (i) and (ii) to eliminate T,

$$\therefore 17g - 15g = 32f.$$

$$\therefore f = \frac{2g}{32} = \frac{2 \times 32}{32} = 2 \text{ ft. per sec.}^2$$

EXERCISES I

(Assume g = 32 ft. per sec.² or 980 cm. per sec.²)

1. A car moving with a velocity of 30 m.p.h. accelerates uniformly at 2 ft./sec.² until it reaches a velocity of 45 m.p.h. Calculate (i) the time taken, (ii) the distance travelled during the acceleration, (iii) the velocity attained 100 yds. from the place where the acceleration began.

2. A ball of mass 4 oz. is thrown vertically upwards with an initial speed of 60 m.p.h. Calculate (i) the time taken to return to the thrower, (ii) the maximum height reached, (iii) the kinetic and potential energies of the ball when half-way up.

3. The velocity of a ship A relative to a ship B is 10 m.p.h. in a direction N. 45° E. If the velocity of B is 20 m.p.h. in a direction N. 60° W., find the actual velocity of A in magnitude and direction.

4. Calculate the energy of (i) a 50 lb. object held stationary 10 ft. above the ground, (ii) a 2 kilogram object moving with a velocity of 10 metres/sec., (iii) a 10 kilogram object held stationary 5 metres above the ground, (iv) a 20 lb. object moving with a velocity of 30 m.p.h.

5. A 4 lb. ball moving with a velocity of 10 ft. per sec. collides with a 16 lb. ball moving with a velocity of 4 ft. per sec. (i) in the same direction, (ii) in the opposite direction. Calculate the velocity of the balls in each case if they coalesce on impact, and the loss of energy resulting from the impact. State the principle used to calculate the velocity.

6. A ship X moves due north at 30 m.p.h.; a ship Y moves N. 60° W. at 20 m.p.h. Find the velocity of Y relative to X in magnitude and direction. If Y is 10 miles due east of X at this instant, find the closest distance of approach of the two ships.

7. Two buckets of mass 6 lb. are each attached to one end of a long inextensible string passing over a fixed pulley. If a 2 lb. mass of putty is dropped from a height of 4 ft. into one bucket, calculate (i) the initial velocity of the system, (ii) the acceleration of the system, (iii) the loss of energy of the 2 lb. mass due to the impact.

8. State the principle of the conservation of momentum, and describe a collision experiment to illustrate it.

For driving a pile, a heavy weight, the "monkey", is allowed to fall from a height on to the top of the pile. If the monkey weighs 500 lb. wt. and falls through 4 ft. on to a pile of weight 1,000 lb. wt., and there is no recoil, what will be the initial velocity of the pile? How much heat is produced at the impact? (Assume 1,400 ft. lb. wt. = 1 lb. deg. C.) (*L.*)

9. Describe *either* Atwood's machine *or* Fletcher's trolley and experiments made with the one you describe to verify that the acceleration of a body is proportional to the force acting on it. (*L.*)

10A. State Newton's Laws of Motion. How can masses be compared by means of a ballistic balance?

A garden syringe ejects 10 c.c. of water a second through an orifice 1 mm. in diameter. Calculate the backwards thrust on the operator's hands. (*O. & C.*)

10B. Show that a body travelling in a straight line, initially moving with a velocity u and acceleration f, traverses a distance S in time t given by the expression

$$S = ut + \tfrac{1}{2} ft^2.$$

How would you test this relation experimentally for a body starting from rest and moving under a constant acceleration?

A body falls freely from the top of a cliff, and during the last second it falls 11/36 of the whole height. What is the height (in feet) of the cliff? (*C.*)

11. Distinguished between *mass* and *weight*. A body of mass 10 lbs. is transferred to the surface of the moon. Calculate (*a*) its weight, (*b*) the force required to give it an acceleration of 5 ft. per sec.², (*c*) the force required to keep it in uniform motion on a horizontal plane with a coefficient of friction 0·5. Assume that the gravitational acceleration on the moon is 6 ft. per sec.²

A mass of 10 lbs. and specific gravity 2·5 is suspended, completely immersed in water, from a spring balance attached to the roof of a lift. What will be the reading of the balance (*a*) if the lift is moving up with an acceleration of 8 ft. per sec.², (*b*) if the lift is falling freely under gravity? (*O. & C.*)

12. What do you understand by the *conservation of energy*? Illustrate your answer by reference to the energy changes occurring (*a*) in a body whilst falling to and on reaching the ground, (*b*) in an X-ray tube.

The constant force resisting the motion of a car, of mass 1,500 kgm., is equal to one-fifteenth of its weight. If, when travelling at 48 km. per hour, the car is brought to rest in a distance of 50 metres by applying the brakes, find the additional retarding force due to the brakes (assumed constant) and the heat developed in the brakes. (*N.*)

13. Explain what is meant by the relative velocity of one moving object with respect to another.

A ship A is moving eastward with a speed of 15 knots and another ship B, at a given instant 10 nautical miles east of A, is moving southwards with a speed of 20 knots. How long after this instant will the ships be nearest to each other, how far apart will they be then, and in what direction will B be sighted from A? (*C.*)

14. State Newton's Second Law of Motion. Deduce from the law a definition of the unit of force.

A shot of mass 1 lb. strikes a fixed block of wood of mass 11 lb. with a given velocity and penetrates a distance of 6 inches. If the block had been free to move and the shot travelled along a line passing through the centre of mass of the block, how far would the shot have penetrated? (*W.*)

15. Explain what is meant by the principle of conservation of energy for a system of particles not acted upon by any external forces. What modifications are introduced when external forces are operative?

A bobsleigh is travelling at 30 m.p.h. when it starts ascending an incline of 1 in 100. If it comes to rest after travelling 500 ft. up the slope, calculate the proportion of the energy lost in friction and deduce the coefficient of friction between the runners and the snow. (*O. & C.*)

16. A bullet of mass 25 gm. and travelling horizontally at a speed of 200 metres sec.⁻¹ imbeds itself in a wooden block of mass 5 kgm. suspended by cords 3 metres long. How far will the block swing from its position of rest before beginning to return? Describe a suitable method of suspending the block for this experiment and explain briefly the principles used in the solution of the problem. (*L.*)

17. State Newton's Laws of Motion and deduce from them the relation between the distance travelled and the time for the case of a body acted upon by a constant force. Explain the units in which the various quantities are measured.

A fire engine pumps water at such a rate that the velocity of the water leaving the nozzle is 50 ft./sec. If the jet be directed perpendicularly on to a wall and the rebound of the water be neglected, calculate the pressure on the wall (1 cu. ft. water weighs 62·35 lb.). (*O. & C.*)

18. A point *A* moves with constant velocity *u* to the north, while a point *B* moves with velocity *v* to the east. Explain how you would determine the velocity of *A* relative to *B*.

A road running north-south intersects a road running east-west. A car travelling towards the crossing from the west at 20 m.p.h. is 200 yds. from the crossing, when a second car, travelling at 30 m.p.h. towards the crossing from the north, is 400 yds. from the crossing. What is the velocity of the first car relative to the second, and what is the least distance that will separate them? Where are the cars at the moment of closest approach? (*W.*)

19. Derive an expression for the kinetic energy of a moving body.

A vehicle of mass 2 tons travelling at 30 m.p.h. on a horizontal surface is brought to rest in a distance of 40 ft. by the action of its brakes. Calculate the average retarding force. What horse-power must the engine develop in order to take the vehicle up an incline of 1 in 10 at a constant speed of 30 m.p.h. if the frictional resistance is equal to 50 lb. wt.? (*L.*)

20. Define velocity and acceleration. A body is projected from a point above level ground with a velocity of 64 ft. sec.$^{-1}$ at an angle of 60° above the horizontal and takes 4 secs. to reach the ground. Calculate (*a*) the height of the point of projection above the ground, (*b*) the horizontal distance between the point of projection and the point at which the body strikes the ground, (*c*) the maximum height reached by the body. (*L.*)

CHAPTER II

CIRCULAR MOTION

SIMPLE HARMONIC MOTION

1. Angular Velocity.

In the previous chapter we discussed the motion of an object moving in a straight line. There are numerous cases of objects moving in a

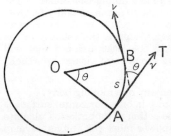

FIG. 19. Circular motion.

curve about some fixed point. The earth and the moon revolve continuously round the sun, for example, and the rim of the balance-wheel of a watch moves to-and-fro in a circular path about the fixed axis of the wheel. In this chapter we shall study the motion of an object moving in a circle with a *uniform speed* round a fixed point O as centre, Fig. 19.

If the object moves from A to B so that the radius OA moves through an angle θ, its *angular velocity*, ω, about O is defined as the *change of the angle per second*. Thus if t is the time taken by the object to move from A to B,

$$\omega = \frac{\theta}{t} \qquad \cdots \qquad (14).$$

Angular velocity is usually expressed in "radians per second". From (14),

$$\theta = \omega t \qquad \cdots \qquad (15).$$

which is analogous to the formula "distance = uniform velocity × time" for motion in a straight line. It will be noted that the time T to describe the circle once, known as the *period* of the motion, is given by

$$T = \frac{2\pi}{\omega}, \qquad \cdots \qquad (16)$$

since 2π radians = 360° by definition.

If s is the length of the arc AB, then $s/r = \theta$, by definition of an angle in radians.

32

$$\therefore \quad s = r\theta.$$

Dividing by t, the time taken to move from A to B,

$$\therefore \quad \frac{s}{t} = r\frac{\theta}{t}.$$

But $s/t =$ the *velocity*, v, of the rotating object, and θ/t is the angular velocity.

$$\therefore \quad v = r\omega \qquad . \quad . \quad . \quad . \quad (17).$$

2. Acceleration of Rotating Object.

When an object is whirled round in a circle at the end of a string, the force (tension) in the rope makes the object move in its path continuously. As we shall now see, the object has a constant *acceleration* towards the centre of the circle.

Suppose the object is at A at some instant; it is then moving with a velocity v along the tangent AT, Fig. 19. If the object moves to B in a small interval of time, the change in velocity along AT

$$= v \cos\theta - v = 0,$$

since θ is so small that $\cos\theta$ is practically equal to $\cos 0°$ or 1. There is, consequently, no acceleration along the tangent.

If we resolve the velocity v at B in a direction parallel to the radius OA, then

change in velocity towards centre $= v \sin\theta.$

$$\therefore \text{ acceleration towards centre} = \frac{v \sin\theta}{t},$$

where t is the time. But $\sin\theta = \theta$ in radians when θ is very small.

$$\therefore \text{ acceleration} = \frac{v\theta}{t} = v\omega,$$

since $\theta/t = \omega$. But $v = r\omega$.

$$\therefore \text{ acceleration} = \omega^2 r, \text{ or } \frac{v^2}{r} \qquad . \quad . \quad . \quad . \quad (18).$$

Thus the rotating object has a constant acceleration *towards the centre* equal to $\omega^2 r$ or v^2/r.

When a stone attached to the end of a string is swung round in a vertical circle, the acceleration towards the centre is provided by the tension in the string. When a racing-car travels round a banked circular track, the acceleration towards the centre is provided by forces at the wheels of the car (p. 34).

3. Centrifugal Force.   The Centrifuge.

The force acting towards the centre on an object of mass m when it rotates in a circle is mv^2/r. Consequently, by Newton's law of action and reaction, there is a force *away from* the centre which is mv^2/r in magnitude, and this is known as the *centrifugal force*. If some water is placed in a vessel attached to the end of a string, the vessel can be whirled in a vertical plane without any water falling out. This is because the centrifugal force on the water (mv^2/r) is greater than its weight (mg).

Cream is separated from milk by rotating the mixture in a vessel. In this case the centrifugal force acting on the milk is greater than that on the cream at the same place, since the cream is less dense, and hence the milk moves away from the centre to the rim. For a similar reason small crystals are separated from the mother-liquors when they are placed in a *centrifuge*, the name given to the rotating vessel. Speeds of 10,000 revs. per minute may be used in centrifuges.

4. Motion of Bicycle Rider Round Circular Track.

When a person on a bicycle rides round a circular track, a frictional force F towards the centre is exerted at the ground, Fig. 20. If we now

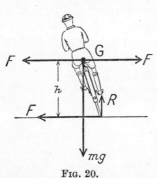

FIG. 20.

Bicycle rider on circular track.

imagine two equal and opposite forces F at the centre of gravity G of the bicycle and rider, each parallel to the force F at the ground, we can see there is a force F at G towards the centre, which has a magnitude mv^2/r poundals, where m is the mass of bicycle and rider. There is also a *couple* (p. 81), tending to overturn the bicycle outwards, which has a moment $F \times h$, where h is the height of G above the ground. If the rider leans inwards towards the centre of the track, the normal reaction R at the ground is equal to mg poundals, since there is no motion vertically, and consequently there is now a restoring couple on the bicycle.

5. Motion of Car (or Train) Round Circular Track.

Suppose a car (or train) is moving with a velocity v round a horizontal circular track of radius r, and let R_1, R_2 be the respective normal reactions at the wheels A, B, and F_1, F_2 the corresponding frictional forces, Fig. 21. If we imagine two equal and opposite forces $(F_1 + F_2)$, at G, the centre of gravity of the car (or train), we have

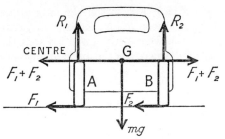

FIG. 21. Car on circular track.

$$F_1 + F_2 = \frac{mv^2}{r}, \qquad \cdots \qquad \text{(i)}$$

and
$$R_1 + R_2 = mg. \qquad \cdots \qquad \text{(ii)}$$

Also, taking moments about G,

$$(F_1 + F_2)h + R_1 a - R_2 a = 0 \qquad \cdot \quad \cdot \quad \text{(iii)},$$

where $2a$ is the distance between the wheels, assuming G is mid-way between the wheels, and h is the height of G above the ground. From these three equations, we find

$$R_2 = \tfrac{1}{2}m\left(g + \frac{v^2 h}{ra}\right)$$

and
$$R_1 = \tfrac{1}{2}m\left(g - \frac{v^2 h}{ra}\right).$$

R_2 never vanishes since it always has a positive value. But if $v^2 = arg/h$, $R_1 = 0$, and the car is about to overturn outwards. R_1 will be positive if $v^2 \smile arg/h$.

6. Motion of Car (or Train) Round Banked Track.

Suppose a car (or train) is moving round a banked track in a circular

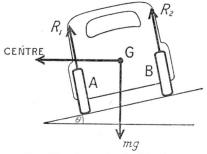

FIG. 22. Car on banked track.

path of horizontal radius r, Fig. 22. If the only forces at the wheels A, B are the normal reactions R_1, R_2 respectively, that is, there is no side-slip or strain at the wheels, the force towards the centre of the track is $(R_1 + R_2) \sin \theta$, where θ is the angle of inclination of the plane to the horizontal.

$$\therefore (R_1 + R_2) \sin \theta = \frac{mv^2}{r} \qquad . \qquad . \qquad . \qquad \text{(i)}$$

For vertical equilibrium, $(R_1 + R_2) \cos \theta = mg$ . . . (ii)

Dividing (i) by (ii), $\qquad \therefore \tan \theta = \frac{v^2}{rg}$ . . . (iii).

Thus for a given velocity v and radius r, the angle of inclination of the track for no side-slip must be $\tan^{-1}(v^2/rg)$. As the speed v increases, the angle θ increases, from (iii). A racing-track is made saucer-shaped because at higher speeds the cars can move towards a part of the track which is steeper and sufficient to prevent side-slip. The outer rail of a curved railway track is raised above the inner rail so that the force towards the centre is largely provided by the component of the reaction at the wheels. It is desirable to bank a road at corners for the same reason as a racing track is banked.

7. Thrust at Ground.

Suppose now that the car (or train) is moving at such a speed that the frictional forces at A, B are F_1, F_2 respectively, each acting towards the centre of the track (not shown in Fig. 22).

Resolving horizontally,

$$\therefore (R_1 + R_2) \sin \theta + (F_1 + F_2) \cos \theta = \frac{mv^2}{r} \qquad . \qquad . \qquad \text{(i)}$$

Resolving vertically,

$$\therefore (R_1 + R_2) \cos \theta - (F_1 + F_2) \sin \theta = mg \qquad . \qquad . \qquad \text{(ii)}$$

Solving, we find

$$F_1 + F_2 = m \left(\frac{v^2}{r} \cos \theta - g \sin \theta \right) \qquad . \qquad . \qquad . \qquad \text{(iii)}.$$

If $\frac{v^2}{r} \cos \theta > g \sin \theta$, then $(F_1 + F_2)$ is positive; and in this case both the thrusts on the wheels at the ground are towards the centre of the track.

If $\frac{v^2}{r} \cos \theta < g \sin \theta$, then $(F_1 + F_2)$ is negative. In this case the force F_2 acts inwards towards the centre of the track, whilst the force F_1 on the wheel A acts outwards.

For stability, we have, by moments about G,

$$(F_1 + F_2)h + R_1a - R_2a = 0$$

$$\therefore (F_1 + F_2)\frac{h}{a} = R_2 - R_1$$

From (iii), $\therefore \dfrac{mh}{a}\left(\dfrac{v^2}{r}\cos\theta - g\sin\theta\right) = R_2 - R_1$ . . (iv).

The reactions R_1, R_2 can be calculated by finding $(R_1 + R_2)$ from equations (i), (ii), and combining the result with equation (iv). This is left as an exercise to the student.

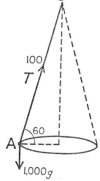

Fig. 23.

EXAMPLE

Explain the action of a centrifuge when used to hasten the deposition of a sediment from a liquid.

A pendulum bob of mass 1 kilogramme is attached to a string 1 metre long and made to revolve in a horizontal circle of radius 60 cm. Find the period of the motion and the tension of the string. (*C.*)

First part. See text, p. 34.

Second part. Suppose A is the bob, and OA is the string, Fig. 23. If T is the tension, and θ is the angle of inclination of OA to the horizontal, then, for motion in the circle,

$$T\cos\theta = \frac{mv^2}{r} = \frac{mv^2}{60} \quad . \quad . \quad . \quad . \quad (i).$$

Since the bob A does not move in a vertical direction, then

$$T\sin\theta = mg \quad . \quad . \quad . \quad . \quad (ii).$$

Now $\cos\theta = 60/100 = 3/5$; hence $\sin\theta = 4/5$.
From (ii),

$$\therefore T = \frac{mg}{\sin\theta} = \frac{1{,}000g}{4/5} = 1{,}250 \text{ gm. wt.}$$

From (i),

$$v = \sqrt{\frac{60\,T\cos\theta}{m}}$$

$$= \sqrt{\frac{60 \times 1{,}250 \times 980 \times 3}{5 \times 1{,}000}} = 210 \text{ cm./sec.}$$

$\therefore$ angular velocity, $\omega = \dfrac{v}{r} = \dfrac{210}{60} = \dfrac{7}{2}$ radians/sec.

$\therefore$ period, $T, = \dfrac{2\pi}{\omega} = \dfrac{2\pi}{7/2} = \dfrac{4\pi}{7}$ sec.

$\therefore T = 1\cdot 8$ sec.

SIMPLE HARMONIC MOTION

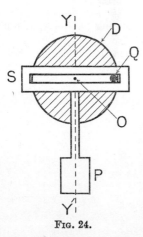

FIG. 24.

When the bob of a pendulum moves to-and-fro through a small angle, the bob is said to be moving with *simple harmonic motion*. The prongs of a sounding tuning fork, and the layers of air near it, are moving with simple harmonic motion, and light waves can be considered due to simple harmonic variations.

We can gain some insight into the analysis of simple harmonic motion by considering a mechanism sometimes used for actuating a pump-plunger P, Fig. 24. The slotted cage S is driven up and down by the pin Q, which rotates with the disc D about the axle O. Consequently the to-and-fro or simple harmonic motion of P is the *projection* of the circular motion of Q on the vertical line YY'.

8. Formulæ in Simple Harmonic Motion.

Consider an object moving round a circle of radius r and centre Z with a uniform angular velocity ω, Fig. 25. If CZF is a fixed diameter, the *foot* of the perpendicular from the moving object to this diameter moves

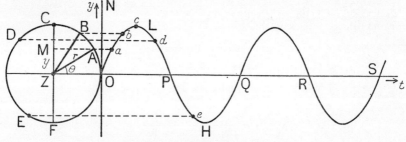

FIG. 25. Simple harmonic motion.

from Z to C, back to Z and across to F, and then returns to Z, while the object moves once round the circle from O in an anti-clockwise direction. The to-and-fro motion along CZF of the foot of the perpendicular is defined as *simple harmonic motion*.

Suppose the object moving round the circle is at A at some instant, where angle OZA = θ, and suppose the foot of the perpendicular from A to CZ is M. The acceleration of the object at A is $\omega^2 r$, and this acceleration is directed along the radius AZ (see p. 33). Hence the acceleration of M towards Z

$$= \omega^2 r \cos AZC = \omega^2 r \sin \theta.$$

But $r \sin \theta = MZ = y$ say.

$$\therefore \text{ acceleration of M towards Z} = \omega^2 y.$$

Now ω^2 is a constant.

$$\therefore \text{ } acceleration \text{ } of \text{ } M \text{ } towards \text{ } Z \propto distance \text{ } of \text{ } M \text{ } from \text{ } Z.$$

It we wish to express mathematically that the acceleration is always directed towards Z, we must say

$$\text{acceleration towards Z} = -\omega^2 y \quad . \quad . \quad . \quad (19).$$

The minus indicates, of course, that the object begins to retard as it passes the centre, Z, of its motion. If the minus were omitted from equation (19) the latter would imply that the acceleration increases as y increases, and the object would then never return to its original position.

We can now form a definition of simple harmonic motion. If a particle is vibrating to-and-fro in such a way that its acceleration is directed towards a fixed point at any instant and is proportional to its distance from that point, the particle is moving with simple harmonic motion.

9. Period, Amplitude. Sine Curve.

The time taken for the foot of the perpendicular to move from C to F and back to C is known as the *period* (T) of the simple harmonic motion. In this time, the object moving round the circle goes exactly once round the circle from C; and since ω is the angular velocity and 2π radians (360°) is the angle described, the period T is given by

$$T = \frac{2\pi}{\omega} \quad . \quad . \quad . \quad . \quad . \quad (20).$$

The distance ZC, or ZF, is the maximum distance from Z of the foot of the perpendicular, and is known as the *amplitude* of the motion. It is equal to r, the radius of the circle.

We have now to consider the variation with time, t, of the distance, y, from Z of the foot of the perpendicular. The distance $y = ZM = r \sin \theta$. But $\theta = \omega t$, where ω is the angular velocity,

$$\therefore y = r \sin \omega t \quad . \quad . \quad . \quad (21).$$

The graph of y v.t is shown in Fig. 25, where ON represents the y-axis and OS the t-axis; since the angular velocity of the object moving round the circle is constant, θ is proportional to the time t. Thus as the foot of the perpendicular along CZF moves from Z to C and back to Z, the graph OLP is traced out; as the foot moves from Z to F and returns to Z, the graph PHQ is traced out. The graph is a *sine curve*. The complete set of values of y from O to Q is known as a cycle.

10. Velocity during S.H.M.

Suppose the object moving round the circle is at A at some instant, Fig. 25. The velocity of the object is $r\omega$, where r is the radius of the circle, and it is directed along the tangent at A. Consequently the velocity parallel to the diameter FC at this instant $= r\omega \cos \theta$, by resolving.

$$\therefore \text{ velocity, } v, \text{ of M along FC} = r\omega \cos \theta.$$

But $\qquad\qquad y = r \sin \theta$

$$\therefore \cos \theta = \sqrt{1 - \sin^2 \theta} = \sqrt{1 - y^2/r^2} = \frac{1}{r}\sqrt{r^2 - y^2}$$

$$\therefore v = \omega\sqrt{r^2 - y^2} \quad . \quad . \quad . \quad (22)$$

This is the expression for the velocity of an object moving with simple harmonic motion. The maximum velocity, v_m, corresponds to $y = 0$, and hence

$$v_m = \omega r.$$

Summarising our results for simple harmonic motion:

(1) If the acceleration of an object $= -\omega^2 y$, where y is the distance or displacement of the object from a fixed point, the motion is simple harmonic motion.

(2) The period, T, of the motion $= 2\pi/\omega$, where T is the time to make a complete to-and-fro movement.

(3) The amplitude, r, of the motion is the maximum distance on either side of the fixed point of the vibrating object.

(4) The velocity at any instant, v, $= \omega\sqrt{r^2 - y^2}$; the maximum velocity $= \omega r$.

EXAMPLE

What is *simple harmonic motion*? Show how it is related to the uniform motion of a particle with velocity v in a circle of radius a.

A steel strip, clamped at one end, vibrates with a frequency of 20 cycles per sec. and an amplitude of 5 mm. at the free end. Find (a) the velocity of the end when passing through the zero position, (b) the acceleration at the maximum displacement. (*L.*)

First part. For definition of simple harmonic motion, see p. 39. The foot of the perpendicular from the particle to the diameter moves with simple harmonic motion as the particle proceeds round the circle. See p. 39.

Second part. Suppose $y = r \sin \omega t$ represents the vibration of the strip where r is the amplitude.

(a) The velocity, $v, = \omega\sqrt{r^2 - y^2}$ (p. 40). When the end of the strip passes through the zero position $y = 0$; and the maximum speed, v_m, is given by

$$v_m = \omega r.$$

Now $\omega = 2\pi f = 2\pi \times 20$, and $r = 0.5$ cm.

$$\therefore v_m = 2\pi \times 20 \times 0.5 = 62.8 \text{ cm./sec.}$$

(b) The acceleration $= -\omega^2 y = -\omega^2 r$ at the maximum displacement.

$$\therefore \text{acceleration} = (2\pi \times 20)^2 \times 0.5$$
$$= 7,894 \text{ cm./sec.}^2$$

11. Simple Pendulum.

We shall now study some cases of simple harmonic motion. Consider a *simple pendulum*, which consists of a small mass m attached to the end of a length l of wire, Fig. 26. If the other end of the wire is attached to a fixed point P and the mass is displaced slightly, it oscillates to-and-fro along the arc of a circle of centre P. We shall now show that the motion of the mass about its original position O is simple harmonic motion.

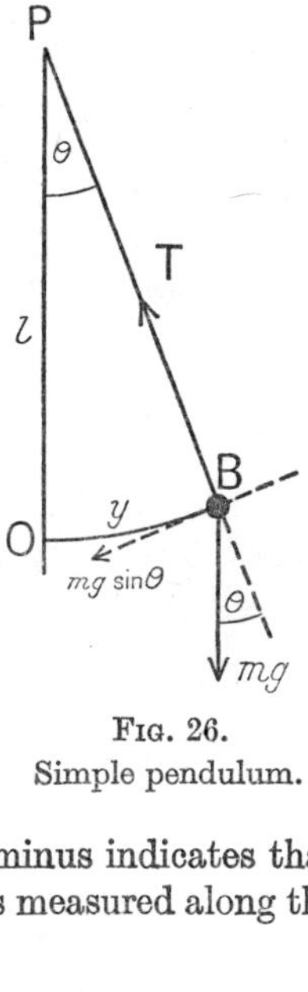

Suppose that the vibrating mass is at B at some instant, where $OB = y$ and angle $OPB = \theta$. At B, the force pulling the mass towards O is directed along the tangent at B, and is equal to $mg \sin \theta$. The tension, T, in the wire has no component in this direction, since PB is perpendicular to the tangent at B. Thus, since force = mass × acceleration (p. 13),

$$- mg \sin \theta = mf,$$

FIG. 26.
Simple pendulum.

where f is the acceleration along the arc OB; the minus indicates that the force is towards O, while the displacement, y, is measured along the arc from O in the opposite direction. *When θ is small, sin θ = θ in* radians; also $\theta = y/l$. Hence,

$$- mg\theta = - mg\frac{y}{l} = mf$$

$$\therefore f = -\frac{g}{l}y = - \omega^2 y,$$

where $\omega^2 = g/l$. Since the acceleration is proportional to the distance y from a fixed point, the motion of the vibrating mass is simple harmonic motion (p. 40). Further, from p. 40, the period $T = 2\pi/\omega$.

$$\therefore T = \frac{2\pi}{\sqrt{g/l}} = 2\pi\sqrt{\frac{l}{g}} \qquad . \quad . \quad . \quad . \quad (23).$$

At a given place on the earth, where g is constant, the formula shows that the period T depends only on the length, l, of the pendulum. Moreover, the period remains constant even when the amplitude of the vibrations diminish owing to the resistance of the air. This result was first obtained by Galileo, who noticed a swinging lantern one day, and timed the oscillations by his pulse (there were no clocks in his day). He found that the period remained constant although the swings gradually diminished in amplitude.

12. Determination of g by Simple Pendulum.

The acceleration due to gravity, g, can be found by measuring the period, T, of a simple pendulum corresponding to a few different lengths, l, from 80 cm. to 180 cm. for example. To perform the experiment accurately: (i) Fifty oscillations should be timed, (ii) a small angle of swing is essential, less than 10°, (iii) a small sphere should be tied to the

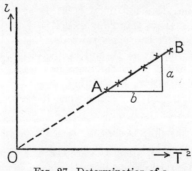

Fig. 27. Determination of g.

end of a thread to act as the mass, and its radius added to the length of the thread to determine l.

A graph of l against T^2 is now plotted, and a straight line AB, which should pass through the origin, is then drawn to lie evenly between the points, Fig. 27.

Now
$$T = 2\pi \sqrt{\frac{l}{g}},$$

$$\therefore T^2 = \frac{4\pi^2 l}{g}$$

$$\therefore g = 4\pi^2 \times \frac{l}{T^2} \quad . \quad . \quad . \quad . \quad (24)$$

The gradient a/b of the line AB is the magnitude of l/T^2; and by substituting in (24), g can then be calculated.

13. Magnitudes of g.

The first determination of g was by the simple pendulum method. The magnitude of g, which is determined nowadays by much more accurate methods, varies all over the globe, according to the longitude and latitude, and altitude, of the place concerned. Some of the values obtained are shown below:

PLACE	g (CM. PER SEC.^{2})
National Physical Laboratory, London	981·181
Cavendish Laboratory, Cambridge	981·266
Greenwich Observatory	981·188
Washington	980·080
Paris Observatory	980·943
Cape Town Observatory	979·659
Melbourne	979·987
Potsdam	981·274
Ottawa	980·607
Calcutta	978·816

14. Proportionality of Weight and Mass.

The simple pendulum experiment can be used to show that the weight W of an object is directly proportional to its mass m. Consider again a vibrating object B of mass m. See Fig. 26, p. 41. Then, since force = mass $\times$ acceleration, and W is the weight acting vertically,

$$- W \sin \theta = mf.$$

But $\sin \theta = \theta$ in radians when the angle is small; and $\theta = y/l$, where $y = OB$.

$$\therefore - W\frac{y}{l} = mf$$

$$\therefore f = -\frac{W}{ml}y = -\omega^2 y,$$

where $\omega^2 = W/ml$.

$$\therefore \text{ period of motion, } T, = 2\pi\sqrt{\frac{ml}{W}}$$

$$\therefore \frac{T^2}{4\pi^2 l} = \frac{m}{W} \quad . \quad . \quad . \quad . \quad . \quad . \quad \text{(i)}$$

Now experiment with varying lengths, l, of the simple pendulum reveals that the square of the period, T^2, is directly proportional to l, or $T^2/l = $ constant. See Fig. 27. Hence, from (i),

$$\frac{m}{W} = \text{constant}$$

$$\therefore W \propto m.$$

$$\therefore \text{ weight of object } \propto \text{ mass of object.}$$

15. Simple Pendulum Suspended from Inaccessible Point.

Suppose a simple pendulum is suspended from an inaccessible point, for example from the ceiling of a very tall room, the string reaching almost to the floor. If h is the height of the room and T_1 is the period, then

$$T_1 = 2\pi\sqrt{\frac{h}{g}} \quad . \quad . \quad . \quad \text{(i)}$$

To find the acceleration due to gravity, suppose a measured length a of the thread is cut off and the new period T_2 is measured. Then

$$T_2 = 2\pi\sqrt{\frac{h-a}{g}} \quad . \quad . \quad . \quad \text{(ii)}.$$

From (i), $\qquad g\frac{T_1^2}{4\pi^2} = h,$

and from (ii) $\qquad g\frac{T_2^2}{4\pi^2} = h - a.$

Subtracting, $\therefore \dfrac{g}{4\pi^2}(T_1{}^2 - T_2{}^2) = a$

$$\therefore g = \frac{4\pi^2 a}{T_1{}^2 - T_2{}^2}.$$

Thus g can be calculated from measurements of a, T_1, and T_2. The height of the room is then given by $gT_1{}^2/4\pi^2$ from (i).

16. The Spiral Spring or Elastic Thread.

When a weight is suspended from the end of a spring or an elastic thread, experiment shows that the extension of the spring, i.e., the increase in length, is proportional to the weight, provided that the elastic limit of the spring is not exceeded (see p. 137). Generally, then, *the tension (force)*, T, *in a spring is proportional to the extension x produced*, i.e., $T = kx$, where k is a constant of the spring.

Consider a spring or an elastic thread PA of length l suspended from a fixed point P, Fig. 28. When a mass m is placed on it, the spring stretches to O by a length a given by

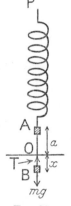

$$mg = ka, \quad \cdot \quad \cdot \quad \cdot \quad \cdot \quad \text{(i)}$$

since the tension in the spring is then mg. If the mass is pulled down a little and then released, it vibrates up-and-down above and below O. Suppose at an instant that B is at a distance x below O. The tension T of the spring at B is then equal to $k(a + x)$, and hence the force towards O $= k(a + x) - mg$. Since force = mass $\times$ acceleration,

Fig. 28.
Spiral Spring

$$\therefore -[k(a + x) - mg] = mf;$$

the minus indicates that the net force is upward at this instant, whereas the displacement x is measured from O in the opposite direction at the same instant. From this equation,

$$-ka - kx + mg = mf.$$

But, from (i), $mg = ka$

$$\therefore -kx = mf$$

$$\therefore f = -\frac{k}{m}x$$

$$\therefore \quad = -\omega^2 x,$$

where $\omega^2 = k/m$. Thus the motion is simple harmonic about O, and the period T is given by

$$T = \frac{2\pi}{\omega} = 2\pi\sqrt{\frac{m}{k}} \quad . \quad . \quad . \quad (25).$$

Also, since $mg = ka$, it follows that $m/k = a/g$.

$$\therefore T = 2\pi\sqrt{\frac{a}{g}} \quad . \quad . \quad . \quad (26).$$

From (25), it follows that $T^2 = 4\pi^2 m/k$. Consequently a graph of T^2 v. m should be a straight line passing through the origin. In practice, when the load m is varied and the corresponding period T is measured, a straight line graph is obtained when T^2 is plotted against m, thus verifying indirectly that the motion of the load was simple harmonic. The graph does not pass through the origin, however, owing to the mass and the movement of the various parts of the spring, which has not been taken into account in the foregoing theory.

17. Determination of g by Spiral Spring.

The mass s of a vibrating spring should also be taken into account, in addition to the mass m suspended at the end. Theory beyond the scope of this book then shows that the period of vibration, T, is given by

$$T = 2\pi\sqrt{\frac{m + \lambda s}{k}} \quad . \quad . \quad . \quad \text{(i)}$$

where λ is approximately $1/3$ and k is the elastic constant of the spring Squaring (i) and re-arranging,

$$\therefore \frac{k}{4\pi^2}T^2 = m + \lambda s \quad . \quad . \quad . \quad . \quad \text{(ii)}$$

Thus, since λ, k, s are constants, a graph of T^2 vs. m should be a straight line when m is varied and T observed. A straight line graph verifies indirectly that the motion of the mass at the end of the spring is simple harmonic. Further, the magnitude of $k/4\pi^2$ can be found from the slope of the line, and hence k can be calculated.

If a mass M is placed on the end of the spring, producing a steady extension a less than the elastic limit, then $Mg = ka$.

$$\therefore g = \frac{a}{M} \times k \quad . \quad . \quad . \quad \text{(iii)}$$

By attaching different masses to the spring, and measuring the corresponding extension, the magnitude of a/M can be found by plotting a v. M and measuring the slope of the line. This is called the "static" experiment on the spring. From the magnitude of k obtained in the "dynamic" experiment when the period was determined for different loads, the value of g can be found by substituting the magnitudes of a/M and k in (iii).

18. Oscillations of a Liquid in a U-Tube.

If the liquid on one side of a U-tube T is depressed by blowing gently down that side, the levels of the liquid will oscillate for a short time about their respective initial positions O, C, before finally coming to rest, Fig. 29.

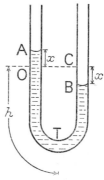

FIG. 29.
Oscillation of liquid.

The period of oscillation can be found by supposing that the level of the liquid on the left side of T is at A at some instant, at a height x above its original (undisturbed) position O. The level B of the liquid on the other side is then at a depth x below its original position C, and hence the excess pressure on the whole liquid, as shown on p. 102,

$$= \text{excess height} \times \text{density of liquid} \times g$$

$$= 2x\rho g.$$

Now pressure = force per unit area.

∴ force on liquid = pressure × area of cross-section of the tube

$$= 2x\rho g \times a,$$

where a is the cross-sectional area of the tube.

This force causes the liquid to accelerate. The mass of liquid in the U-tube = volume × density = $2ha\rho$, where $2h$ is the total length of the liquid in T. Now the acceleration, f, towards O or C is given by

$$\text{force} = \text{mass} \times f,$$

and hence

$$- 2x\rho ga = 2ha\rho f.$$

The minus indicates that the force towards O is opposite to the displacement measured from O at that instant.

$$\therefore f = -\frac{g}{h}x$$

$$= -\omega^2 x,$$

where $\omega^2 = \dfrac{g}{h}$. The motion of the liquid about O (or C) is thus simple harmonic, and the period T is given by

$$T = \frac{2\pi}{\omega} = 2\pi \sqrt{\frac{h}{g}} \qquad \text{(27)}.$$

EXAMPLES

1. Define *simple harmonic motion* and state the relation between displacement from its mean position and the restoring force when a body executes simple harmonic motion.

A body is supported by a spiral spring and causes a stretch of 1·5 cm. in the spring. If the mass is now set in vertical oscillation of small amplitude, what is the periodic time of the oscillation? (*L.*)

First part. Simple harmonic motion is the motion of an object whose acceleration is proportional to its distance from a fixed point and is always directed towards that point. The relation is: Restoring force $= -k \times$ distance from fixed point, where k is a constant.

Second part. Let m be the mass of the body in grams. Then

$$mg = k \times 1\cdot5, \qquad \cdot \quad \cdot \quad \cdot \quad \cdot \quad \cdot \quad \cdot \qquad \text{(i)}$$

where k is a constant of the spring. Suppose the vibrating body is x cm below its original position at some instant and is moving downwards. Then since the extension is $(x + 1\cdot5)$ cm., the net downward force

$$= mg - k\,(x + 1\cdot5)$$
$$= mg - k \times 1\cdot5 - k\,x$$
$$= -k$$

from (i).   Now mass $\times$ acceleration $=$ force.

$$\therefore m \times \text{acceleration} = -k\,x$$

$$\therefore \text{acceleration} = -\frac{k}{m}x$$

But, from (i),

$$\frac{k}{m} = \frac{g}{1\cdot5}$$

$$\therefore \text{acceleration} = -\frac{g}{1\cdot5}\,x = -\omega^2 x,$$

where $\omega^2 = g/1\cdot5$.

$$\therefore \text{period } T = \frac{2\pi}{\omega} = 2\pi\sqrt{\frac{1\cdot5}{g}} = 2\pi\sqrt{\frac{1\cdot5}{980}}$$
$$= 0\cdot25 \text{ sec.}$$

2. The bob of a long pendulum is suspended by string from a point on the ceiling of a room, and observations of the period, T, with the height, l, of the bob above the floor are taken when the length of the pendulum is shortened by cutting off string. Explain how the height of the room, and the acceleration g due to gravity, can be determined from a suitable graph between T and l.

Suppose h is the height of the room. The length of the pendulum is then $(h - l)$, and hence

$$T = 2\pi \sqrt{\frac{h - l}{g}}.$$

Squaring, $\qquad\qquad \therefore T^2 = \frac{4\pi^2}{g}h - \frac{4\pi^2 l}{g} \qquad \text{\textbullet}\quad\text{\textbullet}\quad\text{\textbullet}\qquad \text{(i)}$

Since h and g are constants, it follows from (i) that *a straight line graph is obtained when T^2 is plotted against l*, Fig. 30. From (i), the slope, m, of the

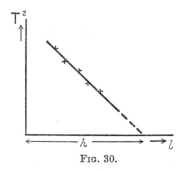

FIG. 30.

T^2 v. l graph is given numerically by $4\pi^2/g$. Thus

$$g = \frac{4\pi^2}{m},$$

and hence g can be calculated.

From (i), when T^2 is zero,

$$\frac{4\pi^2}{g}h - \frac{4\pi^2}{g}l = 0.$$

$$\therefore l = h \text{ in this case.}$$

The height h of the room is thus given by the intercept on the l-axis when the straight line graph is produced to intersect it (Fig. 30).

3. Define simple harmonic motion and show from your definition that the bob of a simple pendulum oscillates in simple harmonic motion provided its amplitude of vibration is small. Obtain an expression for the period.

A small bob of mass 50 gm. oscillates as a simple pendulum, with amplitude 5 cm. and period 2 sec. Find the velocity of the bob and the tension in the supporting thread, when the velocity of the bob is a maximum. (*W.*)

First part.   See text.

Second part.   The velocity, v, of the bob is a maximum when it passes through its original position. With the usual notation (see p. 40), the maximum velocity v_m is given by

$$v_m = \omega r,$$

where r is the amplitude of 5 cm. Since $T = 2\pi/\omega$,

$$\therefore \quad \omega = \frac{2\pi}{T} = \frac{2\pi}{2} = \pi \quad . \quad . \quad . \quad . \quad . \quad \text{(i)}$$

$$\therefore \quad v_m = \omega a = \pi \times 5 = 15\cdot7 \text{ cm. per sec.}$$

Suppose P is the tension in dynes in the thread. The net force towards the centre of the circle along which the bob moves is then given by $(P - mg)$, or $(P - 50g)$. The acceleration towards the centre of the circle, which is the point of suspension, is v_m^2/l, where l is the length of the pendulum.

$$\therefore P - 50g = \frac{50 v_m^2}{l}$$

$$\therefore P = 50g + \frac{50 v_m^2}{l}$$

Now
$$T = 2\pi \sqrt{\frac{l}{g}}$$

$$\therefore l = \frac{gT^2}{4\pi^2} = \frac{g \times 4}{4\pi^2} = \frac{g}{\pi^2}$$

$$\therefore P = 50g + \frac{50(5\pi)^2 \pi^2}{g} \text{ , from above.}$$

$$= 50g + \frac{1250\pi^4}{g}$$

$$= 50\cdot13g \text{ dynes.}$$

$$\therefore P = 50\cdot13 \text{ gm. wt.}$$

GRAVITATION

19. Kepler's Laws.

The motion of the planets in the heavens had excited the interest of the earliest scientists, and Babylonian and Greek astronomers were able to predict their movements fairly accurately. It was considered for some time that the earth was the centre of the universe, but about 1542 COPERNICUS suggested that the planets revolved round the sun as centre. A great advance was made by KEPLER about 1609. He had studied for many years the records of observations on the planets made by TYCHO BRAHE, and he enunciated three laws known by his name. These state:

(1) The planets describe ellipses about the sun as one focus.

(2) The line joining the sun and the planet sweeps out equal areas in equal times.

(3) The squares of the periods of revolution of the planets are proportional to the cubes of their mean distances from the sun.

The third law was announced by Kepler in 1619.

20. Newton's Law of Gravitation.

About 1666, at the early age of 24, NEWTON discovered a universal law known as the *law of gravitation*.

He was led to this discovery by considering the motion of a planet moving in a circle round the sun as centre. The force acting on the planet of mass m is $mr\omega^2$, where r is the radius of the circle and ω is the angular velocity of the motion (p. 33). Since $\omega = 2\pi/T$, where T is the period of the motion,

$$\text{force on planet} = mr\left(\frac{2\pi}{T}\right)^2 = \frac{4\pi^2 mr}{T^2}.$$

This is equal to the force of attraction of the sun on the planet. *Assuming an inverse-square law,* then

$$\text{force on planet} = \frac{k}{r^2},$$

where k is a constant.

$$\therefore \frac{k}{r^2} = \frac{4\pi^2 mr}{T^2}$$

$$\therefore T^2 = \frac{4\pi^2 m}{k} r^3$$

$$\therefore T^2 \propto r^3,$$

since m, k, π are constants.

Now Kepler had announced that the squares of the periods of revolution of the planets are proportional to the cubes of their mean distances from the sun (see above). Newton thus suspected that *the force between the sun and the planet was inversely proportional to the square of the distance between them.* The great scientist now proceeded to test the inverse-square law by applying it to the case of the moon's motion round the earth. The moon has a period of revolution, T, about the earth of approximately 27·3 days, and the force on it $= mR\omega^2$, where R is the radius of the moon's orbit and m is its mass.

$$\therefore \text{force} = mR\left(\frac{2\pi}{T}\right) = \frac{4\pi^2 mR}{T^2}.$$

If the planet were at the earth's surface, the force of attraction on it due to the earth would be mg, where g is the acceleration due to gravity. Assuming that the force of attraction varies as the inverse square of the distance between the earth and the moon,

$$\therefore \frac{4\pi^2 mR}{T^2} : mg = \frac{1}{R^2} : \frac{1}{r^2},$$

where r is the radius of the earth.

$$\therefore \frac{4\pi^2 R}{T^2 g} = \frac{r^2}{R^2},$$

$$\therefore g = \frac{4\pi^2 R^3}{r^2 T^2} \qquad . \qquad . \qquad . \qquad (28)$$

Newton substituted the then known values of R, r, and T, but was disappointed to find that the answer for g was not near to the observed value, 32 ft. per sec.[2]. Some years later, he heard of a new estimate of the radius of the moon's orbit, and on substituting its value he found that the result for g was close to 32 ft. per sec.[2]. Newton saw that a universal law could be formulated for the attraction between any two particles of matter. His *law of gravitation* states: *The force of attraction between two given masses is inversely proportional to the square of their distance apart.*

21. Gravitational Constant, G, and its Determination.

From Newton's law, it follows that the force of attraction, F, between two masses m, M at a distance r apart is given by $F \propto \dfrac{mM}{r^2}$.

$$\therefore F = G\frac{mM}{r^2}, \qquad . \qquad . \qquad . \qquad (29)$$

where G is a universal constant known as the *gravitational constant*.

G can be defined as numerically equal to the force in dynes between two masses of 1 gram placed 1 cm. apart, and its dimensions are given by $[G] = [F][r^2]/[mM] = [MLT^{-2} \times L^2]/[M^2] = [M^{-1}L^3T^{-2}]$.

A celebrated experiment to measure G was carried out by C. V. Boys in 1895, using a method similar to one of the earliest determinations of G by CAVENDISH in 1798. Two identical balls, a, b, of gold, 0·2 in. in diameter, were suspended by a long and a short fine quartz fibre respectively from the ends, C, D, of a highly-polished bar CD, Fig. 31. Two large identical lead spheres, A, B, $4\frac{1}{2}$ ins. in diameter, were brought into position near a, b respectively, and as a result of the

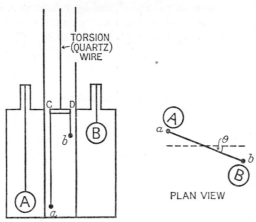

FIG. 31. Boys' experiment (*not to scale*).

attraction between the masses, two equal but opposite forces acted on
CD. The bar was thus deflected, and the angle of deflection, θ, was
measured by a lamp and scale method by light reflected from CD. The
high sensitivity of the quartz fibres enabled the small deflection to be
measured accurately, and the small size of the apparatus allowed it to
be screened considerably from air convection currents.

22. Calculation for G.

Suppose d is the distance between a, A, or b, B, when the deflection
is θ. Then if m, M are the respective masses of a, A,

$$\text{couple on } CD = G\frac{mM}{d^2} \times CD.$$

But $$\text{couple} = c\theta,$$

where c is the couple in the torsion wire per unit radian of twist.

$$\therefore G\frac{mM}{d^2} \times CD = c\theta$$

$$\therefore G = \frac{c\theta d^2}{mM \times CD} \quad \cdot \quad \cdot \quad \cdot \quad \cdot \quad \text{(i)}$$

The constant c was determined by allowing CD to oscillate through a
small angle and then observing its period of oscillation, T, which was
of the order of 3 minutes. If I is the known moment of inertia of the
system about the torsion wire, then (see p. 71),

$$T = 2\pi\sqrt{\frac{I}{c}}.$$

The constant c can now be calculated, and by substitution in (i), G can be determined. Accurate experiments showed that $G = 6.66 \times 10^{-8}$ c.g.s. HEYL in 1930, and again in 1942, found G to be 6.67×10^{-8} c.g.s.

23. Mass and Density of Earth.

At the earth's surface the force of attraction on a mass m is mg, where g is the acceleration due to gravity. Now it can be shown that it is legitimate in calculations to assume that the mass, M, of the earth is concentrated at its centre, if it is a sphere. Assuming that the earth is spherical and of radius r, it then follows that the force of attraction of the earth on the mass m is GmM/r^2.

$$\therefore G\frac{mM}{r^2} = mg.$$

$$\therefore g = \frac{GM}{r^2}.$$

$$\therefore M = \frac{gr^2}{G}.$$

Thus if g, r, and G are known, the mass of the earth can be calculated, its magnitude is about 5.3×10^{27} grams.

The volume of a sphere is $4\pi r^3/3$, where r is its radius. Thus the density, ρ, of the earth is approximately given by

$$\rho = \frac{M}{V} = \frac{gr^2}{4\pi r^3 G/3} = \frac{3g}{4\pi rG}.$$

By substituting known values of g, G, and r, the density of the earth is found to be about 5·5 gm. per c.c.

It is now believed that gravitational force travels with the speed of light. Thus if the gravitational force between the sun and earth were suddenly to disappear by the vanishing of the sun, it would take about 7 minutes for the effect to be experienced on the earth, which would then fly off along a tangent to its original curved path.

EXAMPLE

Derive an expression for the acceleration of a particle moving along a circular path with uniform speed. Show how this expression, combined with the law of gravitation, leads to the relationship $\omega^2 R^3 = gr^2$, where ω is the mean angular velocity of the moon round the earth, R is the mean radius of the moon's orbit, and r is the radius of the earth. Given that $R = 60r$, and that the period of the moon's rotation around the earth is $27\frac{1}{2}$ days, find R. (C.)

First part. The acceleration $= \omega^2 r$, where r is the radius of the circle, and this is proved on p. 33.

Second part. Suppose M is the mass of the earth, m is the mass of the moon. Then, equating the force towards the centre (earth) to the gravitational pull on the moon, we have

$$G \frac{Mm}{R^2} = mR\omega^2$$

$$\therefore \omega^2 R^3 = GM \qquad . \qquad . \qquad . \qquad . \qquad . \qquad \text{(i)}$$

Now if an object of mass m_1 is situated on the earth's surface, its weight $= m_1 g =$ gravitational pull due to the earth's attraction.

$$\therefore \quad m_1 g = G \frac{Mm_1}{r^2}$$

$$\therefore \quad gr^2 = GM \qquad . \qquad . \qquad . \qquad . \qquad \text{(ii)}$$

From (i) and (ii), $\qquad \therefore \omega^2 R^3 = gr^2 \qquad . \qquad . \qquad . \qquad . \qquad \text{(iii)}.$

Third part. Since $\omega = \dfrac{2\pi}{T} = \dfrac{2\pi}{27\frac{1}{2} \times 24 \times 3600}$ radians per sec.,

$$\text{and } r = \frac{R}{60},$$

then, substituting in (iii),

$$\frac{4\pi^2}{(27\frac{1}{2} \times 24 \times 3600)^2} \times R^3 = 32 \times \frac{R^2}{60^2}$$

$$\therefore R = \frac{32 \times (27\frac{1}{2} \times 24 \times 3600)^2}{4\pi^2 \times 60^2} \text{feet}$$

$$= \frac{32 \times (27\frac{1}{2} \times 24 \times 3600)^2}{4\pi^2 \times 60^2 \times 5280} \text{miles}$$

$$= 240,000 \text{ miles}$$

EXERCISES II

(Assume $g = 32$ ft. per sec.^{2} or 980 cm. per sec.^{2})

Circular Motion; G

1. An object of mass 4 lb. moves round a circle of radius 6 ft. with a constant speed of 30 ft./sec. Calculate (i) the angular velocity, (ii) the force towards the centre.

2. An object of mass 10 lb. is whirled round a horizontal circle of radius 4 ft. by a revolving string inclined to the vertical. If the uniform speed of the object is 20 ft. per sec., calculate (i) the tension in the string in lb. wt., (ii) the angle of inclination of the string to the horizontal.

3. A racing-car of 15 cwt. moves round a banked track at a constant speed of 90 m.p.h. Assuming the total reaction at the wheels is normal to the track, and the horizontal radius of the track is 200 ft., calculate the

angle of inclination of the track to the horizontal and the reaction at the wheels.

4. An object of mass 8 lb. is whirled round in a vertical circle of radius 4 ft. with a constant velocity of 20 ft. per sec. Calculate the maximum and minimum tensions in the string.

5. Calculate the force of attraction between two small objects of mass 5 and 8 kilograms respectively which are 10 cm. apart. ($G = 6 \cdot 7 \times 10^{-8}$ c.g.s.)

6. If the acceleration due to gravity is 980 cm. per sec.^{2} and the radius of the earth is $6 \cdot 4 \times 10^8$ cm., calculate a value for the mass of the earth. ($G = 6 \cdot 7 \times 10^{-8}$ c.g.s.) Give the theory.

7. Assuming that the mean density of the earth is 5·5 gm. per c.c., that the constant of gravitation is $6 \cdot 7 \times 10^{-8}$ c.g.s., and that the radius of the earth is $6 \cdot 4 \times 10^8$ cm., find a value for the acceleration due to gravity at the earth's surface. Derive the formula used.

8. Derive from first principles an expression for the acceleration of a particle describing a circular path with constant speed. Explain why it is desirable to bank the road at corners, and calculate the optimum angle of bank for a curve of radius r to be traversed at a speed v.

A train is travelling round a circular arc of radius 500 ft. which is not banked. The gauge of the railway is 4 ft. 9 in. and the height of the centre of gravity is 3 ft. 6 in. above the track. If there is no pressure on the inner rail, what is the speed of the train? (*O. & C.*)

9. A single pendulum hangs from the roof of a vehicle. During the motion of the vehicle in a horizontal circle of radius 160 ft. the pendulum hangs at an angle of 20° with the vertical. Show in a diagram the forces acting on the pendulum bob, and calculate the speed of the vehicle. Show that the free surface of a liquid contained in a vessel placed in the vehicle would be perpendicular to the pendulum. (*W.*)

10. Show that a body moving in a circle of radius r with speed v has an acceleration of v^2/r towards the centre of the circle. Describe a simple experiment which demonstrates this relation.

Either: Give examples where such an acceleration is made to serve a useful purpose and point out instances in ordinary life where its existence needs to be taken into account.

Or: Solve the following problem: Calculate the angle to the horizontal at which a curved railway track of radius of curvature 880 yd. needs to be "banked" so that the reaction on the track may be normal to the track when a train is travelling along it at 60 m.p.h. (*C.*)

11. Give an account of the torsion balance method of measuring Newton's constant of gravitation, G. Two pieces of apparatus A and B for measuring G by the torsion balance are made of similar materials, and are constructed so that the linear dimensions of all parts of A, except the torsion wires, are n times as great as the corresponding parts of B. The torsion wires are so chosen that the two suspended systems have equal periods. Compare the deflections of the torsion bars of A and B.

Assuming that the moon describes a circular orbit of radius R about the earth in 27 days, and that Titan describes a circular orbit of radius $3 \cdot 2 R$ about Saturn in 16 days, compare the masses of Saturn and the earth. (*O. & C.*)

12. Assuming that the planets are moving in circular orbits, apply Kepler's laws to show that the acceleration of a planet is inversely proportional to the square of its distance from the sun. Explain the significance of this and show clearly how it leads to Newton's law of universal gravitation.

Obtain the value of g from the motion of the moon, assuming that its period of rotation round the earth is 27 days 8 hours and that the radius of its orbit is 60·1 times the radius of the earth. (Radius of earth = $6·36 \times 10^6$ metres.) (*N.*)

13. Explain what is meant by the *gravitation constant* (*G*), and describe an accurate laboratory method of measuring it. Give an outline of the theory of your method.

Assuming that the earth is a sphere of radius 6,370 kilometres and that $G = 6·66 \times 10^{-8}$ c.g.s. units, calculate the mean density of the earth. (*O. & C.*)

Simple Harmonic Motion

14. An object moving with simple harmonic motion has an amplitude of 2 inches and a frequency of 20 cycles per sec. Calculate (i) the period of oscillation, (ii) the acceleration at the middle and end of an oscillation, (iii) the velocities at the corresponding instants.

15. Calculate the length in centimetres of a simple pendulum which has a period of 2 seconds. If the amplitude of swing is 2 inches, calculate the velocity and acceleration of the bob (i) at the end of a swing, (ii) at the middle, (iii) 1 inch from the centre of oscillation.

16. Define *simple harmonic motion*. An elastic string is extended 1 inch when a small weight is attached at the lower end. If the weight is pulled down ¼ inch and then released, show that it moves with simple harmonic motion, and find the period.

17. A uniform wooden rod floats upright in water with a length of 2 ft. immersed. If the rod is depressed slightly and then released, prove that its motion is simple harmonic and calculate the period.

18. A simple pendulum, has a period of 4·2 sec. When the pendulum is shortened by 1 metre, the period is 3·7 sec. From these measurements, calculate the acceleration due to gravity and the original length of the pendulum.

19. What is *simple harmonic motion*? Show how it is related to the uniform motion of a particle with velocity v in a circle of radius r.

A steel strip, clamped at one end, vibrates with a frequency of 50 cycles per sec. and an amplitude of 8 mm. at the free end. Find (*a*) the velocity of the end when passing through the zero position, (*b*) the acceleration at the maximum displacement.

20. Define *simple harmonic motion*. A point P describes a circular path about a centre O with uniform angular velocity. Show that Q, the foot of the perpendicular drawn from P to a fixed diameter of the circle, executes a simple harmonic motion of period

$$T = 2\pi \sqrt{\frac{\text{Displacement of Q from O}}{\text{Acceleration of Q towards O}}}.$$

C

Hence, or otherwise, deduce an expression for the period of oscillation of a simple pendulum.

The point of suspension of a simple pendulum of original length l is fixed. The length of the pendulum is now adjusted so that the period of oscillation is (a) increased by 25%, (b) decreased by 25%. Find the corresponding changes in the height of the bob above the floor. (*L.*)

21. Explain what is meant by simple harmonic motion. Deduce an expression for the periodic time of the vertical oscillations of a mass suspended by a helical spring, the extension of which is proportional to the load. The mass of the spring may be neglected.

Describe in some detail how such an arrangement might be used to obtain an estimate of the acceleration due to gravity. (*N.*)

22. Define simple harmonic motion, and write down expressions for the velocity and the acceleration of a particle moving in simple harmonic motion of period T and amplitude a, when the displacement of the particle from the centre of the oscillation is x.

A body of mass 200 gm. is placed on a horizontal platform which oscillates vertically in simple harmonic motion of period 2 sec. and amplitude 5 cm. Find the maximum and minimum values of the force exerted by the body on the platform. What is the value of this force when the platform is moving through its central position? (*W.*)

23. What is meant by simple harmonic motion? Obtain an expression for the kinetic energy of a body of mass m, which is performing S.H.M. of amplitude a and period $2\pi/\omega$, when its displacement from the origin is x.

Describe an experiment, or experiments, to verify that a mass oscillating at the end of a helical spring moves with simple harmonic motion. (*C.*)

24. State the dynamical condition under which a particle will describe simple harmonic motion. Show that it is approximately fulfilled in the case of the bob of a simple pendulum, and derive, from first principles, an expression for the period of the pendulum.

Explain how it can be demonstrated from observations on simple pendulums, that the weight of a body at a given place is proportional to its mass. (O. & *C.*)

25. Define *simple harmonic motion*. Show that a heavy body supported by a light spiral spring executes simple harmonic motion when displaced vertically from its equilibrium position by an amount which does not exceed a certain value and then released. How would you determine experimentally the maximum amplitude for simple harmonic motion?

A spiral spring gives a displacement of 5 cm. for a load of 500 gm. Find the maximum displacement produced when a mass of 80 gm. is dropped from a height of 10 cm. on to a light pan attached to the spring. (*N.*)

26. Show that when a simple pendulum is slightly displaced from its position of equilibrium and then allowed to swing freely, it performs simple harmonic oscillations and determine their period.

The period of a simple pendulum is increased by 1/100 sec. when the length is increased by 1 cm. Find the original length of the pendulum. (*L.*)

27. Derive an expression for the period of oscillation of a body moving with simple harmonic motion in terms of its acceleration and displacement at any instant.

A weight, hanging from a fixed point by a light elastic string, is given a small vertical displacement and then released. If the extension of the string when the weight hangs at rest is b, find the period of the vertical oscillations of the weight. If $b = 1.5$ ins., what is the greatest velocity of the weight during an oscillation of amplitude 0·5 in.? (*W.*)

28. A test-tube of weight 6 gm. and external diameter 2 cm. is floated vertically in water by placing 10 gm. of mercury at the bottom of the tube. The tube is depressed by a small amount and then released. Find the time of oscillation. (*O. & C.*)

29. Define simple harmonic motion, and show that the total energy (kinetic and potential) of a particle executing simple harmonic motion is proportional (*a*) to the square of the amplitude, (*b*) to the square of the frequency.

The total energy of a particle executing a simple harmonic motion of period 2π sec. is 10,240 ergs. $\pi/4$ sec. after the particle passes the mid-point of the swing its displacement is $8\sqrt{2}$ cm. Calculate the amplitude of the motion and the mass of the particle. (*O. & C.*)

CHAPTER III

MOMENTS OF INERTIA

So far in this book we have considered the equations of motion and other dynamical formulæ associated with a particle. In practice, however, an object is made of millions of particles, each at different places, and we need now to consider formulæ for moving objects.

1. Moment of Inertia, I.

Suppose a rigid object is rotating about a fixed axis O, and a particle A of the object makes an angle θ with a fixed line OY in space at some instant, Fig. 32. The angular velocity, $d\theta/dt$ or ω, of every particle about O is the same, since we are dealing with a rigid body, and the velocity v_1 of A at this instant is given by $r_1\omega$, where $r_1 =$ OA. Thus the kinetic energy of $A = \frac{1}{2}m_1v_1^2 = \frac{1}{2}m_1r_1^2\omega^2$. Similarly, the kinetic energy of another particle of the body $= \frac{1}{2}m_2r_2^2\omega^2$, where r_2 is its distance from O and m_2 is its mass. In this way we see that the kinetic energy, K.E., of the whole object is given by

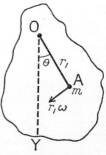

FIG. 32.
Rotating body.

$$\text{K.E.} = \frac{1}{2}m_1r_1^2\omega^2 + \frac{1}{2}m_2r_2\omega^2 + \frac{1}{2}m_3r_3^2\omega^2 + \ldots$$

$$= \frac{1}{2}\omega^2(m_1r_1^2 + m_2r_2^2 + m_3r_3^2 + \ldots)$$

$$= \frac{1}{2}\omega^2(\Sigma mr^2),$$

where Σmr^2 represents the sum of the magnitudes of "mr^2" for all the particles of the object. We shall see shortly how the quantity Σmr^2 can be calculated for a particular object. The magnitude of Σmr^2 is known as the *moment of inertia* of the object about the axis concerned, and we shall denote it by the symbol I. Thus

$$\text{Kinetic energy, K.E.,} = \frac{1}{2}I\omega^2. \qquad . \qquad . \qquad (30)$$

The kinetic energy of a particle of mass m moving with a velocity v is $\frac{1}{2}mv^2$. It will thus be noted that the formula for the kinetic energy of a rotating object is similar to that of a moving particle, the mass m being replaced by the moment of inertia I and the velocity v being replaced by the angular velocity ω.

2. Moment of Forces on a Rigid Body.

The force acting on the particle A in Fig. 32 $= m_1 \times$ acceleration $=$ $m_1 \times \dfrac{d}{dt}(r_1\omega) = m_1 \times r_1\dfrac{d\omega}{dt} = m_1 r_1 \dfrac{d^2\theta}{dt^2}$, since $\omega = \dfrac{d\theta}{dt}$. The moment of this force about the axis O $=$ force $\times$ perpendicular distance from O $= m_1 r_1 \dfrac{d^2\theta}{dt^2} \times r_1$, since the force acts perpendicularly to the line OA.

$$\therefore \text{moment} = m_1 r_1{}^2 \frac{d^2\theta}{dt^2}.$$

$\therefore$ total moment of all forces on body about O

$$= m_1 r_1{}^2 \frac{d^2\theta}{dt^2} + m_2 r_2{}^2 \frac{d^2\theta}{dt^2} + m_3 r_3{}^2 \frac{d^2\theta}{dt^2} + \dots$$

$$= (\Sigma m r^2) \times \frac{d^2\theta}{dt^2},$$

since the angular acceleration, $d^2\theta/dt^2$, about OY is the same for all particles.

$$\therefore \text{total moment about O} = I \frac{d^2\theta}{dt^2}, \qquad \cdot \quad \cdot \quad \cdot \qquad (31)$$

where $I = \Sigma m r^2 =$ moment of inertia about O.

3. Angular Momentum.

The momentum of the particle A about O in Fig. 32 $=$ mass $\times$ velocity $= m_1 \times r_1\omega$. Consequently the *moment* of *the momentum* about O, which is called the *angular momentum* about O,

$$= m_1 r_1 \omega \times r_1 = m_1 r_1{}^2 \omega.$$

$$\therefore \text{total angular momentum} = \Sigma m r^2 \omega = \omega \Sigma m r^2$$

$$= I\omega,$$

where I is the moment of inertia of the body about O.

Angular momentum is analogous to "linear momentum" in the dynamics of a moving particle. Further, the conservation of angular momentum, which corresponds to the conservation of linear momentum, states that the angular momentum about an axis of a given rotating body or system of bodies is constant if no external forces act. Thus when a high diver jumps from a diving board, his moment of inertia can be decreased by curling his body more, in which case his angular velocity is increased, and he may then be able to turn somersaults. Similarly, a dancer on skates can spin faster by folding her arms.

We can now see that the formulæ for the kinetic energy of a rotating object, its angular momentum about an axis, and the moment about the axis of the forces acting on it all contain the moment of inertia, I. Before proceeding further, therefore, we shall calculate the moment of inertia of several objects about a particular axis.

4. Moment of Inertia of Uniform Rod.

(1) *About axis through middle.* The moment of inertia of a small element δx about an axis PQ through its centre O perpendicular to the length $= \left(\dfrac{\delta x}{l}M\right)x^2$, where l is the length of the rod, M is its mass, and x is the distance of the small element from O, Fig. 33.

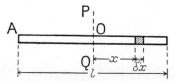

Fig. 33.   Moment of inertia of uniform rod.

$$\therefore \text{ moment of inertia, } I, = 2\int_0^{l/2} \left(\frac{dx}{l}M\right)x^2$$

$$= \frac{2M}{l}\int_0^{l/2} x^2 dx = \frac{Ml^2}{12} \quad . \quad . \quad (32)$$

Thus if the mass of the rod is 60 gm. and its length is 20 cm., the moment of inertia $I = 60 \times 20^2/12 = 2000$ gm. cm.^{2}

(2) *About the axis through one end, A.* In this case, measuring distances x from A instead of O,

$$\text{moment of inertia, } I, = \int_0^l \left(\frac{dx}{l}M\right) \times x^2 = \frac{Ml^2}{3} \quad . \quad . \quad (33)$$

5. Moment of Inertia of Ring.

Every element of the ring is the same distance from the centre. Hence the moment of inertia about an axis through the centre perpendicular to the plane of the ring $= Ma^2$, where M is the mass of the ring and a is its radius.

6. Moment of Inertia of Circular Disc.

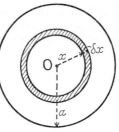

Consider the moment of inertia of a circular disc about an axis through its centre perpendicular to its plane, Fig. 34. If we take a small ring of the disc enclosed between radii x and $x + \delta x$, its mass $= \dfrac{2\pi\, x\, \delta x}{\pi a^2} M$, where a is the radius of the disc and M is its mass. Each element of the ring is distant x from the centre, and hence the moment of inertia of the ring about the axis through $O =$

FIG. 34. Moment of inertia of circular disc.

$$\left(\frac{2\pi\, x\, \delta x}{\pi a^2} M\right) \times x^2$$

$$\therefore \text{ moment of inertia of whole disc} = \int_{0}^{a} \frac{2\pi x dx}{\pi a^2} M \times x^2$$

$$= \frac{Ma^2}{2} \qquad . \qquad . \qquad (34)$$

Thus if the disc weighs 60 gm. and has a radius of 10 cm., its moment of inertia $= 60 \times 10^2/2 = 3000$ gm. cm.^{2}.

7. Moment of Inertia of Cylinder.

If a cylinder is *solid*, its moment of inertia about the axis of symmetry is the sum of the moments of inertia of discs into which we may imagine the cylinder cut. The moment of inertia of each disc $= \frac{1}{2}$ mass $\times a^2$, where a is the radius; and hence, if M is the mass of the cylinder,

$$\text{moment of inertia of solid cylinder} = \tfrac{1}{2}Ma^2 \qquad . \qquad . \qquad \text{(i)}$$

If a cylinder is *hollow*, its moment of inertia about the axis of symmetry is the sum of the moments of inertia of the curved surface and that of the two ends, assuming the cylinder is closed at both ends. Suppose a is the radius, h is the height of the cylinder, and σ is the mass per unit area of the surface. Then

$$\text{mass of curved surface} = 2\pi a h\sigma,$$

and   moment of inertia about axis $=$ mass $\times a^2 = 2\pi a^3 h\sigma$,

since we can imagine the surface cut into rings.

The moment of inertia of one end of the cylinder $=$ mass $\times a^2/2$ $= \pi a^2\sigma \times a^2/2 = \pi a^4\sigma/2$. Hence the moment of inertia of both ends $= \pi a^4\sigma$.

$\therefore$ moment inertia of cylinder, I, $= 2\pi a^3 h\sigma + \pi a^4\sigma$.

The mass of the cylinder, M, $= 2\pi a h\sigma + 2\pi a^2\sigma$

$$\therefore I = \frac{2\pi a^3 h\sigma + \pi a^4\sigma}{2\pi a h\sigma + 2\pi a^2\sigma} M.$$

$$= \frac{2a^2 h + a^3}{2h + 2a} M.$$

$$= \tfrac{1}{2}Ma^2 + \frac{a^2 h}{2h + 2a}M \quad . \quad . \quad . \quad . \quad \text{(ii)}$$

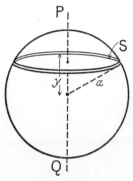

FIG. 35.   Moment of inertia of sphere.

If a hollow and a solid cylinder have the same mass M and the same radius and height, it can be seen from (i) and (ii) that the moment of inertia of the hollow cylinder is greater than that of the solid cylinder about the axis of symmetry. This is because the mass is distributed on the average at a greater distance from the axis in the former case.

8. Moment of Inertia of Sphere.

The moment of inertia of a sphere about an axis PQ through its centre can be found by cutting thin discs such as S perpendicular to the axis, Fig. 35. The volume of the disc, of thickness δy and distance y from the centre,

$$= \pi r^2 \delta y = \pi(a^2 - y^2)\,\delta y.$$

$$\therefore \text{mass } M' \text{ of disc} = \frac{\pi(a^2 - y^2)\,\delta y}{4\pi a^3/3} M$$

$$= \frac{3M}{4a^3}(a^2 - y^2)\,\delta y,$$

where M is the mass of the sphere and a is its radius, since the volume of the sphere $= 4\pi a^3/3$. Now the moment of inertia of the disc about PQ

$$= M' \times \frac{\text{radius}^2}{2}$$

$$= \frac{3M}{4a^3}(a^2 - y^2)\,\delta y \times \frac{(a^2 - y^2)}{2}$$

$$\therefore \text{moment of inertia of sphere} = \frac{3M}{8a^3}\int_{-a}^{+a}(a^2 - y^2)^2 dy$$

$$= \frac{3M}{8a^3} \int_{-a}^{+a} (a^4 - 2a^2y^2 + y^4)\, dy$$

$$= \frac{2}{5} Ma^2 \qquad . \quad . \quad . \quad . \quad (35)$$

Thus if the sphere weighs 10 lb. and has a radius of 2 ft., the moment

of inertia $= \dfrac{2}{5} \times 10 \times 2^2 = 16\, \text{lb. ft.}^2$.

9. Radius of Gyration.

The moment of inertia of an object about an axis, Σmr^2, is sometimes written as Mk^2, where M is the mass of the object and k is a quantity called the *radius of gyration* about the axis. For example, the moment of inertia of a rod about an axis through one end $= Ml^2/3$ (p. 62) $= M(l/\sqrt{3})^2$. Thus the radius of gyration, $k, = l/\sqrt{3} = 0.58l$. The moment of inertia of a sphere about its centre

$$= \frac{2}{5}Ma^2 = M \times \left(\sqrt{\frac{2}{5}}a\right)^2 \cdot \text{ Thus the radius of}$$

gyration, $k, = \sqrt{\dfrac{2}{5}}a = 0.63a$ in this case.

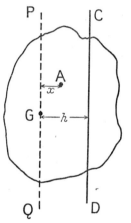

10. Relation Between Moment of Inertia About C.G. and Parallel Axis.

Suppose I is the moment of inertia of a body about an axis CD and I_G is the moment of inertia about a parallel axis PQ through the centre of gravity, G, distant h from the axis CD, Fig. 36. If A is a particle of mass m whose distance from PQ is x, its moment of inertia about CD $= m(h - x)^2$.

Fig. 36. Moment of inertia and parallel axis.

$$\therefore I = \Sigma m(h - x)^2 = \Sigma mh^2 + \Sigma mx^2 - \Sigma 2mhx.$$

Now $\Sigma mh^2 = h^2 \times \Sigma m = Mh^2$, where M is the total mass of the object, and $\Sigma mx^2 = I_G$, the moment of inertia through the centre of gravity. Also, $\qquad \Sigma 2mhx = 2h\Sigma mx = 0$, since Σmx, the sum of the moments about the centre of gravity, is zero; this follows because the moment of the resultant (the weight) about G is zero.

$$\therefore I = I_G + Mh^2 \qquad . \quad . \quad . \quad . \quad (36)$$

From this result, it follows that the moment of inertia, I, of a disc of radius a and mass M about an axis through a point on its circumference $= I_G + Ma^2$, since $h = a =$ radius of disc in this case. But $I_G =$ moment of inertia about the centre $= Ma^2/2$ (p. 63).

$$\therefore \text{ moment of inertia, } I, = \frac{Ma^2}{2} + Ma^2 = \frac{3Ma^2}{2}.$$

Similarly the moment of inertia of a sphere of radius a and mass M about an axis through a point on its circumference $= I_G + Ma^2 = 2Ma^2/5 + Ma^2 = 7Ma^2/5$, since I_G, the moment of inertia about an axis through its centre, is $2Ma^2/5$.

11. Relation Between Moments of Inertia about Perpendicular Axes.

Suppose OX, OY are any two perpendicular axes and OZ is an axis perpendicular to OX and OY, Fig. 37 (i). The moment of inertia, I, of

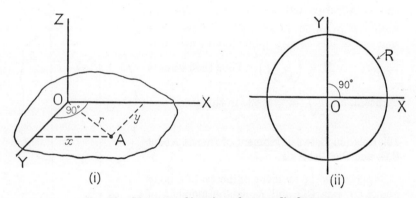

FIG. 37.   Moments of inertia and perpendicular axes.

a body about the axis OZ $= \Sigma mr^2$, where r is the distance of a particle A from OZ and m is its mass. But $r^2 = x^2 + y^2$, where x, y are the distances of A from the axis OY, OX respectively.

$$\therefore I = \Sigma m(x^2 + y^2) = \Sigma mx^2 + \Sigma my^2.$$

$$\therefore I = I_y + I_x, \quad . \quad . \quad . \quad . \quad . \quad (37)$$

where I_y, I_x are the moments of inertia about OY, OX respectively.

As a simple application, consider a ring R and two perpendicular axes OX, OY in its plane, Fig. 37 (ii). Then from the above result,

$$I_y + I_x = I = \text{ moment of inertia through O perpendicular}$$
to ring.

$$\therefore I_y + I_x = Ma^2.$$

But $I_y = I_x$, by symmetry.

$$\therefore I_x + I_x = Ma^2,$$

$$\therefore I_x = \frac{Ma^2}{2}.$$

This is the moment of inertia of the ring about any diameter in its plane.

In the same way, the moment of inertia, I, of a disc about a diameter in its plane is given by

$$I + I = \frac{Ma^2}{2},$$

since the moments of inertia, I, about the two perpendicular diameters are the same and $Ma^2/2$ is the moment of inertia of the disc about an axis perpendicular to its plane.

$$\therefore 2I = \frac{Ma^2}{2}$$

$$\therefore I = \frac{Ma^2}{4}.$$

12. Kinetic Energy of a Rolling Object.

When an object such as a cylinder or ball rolls on a plane, the object is rotating as well as moving bodily along the plane; therefore it has rotational energy as well as translational energy.

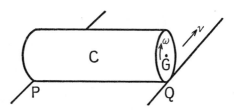

FIG. 38.   Rolling object.

Consider a cylinder C rolling along a plane without slipping, Fig. 38. At any instant the line of contact, PQ, with the plane is at rest, and we can consider the whole of the cylinder to be rotating about this axis. Hence the energy of the cylinder $= \frac{1}{2}I_1\omega^2$, where I_1 is the moment of inertia about PQ and ω is the angular velocity.

But if I is the moment of inertia about a parallel axis through the centre of gravity of the cylinder, M is the mass of the cylinder and a its radius, then

$$I_1 = I + Ma^2,$$

from the result on p. 65.

$$\therefore \text{ energy of cylinder} = \tfrac{1}{2}(I + Ma^2)\omega^2$$
$$= \tfrac{1}{2}I\omega^2 + \tfrac{1}{2}Ma^2\omega^2$$
$$\therefore \text{ Energy} = \tfrac{1}{2}I\omega^2 + \tfrac{1}{2}Mv^2 \qquad . \quad . \qquad (38)$$

since, by considering the distance rolled and the angle then turned, $v = a\omega =$ velocity of centre of gravity. This energy formula is true for any moving object.

As an application of the energy formula, suppose a *ring* rolls along a plane. The moment of inertia about the centre of gravity, its centre, $= Ma^2$ (p. 62); also, the angular velocity, ω, about its centre $= v/a$, where v is the velocity of the centre of gravity.

$$\therefore \text{ kinetic energy of ring} = \tfrac{1}{2}Mv^2 + \tfrac{1}{2}I\omega^2$$

$$= \tfrac{1}{2}Mv^2 + \tfrac{1}{2}Ma^2 \times \left(\frac{v}{a}\right)^2 = Mv^2.$$

By similar reasoning, the kinetic energy of a sphere rolling down a plane

$$= \tfrac{1}{2}Mv^2 + \tfrac{1}{2}I\omega^2$$

$$= \tfrac{1}{2}Mv^2 + \tfrac{1}{2} \times \frac{2}{5}Ma^2 \times \left(\frac{v}{a}\right)^2 = \frac{7}{10}\ Mv^2,$$

since $I = 2Ma^2/5$ (p. 64).

13. Acceleration of Rolling Object.

We can now deduce the acceleration of a rolling object down an inclined plane.

As an illustration, suppose a solid cylinder rolls down a plane. Then
$$\text{kinetic energy} = \tfrac{1}{2}Mv^2 + \tfrac{1}{2}I\omega^2.$$

But moment of inertia, I, about an axis through the centre of gravity parallel to the plane $= \tfrac{1}{2}Ma^2$, and $\omega = v/a$, where a is the radius.

$$\therefore \quad \text{kinetic energy} = \tfrac{1}{2}Mv^2 + \tfrac{1}{4}Mv^2 = \tfrac{3}{4}Mv^2.$$

If the cylinder rolls from *rest* through a distance s, the loss of potential energy $= Mgs \sin \alpha$, where α is the inclination of the plane to the horizontal.

$$\therefore \tfrac{3}{4}Mv^2 = Mgs \sin \alpha$$

$$\therefore v^2 = \frac{4g}{3} s \sin a$$

But $$v^2 = 2fs.$$

$$\therefore 2fs = \frac{4g}{3} s \sin a$$

$$\therefore f = \frac{2g}{3} \sin a \qquad . \qquad . \qquad . \qquad \text{(i)}$$

The acceleration if sliding, and no rolling, took place down the plane is $g \sin a$. The cylinder has thus a smaller acceleration when rolling.

The time t taken to move through a distance s from rest is given by $s = \frac{1}{2}ft^2$. Thus, from (i),

$$s = \tfrac{1}{3}gt^2 \sin a,$$

$$\text{or} \quad t = \sqrt{\frac{3s}{g \sin a}}.$$

If the cylinder is *hollow*, instead of solid as assumed, the moment of inertia about an axis through the centre of gravity parallel to the plane is greater than that for a solid cylinder, assuming the same mass and dimensions (p. 64). The time taken for a hollow cylinder to roll a given distance from rest on the plane is then greater than that taken by the solid cylinder, from reasoning similar to that above; and thus if no other means were available, a time test on an inclined plane will distinguish between a solid and a hollow cylinder of the same dimensions and mass. If a torsion wire is available, however, the cylinders can be suspended in turn, and the period of torsional oscillations determined. The cylinder of larger moment of inertia, the hollow cylinder, will have a greater period, as explained on p. 71.

14. Period of Oscillation of Rigid Body.

On p. 61 we showed that the moment of the forces acting on rotating objects $= I d\omega/dt = I d^2\theta/dt^2$, where I is the moment of inertia about the axis concerned and $d^2\theta/dt^2$ is the angular acceleration about the axis. Consider a rigid body oscillating about a fixed axis O, Fig. 39. The moment of the weight mg (the only external force) about O is $mgh \sin \theta$, or $mgh\theta$ if θ is small, where h is the distance of the centre of gravity from O.

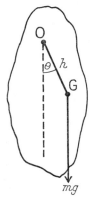

Fig. 39. Oscillation of rigid body.

$$\therefore I\frac{d^2\theta}{dt^2} = -mgh\,\theta,$$

the minus indicating that the moment due to the weight always *opposes* the growth of the angle θ.

$$\therefore \frac{d^2\theta}{dt^2} = \frac{-mgh}{I}\,\theta = -\omega^2\theta,$$

where $\omega^2 = mgh/I$.

$\therefore$ the motion is simple harmonic motion (p. 40),

and   period, $T, = \dfrac{2\pi}{\omega} = \dfrac{2\pi}{\sqrt{mgh/I}} = 2\pi\sqrt{\dfrac{I}{mgh}}$ . . .   (39)

If $I = mk_1{}^2$, where k_1 is the radius of gyration about O,

$$T = 2\pi\sqrt{\frac{mk_1{}^2}{mgh}} = \sqrt{\frac{k_1{}^2}{gh}}$$ . . . .   (40)

15. Compound Pendulum. Since $I = I_G + mh^2 = mk^2 + mh^2$, where I_G is the moment of inertia about the centre of gravity, h is the distance of the axis O from the centre of gravity, and k is the radius of gyration about the centre of gravity, then, from (39),

$$T = 2\pi\sqrt{\frac{I}{mgh}} = 2\pi\sqrt{\frac{mk^2 + mh^2}{mgh}}.$$

$$\therefore T = 2\pi\sqrt{\frac{k^2 + h^2}{gh}}.$$

Hence $T = 2\pi\sqrt{\dfrac{l}{g}}$,

where $l = \dfrac{k^2 + h^2}{h}$ . . .   (i).

Thus $(k^2 + h^2)/h$ is the length, l, of the *equivalent simple pendulum*.

From (i), $h^2 - hl + k^2 = 0.$

$\therefore h_1 + h_2 = l$, and $h_1 h_2 = k^2$,

where h_1 and h_2 are the roots of the equation.

By timing the period of vibration, T, of a long rod about a series of axes at varying distances h on either side of the centre of gravity, and then plotting a graph of T vs . h, two different values of h giving the same period can be obtained, Fig. 40. Suppose h_1, h_2 are the two values. Then from the result just obtained, $h_1 + h_2 = l$, the length of the equivalent simple pendulum. Thus, since $T = 2\pi \sqrt{l/g}$,

$$g = \frac{4\pi^2 l}{T^2} = \frac{4\pi^2(h_1 + h_2)}{T^2}.$$

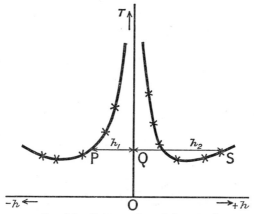

FIG. 40. Compound pendulum graph.

In Fig. 40, $PQ + QS = h_1 + h_2 = l$.

The compound pendulum can provide a very accurate determination of "g". For details of the experiment the reader should consult a text-book of practical physics, such as *Advanced Practical Physics for Students* by Worsnop and Flint (Methuen). See also p. 186.

16. Measurement of Moment of Inertia of Plate.

The moment of inertia of a circular disc or other plate about an axis perpendicular to its plane, for example, can be measured by means of torsional oscillations. The plate is suspended horizontally from a vertical torsion wire, and the period T_1 of torsional oscillations is measured. Then, from (39),

$$T_1 = 2\pi \sqrt{\frac{I_1}{c}}, \qquad \cdot \quad \cdot \quad \cdot \quad \cdot \qquad (i)$$

where I_1 is the moment of inertia and c is the constant (opposing couple per unit radian) of the wire (p. 146). A ring or annulus of *known* moment of inertia I_2 is now placed on the plate concentric with the axis, and the new period T_2 is observed. Then

$$T_2 = 2\pi \sqrt{\frac{I_1 + I_2}{c}} \qquad \cdot \quad \cdot \quad \cdot \qquad (ii).$$

By squaring (i) and (ii), and then eliminating c, we obtain

$$I_1 = \frac{T_1{}^2}{T_2{}^2 - T_1{}^2} \cdot I_2.$$

Thus knowing T_1, T_2, and I_2, the moment of inertia I_1 can be calculated.

17. Measurement of Moment of Inertia of Flywheel.

The moment of inertia of a flywheel W about a horizontal axle A can be determined by tying one end of some string to a pin on the axle, winding the string round the axle, and attaching a mass M to the other end of the string, Fig. 41. The length of string is such that M reaches

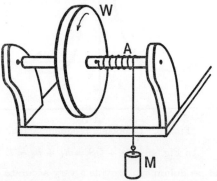

FIG. 41.   Moment of inertia of fly-wheel.

the floor, when released, at the same instant as the string is completely unwound from the axle.

M is released, and the number of revolutions, n, made by the wheel W up to the occasion when M strikes the ground is noted. The further number of revolutions n_1 made by W until it comes finally to rest, and the time t taken, are also observed by means of a chalk-mark on W.

Now the loss in potential energy of M = gain in kinetic energy of M + gain in kinetic energy of flywheel + work done against friction.

$$\therefore Mgh = \tfrac{1}{2}Mr^2\omega^2 + \tfrac{1}{2}I\omega^2 + nf, \qquad . \qquad . \qquad . \qquad \text{(i)}$$

where h is the distance M has fallen, r is the radius of the axle, ω is the angular velocity, I is the moment of inertia, and f is the energy per turn expended against friction. Since the energy of rotation of the flywheel when the mass M reaches the ground = work done against friction in n_1 revolutions,

$$\tfrac{1}{2}I\omega^2 = n_1 f.$$

$$\therefore f = \tfrac{1}{2}\frac{I\omega^2}{n_1}.$$

Substituting for f in (i),

$$\therefore Mgh = \tfrac{1}{2}Mr^2\omega^2 + \tfrac{1}{2}I\omega^2\left(1 + \frac{n}{n_1}\right) \qquad . \qquad . \qquad \text{(ii)}$$

Since the angular velocity of the wheel when M reaches the ground is ω, and the final angular velocity of the wheel is zero after a time t, the average angular velocity $= \omega/2 = 2\pi n_1/t$. Thus $\omega = 4\pi n_1/t$. Knowing ω and the magnitude of the other quantities in (ii), the moment of inertia I of the flywheel can be calculated.

EXAMPLES

1. A solid cylinder (i) slides down, (ii) rolls down a smooth plane inclined at 30° to the horizontal without slipping. Compare the accelerations down the plane in each case if the cylinder starts from rest.

(i) When the cylinder slides down the plane, its acceleration down the plane, f, $= g\sin 30° = 32\sin 30° = 16$ ft. per sec.^{2}.

(ii) When the cylinder rolls down the plane, its gain of kinetic energy

$$= \tfrac{1}{2}I\omega^2 + \tfrac{1}{2}Mv^2 \text{ (p. 68)}$$

$$= \tfrac{1}{2}(\tfrac{1}{2}Ma^2)\left(\frac{v}{a}\right)^2 + \tfrac{1}{2}Mv^2,$$

since $I =$ moment of inertia about centre of gravity $= Ma^2/2$ and $\omega = v/a$.

$$\therefore \text{ gain of kinetic energy} = \tfrac{3}{4}Mv^2.$$

But loss of potential energy $= Mgs\sin 30°$, where s is the distance travelled along the plane.

$$\therefore \tfrac{3}{4}Mv^2 = Mgs\sin 30°.$$

$$\therefore v^2 = \frac{4g}{3}s\sin 30°.$$

But $$v^2 = 2fs,$$

where f is the acceleration, since the initial velocity is zero.

$$\therefore 2fs = \frac{4g}{3}s\sin 30°$$

$$\therefore f = \frac{2g}{3}\sin 30° = \frac{2\times 32}{3}\sin 30°$$

$$= 10\tfrac{2}{3} \text{ ft. per sec.}^2.$$

$\therefore$ ratio of accelerations $= 16 : 10\tfrac{2}{3} = 3 : 2$.

2. Calculate the period of oscillation of (i) a uniform rod 12 ft. long about one end, (ii) a hoop of radius 2 ft. about an axis through its circumference perpendicular to its plane. What is the length of the equivalent simple pendulum in each case?

(i) The period of oscillation of the rod, T, $= 2\pi \sqrt{\dfrac{I}{mgh}}$ (p. 70).

But $I = ml^2/3$, where l is the length of the rod (p. 62), and $h =$ distance of centre of gravity from axis $= l/2$.

$$\therefore T = 2\pi \sqrt{\frac{ml^2/3}{mgl/2}} = 2\pi \sqrt{\frac{2\,l}{3\,g}} \qquad \cdots \qquad (i)$$

$$= 2\pi \sqrt{\frac{2}{3} \times \frac{12}{32}} = 3{\cdot}14 \text{ sec.}$$

The simple pendulum period, $T = 2\pi \sqrt{\dfrac{\text{length.}}{g}}$ From (i) it follows that

$$\text{length of equivalent simple pendulum} = \frac{2}{3}l = \frac{2}{3} \times 12 = 8 \text{ ft.}$$

(ii) The moment of inertia, I, of the hoop about an axis through its circumference $= \mathrm{I_G} + Mh^2 = Ma^2 + Ma^2$, since $I_G = Ma^2$ and $h = a$ (see p. 65).

$$\therefore I = 2Ma^2$$

$$\therefore \text{period}, T, = 2\pi \sqrt{\frac{I}{Mgh}} = 2\pi \sqrt{\frac{2Ma^2}{Mga}}.$$

$$= 2\pi \sqrt{\frac{2a}{g}} = 2\pi \sqrt{\frac{2 \times 2}{32}} = 2{\cdot}2 \text{ sec.}$$

Since period, T, of simple pendulum $= 2\pi \sqrt{\dfrac{\text{length}}{g}}$,

$$\text{length of equivalent simple pendulum} = 2a = 4 \text{ ft.}$$

3. Define the moment of inertia of a body about a given axis. Describe how the moment of inertia of a fly-wheel can be determined experimentally.

A horizontal disc rotating freely about a vertical axis makes 100 r.p.m. A small piece of wax of mass 10 gm. falls vertically on to the disc and adheres to it at a distance of 9 cm. from the axis. If the number of revolutions per minute is thereby reduced to 90, calculate the moment of inertia of the disc. (N.)

First part. See text.

Second part. Let $I =$ moment of inertia of disc. Then if ω_1, ω_2 are the initial and final angular velocities,
the respective angular momentum about the axis $= I\omega_1$, $I\omega_2$ (p. 61). The angular momentum of the wax about the axis $= mr\omega_2 \times r = mr^2\omega_2$,

where $r = 9$ cm., $m = 10$ gm. Since the angular momentum is constant,

$$\therefore I\omega_1 = I\omega_2 + mr^2\omega_2$$
$$\therefore I(\omega_1 - \omega_2) = mr^2\omega_2$$
$$\therefore I = mr^2\left(\frac{\omega_2}{\omega_1 - \omega_2}\right)$$
$$= 10 \times 9^2 \times \left(\frac{90}{100 - 90}\right), \text{ from above,}$$
$$= 7,290 \text{ gm. cm}^2.$$

EXERCISES III

1. A uniform rod has a mass of 60 gm. and a length a 20 cm. Calculate the moment of inertia about an axis perpendicular to its length (i) through its centre, (ii) through one end. Prove the formulæ used.

2. What is the *Theorem of Parallel Axes?* A uniform disc has a mass of 4 lb. and a radius of 6 ft. Calculate the moment of inertia about an axis perpendicular to its plane (i) through its centre, (ii) through a point of its circumference.

3. What is the *Theorem of Perpendicular Axes?* A ring has a radius of 20 cm. and a mass of 100 gm. Calculate the moment of inertia about an axis (i) perpendicular to its plane through its centre, (ii) perpendicular to its plane passing through a point on its circumference, (iii) in its plane passing through the centre.

4. What is the formula for the kinetic energy of (i) a particle, (ii) a rigid body rotating about an axis through its centre of gravity, (iii) a rigid body rotating about an axis through any point? Calculate the kinetic energy of a disc of mass 5 lb. and radius 2 ft. rolling along a plane with a uniform velocity of 10 ft. per sec.

5. A sphere rolls down a plane inclined at 30° to the horizontal. Find the acceleration and velocity of the sphere after it has moved 16 ft. from rest along the plane, assuming the moment of inertia of a sphere about a diameter is $2Ma^2/5$, where M is the mass and a is the radius.

6. A uniform rod of length 9 ft. is suspended at one end so that it can move about an axis perpendicular to its length, and is held inclined at 60° to the vertical and then released. Calculate the angular velocity of the rod when (i) it is inclined at 30° to the vertical, (ii) reaches the vertical.

7. Define the *moment of inertia* of a rigid object about an axis.
A ring of radius 6 ft. oscillates about an axis on its circumference which is perpendicular to the plane of the ring. Calculate the period of oscillation. Give an explanation of any formula used.

8. Derive an expression for the moment of inertia of a uniform circular disc of mass M, radius r, about a central axis perpendicular to its plane. How would you determine this moment of inertia experimentally?

A circular disc of mass 800 gm., radius 10 cm., is suspended by a wire through its centre perpendicular to its plane and makes 50 torsional oscillations in 59·8 sec. When an annulus is placed symmetrically on the disc, the system makes 50 oscillations in 66·4 sec. Calculate the moment of inertia of the annulus about the axis of rotation. (N.)

9. What is meant by "moment of inertia"? Explain the importance of this concept in dealing with problems concerning rotating bodies.

Describe, with practical details, how you would determine whether a given cylindrical body were hollow or not without damaging it. (C.)

10. Define *moment of inertia*, and find an expression for the kinetic energy of a rigid body rotating about a fixed axis.

A sphere, starting from rest, rolls (without slipping) down a rough plane inclined to the horizontal at an angle of 30°, and it is found to travel a distance of 1,350 cm. in the first 3 secs. of its motion. Assuming that F, the frictional resistance to the motion, is independent of the speed, calculate the ratio of F to the *weight* of the sphere. (For a sphere of mass m and radius r, the moment of inertia about a diameter is $\frac{2}{5}mr^2$.) (O. & C.)

11. Obtain an expression for the moment of inertia of a uniform circular cylinder of mass M and radius a about its axis. If such a cylinder is set in rotation about its axis with angular velocity ω, find its kinetic energy.

A uniform circular disc of mass 500 gm. and radius 50 cm. can rotate in its own plane about a fixed horizontal axis passing through a point on its circumference. If the disc is pulled aside until its centre of gravity is on the same horizontal level as the axis and then released, find the linear velocity of the centre of gravity as it passes through its equilibrium position. (W.)

12. A flat plate of irregular shape is pierced by a number of small holes, distributed at random, through which a knitting needle can pass easily. Describe how, using the plate and the needle, you would find the acceleration due to gravity and give the theory of the method.

A thin uniform rod swings as a pendulum about a horizontal axis at one end, the periodic time being 1·65 sec. If the mass of the rod is 125 gm., what is (a) its length, (b) its moment of inertia about the horizontal axis? (N.)

13. Explain the meaning of the term *moment of inertia*. Describe in detail how you would find experimentally the moment of inertia of a bicycle wheel about the central line of its hub.

A uniform cylinder 20 cm. long, suspended by a steel wire attached to its mid-point so that its long axis is horizontal, is found to oscillate with a period of 2 secs. when the wire is twisted and released. When a small thin disc, of mass 10 gm., is attached to each end the period is found to be 2·3 secs. Calculate the moment of inertia of the cylinder about the axis of oscillation. (N.)

14. Obtain an expression for the period of small oscillations of a compound pendulum. A circular hoop oscillates in its own plane about a horizontal axis normal to its plane and passing through its circumference. A simple pendulum of length 100 cm. swings with the same period as the hoop. Find the radius of the hoop. (W.)

CHAPTER IV

STATICS

1. Statics

1. Statics is a subject which concerns the *equilibrium* of forces, such as the forces which act on a bridge. In Fig. 42 (i), for example, the joint O of a light bridge is in equilibrium under the action of the two forces P, Q acting in the girders meeting at O and the reaction S of the masonry at O.

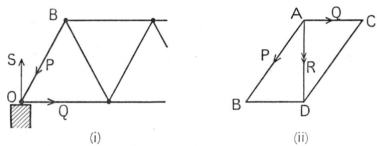

FIG. 42.   Equilibrium of forces.

2. Parallelogram of Forces.

A force is a vector quantity, i.e., it can be represented in magnitude and direction by a straight line (see p. 6). If AB, AC represent the forces P, Q respectively at the joint O, their *resultant*, R, is represented in magnitude and direction by the diagonal AD of the parallelogram ABDC which has AB, AC as two of its adjacent sides, Fig. 42 (ii). This is known as the *parallelogram of forces*, and is exactly analogous to the parallelogram of velocities discussed on p. 7.

By trigonometry for triangle ABD, we have

$$AD^2 = BA^2 + BD^2 - 2BA \cdot BD \cos ABD.$$

$$\therefore R^2 = P^2 + Q^2 + 2PQ \cos \theta,$$

where $\theta =$ angle BAC, the angle between the forces P, Q, $= 180° -$ angle ABD. This formula enables R to be calculated when P, Q and the angle between them are known. The angle BAD, or a, between the resultant R and the force P can then be calculated from the relation

77

$$\frac{R}{\sin \theta} = \frac{Q}{\sin a},$$

applying the sine rule to triangle ABD and noting that angle ABD = $180° - \theta$.

Resolved component. On p. 7 we saw that the effective part, or resolved component, of a vector quantity X in a direction θ inclined to it is given by $X \cos \theta$. Thus the resolved component of a force P in a direction making an angle of 30° with it is $P \cos 30°$; in a perpendicular direction to the latter the resolved component is $P \cos 60°$, or $P \sin 30°$. In Fig. 42 (i), the downward component of the force P on the joint of O is given by $P \cos$ BOS.

3. Forces in Equilibrium.   Triangle of Forces.

Since the joint O is in equilibrium, Fig. 42 (i), the resultant of the forces P, Q in the rods meeting at this joint is equal and opposite to the reaction S at O. Now the diagonal AD of the parallelogram ABDC in Fig. 42 (ii) represents the resultant R of P, Q since ABDC is the parallelogram of forces for P, Q; and hence DA represents the force S. Consequently the sides of the triangle ABD represent the three forces at O in magnitude and direction: This result can be generalised as follows. *If three forces are in equilibrium, they can be represented by the three sides of a triangle taken in order.* This theorem in Statics is known as the *triangle of forces.* In Fig. 42 (ii), AB, BD, DA, in this order, represent P, Q, S respectively in Fig. 42 (i).

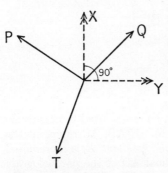

FIG. 43.   Resolution of forces.

We can derive another relation between forces in equilibrium. Suppose X, Y are the respective algebraic sums of the resolved components in two perpendicular directions of three forces P, Q, T in equilibrium, Fig. 43. Then, since X, Y can each be represented by the sides of a *rectangle* drawn to scale, their resultant R is given by

$$R^2 = X^2 + Y^2 \quad . \quad . \quad . \quad . \quad . \quad (i)$$

Now if the forces are in equilibrium, R is zero. It then follows from (i) that X must be zero and Y must be zero. Thus *if forces are in equilibrium the algebraic sum of their resolved components in any two perpendicular directions is respectively zero.* This result applies to any number of forces in equilibrium (p. 83).

4. Moments.

When the steering-wheel of a car is turned, the applied force is said to exert a *moment,* or turning-effect, about the axle attached to the wheel. The magnitude of the moment of a force P about a point O is defined as *the product of the force P and the perpendicular distance OA from O to the line of action of P*, Fig. 44 (i). Thus

$$\text{moment} = P \times \text{AO}.$$

The magnitude of the moment is expressed in dyne cm. when P is in dynes and AO is in cm.; or in lb. wt. ft. if P is in lb. wt. and AO is in feet. We shall say that an anticlockwise moment is positive in sign, and that a clockwise moment is negative in sign.

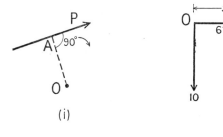

(i)

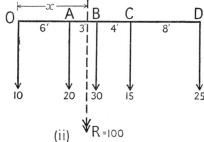

(ii)

FIG. 44. Moments of forces.

5. Parallel Forces.

If a bridge carries loads of 10, 20, 30, 15, and 25 cwt. at O, A, B, C, D respectively, the resultant R of the weights, which are parallel forces, is equal to their sum, Fig. 44 (ii). Thus

resultant, R, $= 10 + 20 + 30 + 15 + 25 = 100$ cwt.

Experiment and theory show that *the moment of the resultant of a number of forces about any point is equal to the algebraic sum of the moments of the individual forces about the same point.* This result enables us to find where the resultant R acts. Taking moments about O for all the forces in Fig. 44 (ii), we have

$$(20 \times 6) + (30 \times 9) + (15 \times 13) + (25 \times 21),$$

because the distances between the forces are 6 ft., 3 ft., 4 ft., 8 ft., as shown. If x ft. is the distance of the line of action of R from O, the moment of R about O $= R \times x = 100 \times x$.

$$\therefore 100\,x = (20 \times 6) + (30 \times 9) + (15 \times 13) + (25 \times 21),$$

from which $\qquad\qquad x = 11 \cdot 1$ ft.

The resultant of a number of forces *in equilibrium* is zero; and the moment of the resultant about any point is hence zero. It therefore follows that the algebraic sum of the moments of all the forces about any point is zero when those forces are in equilibrium.

6. Equilibrium of Three Coplanar Forces Acting on Rigid Body.

If any object is in equilibrium under the action of *three* forces, the resultant of two of the forces must be equal and opposite to the third force. Thus the line of action of the third force must pass through the point of intersection of the lines of action of the other two forces.

As an example of calculating unknown forces in this case, suppose that a 12 ft. ladder of 20 lb. wt. is placed at an angle of 60° to the horizontal, with one end B leaning against a smooth wall and the other end A on the ground, Fig. 45. The force R at B on the ladder is called the *reaction* of the wall, and if the latter is smooth, R acts perpendicularly to the wall. Assuming the weight, W, of the ladder acts at its mid-point G, the forces W and R meet at O, as shown. Consequently the frictional force F at A passes through O.

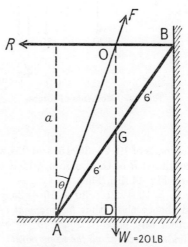

FIG. 45.   Equilibrium of ladder.

The *triangle of forces* can be used to find the unknown forces R, F. Since DA is parallel to R, AO is parallel to F, and OD is parallel to W, the triangle of forces is represented by AOD. By means of a scale drawing R and F can be found, since

$$\frac{W(20)}{\text{OD}} = \frac{F}{\text{AO}} = \frac{R}{\text{DA}}.$$

A quicker method is achieved by taking moments about A for all the forces. The algebraic sum of the moments is zero about any point since the object is in equilibrium, and hence

$$R \cdot a - W \cdot AD = 0,$$

where a is the perpendicular from A to R. (F has zero moment about A.)
But $a = 12 \sin 60°$, and AD $= 6 \cos 60°$.

$$\therefore R \times 12 \sin 60° - 20 \times 6 \cos 60° = 0.$$

$$\therefore R = 10 \frac{\cos 60°}{\sin 60°} = 5 \cdot 77 \text{ lb.}$$

Suppose θ is the angle F makes with the vertical.

Resolving the forces vertically, $F \cos \theta = W = 20$ lb.

Resolving horizontally, $F \sin \theta = R = 5 \cdot 77$ lb.

$$\therefore F^2 \cos^2\theta + F^2 \sin^2\theta = F^2 = 20^2 + 5 \cdot 77^2.$$

$$\therefore F = \sqrt{20^2 + 5 \cdot 77^2} = 20 \cdot 8 \text{ lb.}$$

7. Couples and their Moments.

There are many examples in practice where two forces, acting together, exert a moment or turning-effect on some object. As a very simple case, suppose two strings are tied to a wheel at X, Y, and *two equal and opposite forces*, P, are exerted tangentially to the wheel, Fig. 46 (i). If the wheel is pivoted at its centre, O, it begins to rotate about O in an anticlockwise direction.

Two equal and opposite forces whose lines of action do not coincide are said to constitute a *couple* in Mechanics. The two forces always have a turning-effect, or moment, which is defined by

moment = one force × perpendicular distance between forces .   (42)

Since XY is perpendicular to each of the forces P in Fig. 46 (i), the

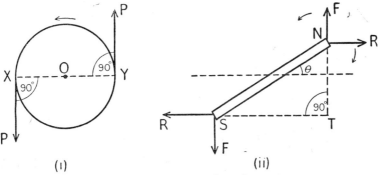

Fɪɢ. 46.   Moments of couples.

moment of the couple acting on the wheel $= P \times XY = P \times$ diameter of wheel. Thus if $P = 10$ lb. wt. and the diameter is 6 ft., the moment of the couple $= 60$ lb. wt. ft.

In Magnetism, we meet cases in which a magnet is kept in equilibrium by two couples acting on it, Fig. 46 (ii) represents a magnet NS in equilibrium under the action of a couple due to the forces F and an opposing couple due to the forces R. The former couple has a clockwise moment $= F \times ST$: the latter couple has an anticlockwise moment $= R \times NT$. Since the magnet does not move, the moments are equal,

$$\therefore F \times ST = R \times NT$$

$$\therefore F = R \times \frac{NT}{ST} = R \tan \theta,$$

where θ is the angle NST.

8. Work Done by a Couple.

Suppose two equal and opposite forces F act tangentially to a wheel W, and rotate it through an angle θ while the forces keep tangentially to the wheel, Fig. 47. The moment of the couple is then constant. The

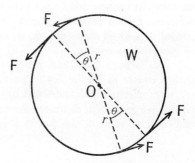

FIG. 47.   Work done by couple.

work done by each force $= F \times$ distance $= F \times r\theta$, since $r\theta$ is the distance moved by a point on the rim if θ is in radians.

$\therefore$ total work done by couple $= Fr\theta + Fr\theta = 2Fr\theta$.

But moment of couple $= F \times 2r = 2Fr$

$\therefore$ work done by couple $=$ moment of couple $\times \theta$. . . . (43)

Although we have chosen a simple case, the result for the work done by a couple is always given by *moment* $\times$ *angle of rotation*. In the formula, it should be carefully noted that θ is in radians. Thus suppose $F = 100$ gm. wt. $= 100 \times 980$ dynes, $r = 4$ cm., and the wheel makes 5 revolutions while the moment of the couple is kept constant. Then

angle of rotation $= 2\pi \times 5$ radians,

and   moment of couple $= (100 \times 980) \times (2 \times 4)$ cm. dyne.

$$\therefore \text{ work done} = (100 \times 980) \times 2 \times 4 \times 2\pi \times 5 =$$
$$2 \cdot 46 \times 10^7 \text{ ergs.}$$

9. Equilibrium of any Number of Coplanar Forces.

On p. 80 we showed how unknown forces could be calculated when an object is in equilibrium under the action of three forces. If an object is in equilibrium under any number of coplanar forces their resultant in any direction is zero. Consequently the algebraic sum of the resolved components of all the forces in any two perpendicular directions is respectively zero (see p. 78). But this cannot be the only condition satisfied by the forces, because they might reduce to two equal and opposite forces whose lines of action do not coincide. In this case the algebraic sum of the resolved components is zero, but the forces are not in equilibrium because they reduce to a couple. We must therefore stipulate in addition that the algebraic sum of the moments of the forces about any point must be zero, in which case there cannot be a couple. Summarizing, the necessary conditions of equilibrium of any number of coplanar forces are:

(1) The algebraic sum of the resolved components of all the forces in any two perpendicular directions must be respectively zero.

(2) The algebraic sum of the moments of the forces about any point must be zero.

10. Equilibrium of Parallel Forces.

If an object such as a bridge is in equilibrium under the action of any number of parallel forces, it follows that:

(1) the sum of the forces in one direction = the sum of the forces in the opposite direction:

(2) the algebraic sum of the moments of all the forces about any point is zero.

As a simple example of the equilibrium of parallel forces, suppose a

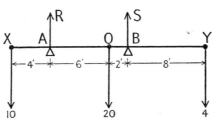

Fig. 48.   Equilibrium of parallel forces.

light beam XY rests on supports A,B, and has loads of 10, 20, and 4 lb. concentrated at X, O, Y respectively, Fig. 48. Let R, S be the reactions at A,B respectively. Then, for equilibrium in a vertical direction,

$$R + S = 10 + 20 + 4 = 34 \text{ lb. wt.} \qquad . \quad . \quad \text{(i)}$$

To find R, we take moments about a suitable point such as B, in which case the moment of S is zero. Then, for the remaining four forces,

$$+ 10 \cdot 12 + 20 \cdot 2 - R \cdot 8 - 4 \cdot 8 = 0,$$

from which $R = 16$ lb. wt. From (i), it follows that $S = 34 - 16 = 18$ lb. wt.

11. Centre of Gravity.

Every particle is attracted towards the centre of the earth by the force of gravity, and the *centre of gravity* of a body is the point where the *resultant* force of attraction acts. In the simple case of a ruler, the centre of gravity is the point of support when the ruler is balanced. A similar method can be used to find roughly the centre of gravity of a flat plate. A more accurate method consists of suspending the object in turn from two points on it, so that it hangs freely in each case, and finding the point of intersection of a plumb-line, suspended in turn from each point of suspension. This experiment is described in elementary books.

An object can be considered to consist of many small particles. The forces on the particles due to the attraction of the earth are all parallel since they act vertically, and hence their resultant is the sum of all the forces. The resultant is the *weight* of the whole object, of course. In the case of a rod of uniform cross-sectional area, the weight of a particle A at one end, and that of a corresponding particle A' at the other end. have a resultant which acts at the mid-point O of the rod, Fig. 49,

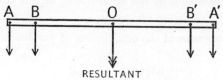

RESULTANT

FIG. 49.   Centre of gravity of uniform rod.

Similarly, the resultant of the weight of a particle B, and that of a corresponding particle at B', have a resultant acting at O. In this way, i.e., by symmetry, it follows that the resultant of the weights of all the particles of the rod acts at O, and hence the centre gravity of a uniform rod is at its mid-point.

The *centre of mass* of an object is the point where the total mass acts. Except for enormous objects, the centre of mass is situated at the same place as the centre of gravity.

12. Positions of Centre of Gravity.

The following are the positions of the centre of gravity (C.G.) of some objects:

(1) *Circular disc.* The C.G. is at the centre.

(2) *Circular wire.* The C.G. is at its centre of the circle.

(3) *Triangular lamina or plate.* The C.G. is at the point of inter-

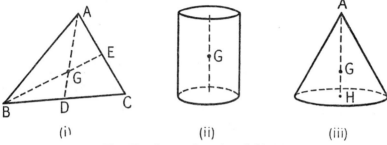

(i)   (ii)   (iii)

FIG. 50.   Centre of gravity of objects.

section of the medians, which are the lines joining the points of the triangle such as A, B to the mid-points of the opposite sides, D, E, Fig. 50 (i). It can be shown that $AG = \frac{2}{3} AD$, where $BD = DC$ and G is the centre of gravity, and hence the C.G. is two-thirds of the way along the median from a point of the triangle.

(4) *Parallelogram, rectangle, or square lamina.* The C.G. is at the point of intersection of the diagonals.

(5) *Curved surface of a hollow cylinder.* The C.G. is at the mid-point of the axis of the cylinder, Fig. 50 (ii).

(6) *Solid cylinder.* The C.G. is at the mid-point of the axis of the cylinder.

(7) *Right solid cone.* The C.G. is three-quarters of the way along the axis from the apex, i.e., $AG = \frac{3}{4}AH$, Fig. 50 (iii).

13. Centre of Gravity of Combined Objects.

The position of the centre of gravity of *combined objects* can be found by applying the law of moments for parallel forces, since the weights are parallel forces. This law states:

The moment of the resultant (total) weight about any point = the algebraic sum of the moments, in the same direction, of the separate weights about the same point (see p. 79).

The following example illustrates how this principle is applied:

EXAMPLE

What is meant by (a) the centre of mass of a body, (b) the centre of gravity of a body?

A cylindrical can is made of a material weighing 10 gm./sq. cm. and has no lid. The diameter of the can is 25 cm. and its height 50 cm. Find the position of the centre of mass when the can is half full of water. (C.)

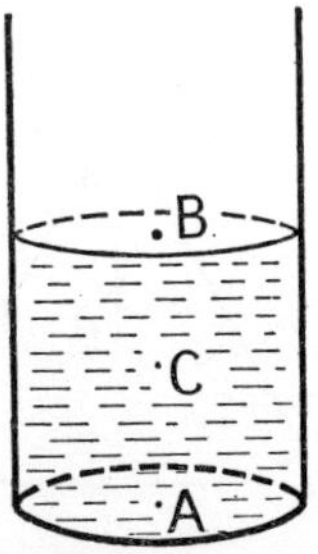

First part. The "centre of mass" is the point where the resultant mass of the body acts; the "centre of gravity" is the point where the resultant *weight* of the body acts.

Second part. The area of the base $= \pi r^2 = \pi \times \left(\dfrac{25}{2}\right)^2$ sq.cm.; hence the mass is $\pi \times (25/2)^2 \times 10$ gm., and acts at A, the centre of the base, Fig. 51.

The mass of the curved surface of the centre $= 2\pi rh \times 10$ gm. $= 2\pi \times (25/2) \times 50 \times 10$ gm., and acts at B, half-way along the axis.

FIG. 51.

The mass of water $= \pi r^2 h$ gm. $= \pi \times (25/2)^2 \times 25$ gm., and acts at C, the mid-point of AB.

Thus the resultant mass in grams

$$= \frac{\pi \times 625 \times 10}{4} + \frac{2\pi \times 25 \times 50 \times 10}{2} + \frac{\pi \times 625 \times 25}{4}$$

$$= \pi \times 625 \times 28\tfrac{3}{4}$$

Taking moments about A,

$$\therefore \pi \times 625 \times 28\tfrac{3}{4} \times x = (\pi \times 12500) \times \text{AB} + \left(\pi \times \frac{625 \times 25}{4}\right) \times \text{AC}$$

where x is the distance of the centre of mass from A.

$$\therefore 28\tfrac{3}{4} x = 20 \times 25 + \frac{25}{4} \times 12\tfrac{1}{2}$$

$$\therefore \quad x = 20 \cdot 1$$

$\therefore$ centre of mass is $20 \cdot 1$ cm. from the base.

14. Machines.

A *machine* is an instrument which enables a force W to be applied at a certain point by the application of another force P at a different point. A pulley system, for example, enables a heavy load, W, to be raised by a smaller force or effort, P.

The *mechanical advantage* (M.A.) of a machine is defined by the ratio

$$\text{M.A.} = \frac{\text{load } (W)}{\text{effort } (P)} \qquad \cdot \quad \cdot \quad \cdot \quad \cdot \quad \cdot \quad \cdot \quad (44)$$

The *velocity ratio* (V.R.) of the machine is defined by the ratio

$$\text{V.R.} = \frac{\text{distance per sec. moved by effort } (x)}{\text{distance per sec. moved by load } (y)} \quad \cdot \quad (45)$$

On account of friction, for example, the energy, or work, obtained from a machine is always less than the energy, or work, supplied to it. The *efficiency*, η, of the machine is defined by

$$\eta = \frac{\text{work or energy obtained}}{\text{work or energy supplied}} \qquad \cdot \quad \cdot \quad \cdot \quad (46)$$

$$= \frac{\text{work done on load, } W \times y}{\text{work done by effort, } P \times x},$$

since work $=$ force $\times$ distance. But $W/P =$ mechanical advantage (M.A.), and $x/y =$ velocity ratio (V.R.).

$$\therefore \eta = \frac{\text{M.A.}}{\text{V.R.}}$$

In practice, therefore, the mechanical advantage is less than the velocity ratio, which is independent of friction. If the machine were perfect, i.e., if no energy were lost, the two quantities would be equal.

15. Levers.

A *lever* is a machine in which a load, W, is attached to one point of a rod, which is capable of rotating about another point known as the *fulcrum*. The effort, P, is applied at another point of the rod. In the **first class** of levers, the load W and the effort P are on opposite sides of the fulcrum O, and P is further from the fulcrum than W., Fig. 52 (i).

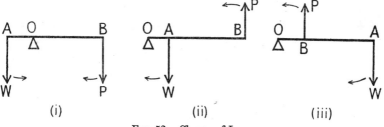

(i)   (ii)   (iii)

Fig. 52.   Classes of Levers.

Taking moments about O, we have $W \cdot OA = P \cdot OB$, or $W/P = OB/OA$. The mechanical advantage is thus equal to the ratio of the "arms" of the lever. Examples of this class of lever are the crowbar, pincers, and pliers.

In the **second class** of levers the load W and the effort P are on the same side of the fulcrum, O, with W nearer to O than P, Fig. 52 (ii). By taking moments about O, the mechanical advantage, $W/P = OB/OA$. Examples of this class of levers are the wheelbarrow, the nut-cracker, and the oar. In the **third class** of levers the load W and the effort P are on the same side of the fulcrum, O, but the load is further away from the fulcrum than the effort, Fig. 52 (iii). Examples of this class of levers are the coal-tongs and the human arm. By taking moments about O, the mechanical advantage, W/P, $= OB/OA$, which is less than unity, unlike the other two classes of levers.

16. Common Balance.

The common balance is basically a lever of the first class whose two arms are equal, Fig. 53. The fulcrum, about which the beam and pointer tilt, is an agate wedge resting on an agate plate; agate wedges, B, at the ends of the beam, support the scale-pans. The centre of gravity of the

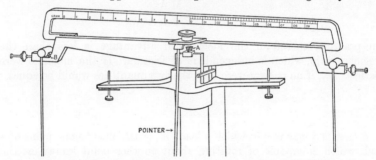

FIG. 53.   Top of Common Balance; beam tilted by small load.

beam and pointer is vertically below the fulcrum, to make the arrangement stable. The weight placed on the two scale-pans are equal when there is a "balance".

On rare occasions the arms of the balance are slightly unequal. The weight W of an object is then determined by finding the respective weights W_1, W_2 required to balance it on each scale-pan. Suppose a, b are the lengths of the respective arms. Then, taking moments,

$$\therefore W_1 \cdot a = W \cdot b, \text{ and } W \cdot a = W_2 \cdot b.$$

$$\therefore \frac{W}{W_1} = \frac{a}{b} = \frac{W_2}{W}$$

$$\therefore W^2 = W_1 W_2$$

$$\therefore \; W = \sqrt{W_1 W_2}$$

Thus W can be found from the two weights W_1, W_2.

17. Sensitivity of a Balance.

A balance is said to be very *sensitive* if a small difference in weights on the scale-pans causes a large deflection of the beam. To investigate the factors which affect the sensitivity of a balance, suppose a weight W_1 is placed on the left scale-pan and a slightly smaller weight W_2 is

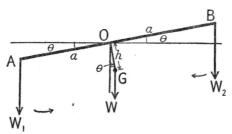

FIG. 54.   Sensitivity of balance.

placed on the right scale-pan, Fig. 54. The beam AOB will then be inclined at some angle θ to the horizontal, where O is the fulcrum.

The weight W of the beam and pointer acts at G, at a distance h below O. Suppose AO = OB = a. Then, taking moments about O,

$$W_1 a \cos \theta = Wh \sin \theta + W_2 a \cos \theta$$

$$\therefore (W_1 - W_2)a \cos \theta = Wh \sin \theta$$

$$\therefore \tan \theta = \frac{(W_1 - W_2)a}{Wh}$$

Thus for a given value of $(W_1 - W_2)$, the difference of the weights on the scale-pans, θ will increase when a increases and W, h both decrease. In theory, then, a sensitive balance must be light and have long arms, and the centre of gravity of its beam and pointer must be very close to the fulcrum. Now a light beam will not be rigid. Further, a beam with long arms will take a long time to settle down when it is deflected. A compromise must therefore be made between the requirements of sensitivity and those of design.

If the knife-edges of the scale-pan and of the beam are in the same plane, the balance has the same sensitivity over a considerable range of loads, because the two scale-pans and the weights on them rise and fall respectively by the same amount. When the knife-edge of the beam is below the knife-edges of the two scale-pans, the sensitivity increases with the load; the reverse is the case if the knife-edge of the beam is above those of the scale-pans.

18. Buoyancy Correction in Weighing.

In very accurate weighing, a correction must be made for the buoyancy of the air. Suppose the body weighed has a density ρ and a mass m. From Archimedes principle (p. 97), the upthrust due to the air of density σ is equal to the weight of air displaced by the body, and hence the net downward force $= \left(m - \dfrac{m}{\rho} . \sigma \right) g$, since the volume of the body is m/ρ. Similarly, if the weights restoring a balance have a total mass m_1 and a density ρ_1, the net downward force $= \left(m_1 - \dfrac{m_1}{\rho_1} . \sigma \right) g$.

Since there is a balance,

$$m - \frac{m\sigma}{\rho} = m_1 - \frac{m_1\sigma}{\rho_1}$$

$$\therefore m = m_1 \frac{\left(1 - \dfrac{\sigma}{\rho_1} \right)}{1 - \dfrac{\sigma}{\rho}}$$

Thus knowing the density of air, σ, and the densities ρ, ρ_1, the true mass m can be found in terms of m_1. The pressure and temperature of air, which may vary from day to day, affects the magnitude of its density σ, from the gas laws; the humidity of the air is also taken into account in very accurate weighing, as the density of moist air differs from that of dry air.

EXAMPLES

1. What is meant by (a) the *mechanical advantage*, (b) the *velocity ratio*, (c) the *efficiency* of a machine? A forearm is held horizontally, with the upper part of the arm vertical, and a 500 gm. weight is held in the hand so that its centre of gravity is 30 cm. from the elbow joint. Assuming that the lower and upper ends of the biceps muscles are attached at points 5 cm. and 12 cm. from the elbow joint, and that the lever system is perfectly efficient, find (i) the tension in the muscle, (ii) the velocity ratio of the system. (Neglect the weight of the forearm itself.) (*L.*)

First part. See text.

Second part. Suppose O is the elbow joint, C is the 500 gm. wt., A is the point of attachment of the lower end of the bicep muscle, and B is that of the upper end, Fig. 55. If T is the tension in the muscle AB, then, taking moments about O,

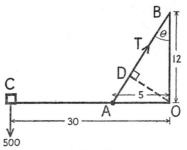

FIG. 55.

$$T \times OD = 500 \times OC.$$

But $OD = 12 \sin \theta = 12 \times \frac{5}{13}$cm., since $AB = \sqrt{12^2 + 5^2} = 13$, and $OC = 30$ cm.

$$\therefore T \times 12 \times \frac{5}{13} = 500 \times 30$$

$$\therefore T = \frac{500 \times 30 \times 13}{12 \times 5} = 3250 \text{ gm. wt.}$$

The velocity ratio of the system is equal to the mechanical advantage if the lever system is perfectly efficient (p. 87). Thus velocity ratio =

mechanical advantage $= \frac{3250}{500} = 6.5.$

2 State the conditions of equilibrium of a rigid body under coplanar forces. How would you illustrate one of the conditions stated? A trap-door is hinged at one end and held in a horizontal position by a cord of length 4 ft. attached to the mid-point of the opposite edge, and fixed to a point 3 ft. vertically above the mid-point of the hinge. Find the tension in the cord and the reaction at the hinge if the weight of the trap-door is 20 lb. (*C.*)

First part. See text.

Second part. Suppose AB is the trap-door section, AC is the cord attached to C, and B is the section of the hinge, Fig. 56. Since there are

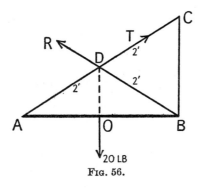

FIG. 56.

92 MECHANICS AND PROPERTIES OF MATTER

3 forces acting on the trap-door, and its weight acts vertically at O, it follows that the reaction R at B passes through D, the point of intersection of the weight and T, the tension. Further, since AO = OB, AD = DC. Hence D is the centre of the circle which can be drawn round the triangle ACB, and thus DB = DC = 2 ft.

One method of finding R and T is to note that triangle CBD is the triangle of forces for the system. CB represents the 20 lb. wt., DC represents T, and BD represents R. Now CD = DB. Hence $T = R$. Further, as BC = 3 ft. and DC = 2 ft., we have

$$\frac{T}{2} = \frac{20}{3}$$

$$\therefore T = \frac{40}{3} = 13\frac{1}{3} \text{ lb. wt.} = R.$$

An alternative method is to take moments about B to eliminate R, and then to take moments about A to eliminate T. This is left as an exercise to the student.

3. State what is meant by *scalar* and *vector* quantities, giving examples of each.

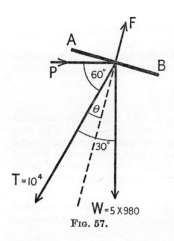

FIG. 57.

Explain how a flat kite can be flown in a wind that is blowing horizontally. The line makes an angle of 30° with the vertical and is under a tension of 10^4 dynes; the mass of the kite is 5 gm. What angle will the plane of the kite make with the vertical, and what force will the wind exert on it? (*O. & C.*)

First part. See text.

Second part. When the kite AB is inclined to the horizontal, the wind blowing horizontally exerts an upward force F normal to AB, Fig. 57. For equilibrium of the kite, F must be equal and opposite to the resultant of the tension T, 10,000 dynes, and the weight W, 5×980 or 4900 dynes. By drawing the parallelogram of forces for the resultant of T and W, F and the angle θ between F and T can be found. θ is nearly 10°, and F is about 14800 dynes.

The angle between AB and the vertical = $60° + \theta = 70°$ (approx.). Also, since F is the component of the horizontal force P of the wind.

$$P \cos (60° + \theta) = F.$$

$$\therefore P = \frac{F}{\cos (60° + \theta)} = \frac{14,800}{\cos 70°}$$

$$= 43,300 \text{ dynes (approx.)}$$

EXERCISES IV

1. A flat plate is cut in the shape of a square of side 2 ins., with an equilateral triangle of side 2 ins. adjacent to the square. Calculate the distance of the centre of gravity from the apex of the triangle.

2. The foot of a uniform ladder is on a rough horizontal ground, and the top rests against a smooth vertical wall. The weight of the ladder is 40 lb., and a boy weighing 80 lb. stands on the ladder one-quarter of its length from the bottom. If the inclination of the ladder to the horizontal is 30°, find the reaction at the wall and the total force at the ground.

3. A rectangular plate ABCD has two forces of 10 lb. wt. acting along AB and DC in opposite directions. If AB = 3 ft., BC = 5 ft., what is the moment of the couple acting on the plate? What forces acting along BC and AD respectively are required to keep the plate in equilibrium?

4. A hollow metal cylinder 2 ft. tall has a base of diameter 14 ins. and is filled with water to a height of (i) 1 ft., (ii) 6 ins. Calculate the distance of the centre of gravity in feet from the base in each case if the cylinder has no top. (Metal weighs 3 lb. per sq. ft. of surface; density of water = 62·5 lb. per cu. ft. Assume $\pi = 22/7$.)

5. A trap-door 4 ft. by 4 ft. is kept horizontal by a string attached to the mid-point of the side opposite to that containing the hinge. The other end of the string is tied to a point 3 ft. vertically above the hinge. If the trap-door weight is 5 lb., calculate the tension in the string and the reaction at the hinge.

6. Two smooth inclined planes are arranged with their lower edges in contact; the angles of inclination of the plane to the horizontal are 30°, 60° respectively, and the surfaces of the planes are perpendicular to each other. If a uniform rod rests in the principal section of the planes with one end on each plane, find the angle of inclination of the rod to the horizontal.

7. Describe and give the theory of an accurate beam balance. Point out the factors which influence the sensitivity of the balance. Why is it necessary, in very accurate weighing, to take into account the pressure, temperature, and humidity of the atmosphere? (*O. & C.*)

8. Summarise the various conditions which are being satisfied when a body remains in equilibrium under the action of three non-parallel forces.

A wireless aerial attached to the top of a mast 20 ft. high exerts a horizontal force upon it of 60 lb. wt. The mast is supported by a stay-wire running to the ground from a point 6 ft. below the top of the mast, and inclined at 60° to the horizontal. Assuming that the action of the ground on the mast can be regarded as a single force, draw a diagram of the forces acting on the mast, and determine by measurement or by calculation the force in the stay-wire. (*C.*)

9. A rigid body is in equilibrium under the action of three forces, one of which is its weight; state the conditions which the system of forces must satisfy. Would your statement require modification if the forces were more than three in number?

A rod AB of mass 30 lb. and 10 ft. long has its centroid at a point distant 4 ft. from A. The rod is hinged at A so as to be rotatable about A in a vertical plane, but is maintained in an inclined position by a thin horizontal cord attached at B and secured at a point C which is 6 ft. directly above the hinge at A. CB is 8 ft. Find graphically, or otherwise, the reaction at the hinge and the tension in the cord. (*W*.),

10. Give an account of the essential features of a good physical balance. Describe how, using a balance with slightly unequal arms, (*a*) the true mass of a body, (*b*) the ratio of the arms, may be determined. (*L*.)

11. Three forces in one plane act on a rigid body. What are the conditions for equilibrium?
The plane of a kite of mass 12 lb. is inclined to the horizon at 60°. The resultant thrust of the air on the kite acts at a point 10 ins. above its centre of gravity, and the string is attached at a point 12 in. above the centre of gravity. Find the thrust of the air on the kite, and the tension in the string. (*C*.)

12. Describe a good type of physical beam balance and point out the conditions which such a balance should fulfil. On what does the sensitivity of the balance depend?   How would you determine the sensitivity experimentally?
A body is weighed first in the left- and then in the right-hand pan of a balance, the respective weights being 9·842 gm. and 9·833 gm. Find the true weight of the body and the ratio of the lengths of the arms of the balance. (*N*.)

13. The beam of a balance weighs 150 gm. and its moment of inertia is 5,000 gm. cm.². Each arm of the balance is 10 cm. long. When set swinging the beam makes one complete oscillation in 6 sec. How far is the centre of gravity of the beam below its point of support, and through what angle would the beam be deflected by a weight of 1 milligram placed in one of the scale pans? (*C*.)

CHAPTER V

HYDROSTATICS

1. Density.

The *density* of a substance is defined as its *mass per unit volume*. Thus

$$\text{density, } \rho, = \frac{\text{mass of substance}}{\text{volume of substance}} \quad \cdots \quad (47)$$

The density of steel is 8·5 grams per c.c.; the density of aluminium is 2·7 gm. per c.c.; the density of water at 4° C. is 1 gram per c.c. or about 62½ lb. per cubic foot.

Substances which float on water have a density less than 1 gram per c.c. (p. 97). For example, ice has a density of about 0·9 gm. per c.c.; cork has a density of about 0·25 gm. per c.c. Steel, of density 8·5 gm. per c.c., will float on mercury, whose density is about 13·6 gm. per c.c. at 0° C.

2. Specific Gravity.

The specific gravity, s, of a substance is defined by the relation

$$s = \frac{W}{w}, \quad \cdots \quad (48)$$

where W is the weight of the substance and w is the weight of *an equal volume of water*. Since "specific gravity" is the ratio of two weights, specific gravity is simply a number; it has no units, unlike density. The specific gravity of steel is 8·5; the specific gravity of mercury is 13·6 at 0° C.

If we consider 1 c.c. of the substance, then W in (48) is the *density* of the substance, by definition. As w is then the density of water, the specific gravity of a substance can be defined as "its density relative to that of water". The density of water is 1 gram per c.c. Since the specific gravity of mercury is 13·6, the density of mercury is 13·6 gm. per c.c. The density of mercury is also 13·6 × 62½ or 850 lbs. per cu. ft., since the density of water is 62½ lb. per cu. ft.

3. Determination of Density and Specific Gravity of Liquid.

The density, or specific gravity of a liquid can be measured accurately

FIG. 58. Specific gravity bottle.

by means of a *specific gravity bottle*, which has a tight-fitting glass stopper with a fine hole in it, Fig. 58. The bottle can thus always be filled to a high degree of accuracy with the same volume of liquid, the excess being wiped off. Since 1 gram of water has a volume of 1 c.c., the volume of the bottle is numerically equal to the mass in grams of water, m say, filling it completely. If the bottle is dried, and m_1 grams is the mass of an unknown liquid filling the bottle, then

$$\text{density of liquid, } \rho, = \frac{m_1}{m} \text{ grams per c.c.}$$

The specific gravity of the liquid is also given by the ratio m_1/m, since we have compared the weights of equal volumes of liquid and water.

4. Density of Crystals Soluble in Water.

The density of crystals of copper sulphate, hypo, or other substances soluble in water can be found by using oil and making the following measurements:

(1). Weight of specific gravity bottle empty (m_0).

(2). Wt. of bottle + some crystals . . .(m_1).

(3). Wt. of bottle + crystals + oil filling remainder of bottle (m_2)

(4). Wt. of bottle + oil filling whole bottle (m_3).

The oil used is one in which the crystals are not soluble, for example, paraffin oil can be used for copper sulphate or hypo crystals. From these measurements,

$$\text{weight of crystals} = m_1 - m_0,$$

$$\text{and volume of crystals} = [(m_3 - m_0) - (m_2 - m_1)]/\rho,$$

where ρ is the density of the oil.

$$\therefore \text{ density of crystals} = \frac{m_1 - m_0}{[(m_3 - m_0) - (m_2 - m_1)]/\rho}$$

$$= \frac{(m_1 - m_0)\rho}{(m_3 - m_0) - (m_2 - m_1)}.$$

The density ρ of the oil can be found from a preliminary experiment with a specific gravity bottle, and hence the density of the crystals can be calculated.

5. Density of Sand.

The density of sand or other particles insoluble in water can be found from the following measurements, using a specific gravity bottle:

(1) Weight of specific gravity bottle empty (m_0).

(2) Weight of bottle + some sand (m_1).

(3) Weight of bottle + sand + water filling remainder of bottle (m_2)

(4) Weight of bottle + water filling whole bottle (m_3).

Thus weight of sand $= m_1 - m_0$,

and volume of sand $= (m_3 - m_0) - (m_2 - m_1)$

$$\therefore \text{density of sand} = \frac{m_1 - m_0}{(m_3 - m_0) - (m_2 - m_1)}.$$

6. Archimedes Principle.

An object immersed in a liquid experiences a resultant upward force owing to the pressure of liquid on it. This upward force is called the *upthrust* of the liquid on the object, and ARCHIMEDES was the first person to give the law concerning its magnitude. He stated that *the upthrust is equal to the weight of liquid displaced by the object*, and this is known as *Archimedes' Principle*. Thus if an iron cube of volume 400 c.c. is totally immersed in water of density 1 gm. per c.c., the upthrust on the cube $= 400 \times 1 = 400$ gm. wt. If the same cube is totally immersed in oil of density 0·8 gm. per c.c., the upthrust on it $= 400 \times 0·8 = 320$ gm wt.

As we shall now see, Archimedes' Principle can be used to measure the density, or specific gravity, of solids and liquids.

7. Determination of Density (or Specific Gravity) by Archimedes Principle. Density of Solid.

The density or specific gravity of a solid such as brass or iron can be determined by (1) weighing it in air, m_0 gm. say, (2) weighing it when it is totally immersed in water, m_1 gm. say. Then

upthrust $= m_0 - m_1 =$ wt. of water displaced.

$$\therefore \text{specific gravity of solid} = \frac{m_0}{m_0 - m_1},$$

and density of solid, $\rho, = \frac{m_0}{m_0 - m_1}$ gm. per c.c.

8. Density of Copper Sulphate.

If a solid dissolves in water, such as a copper sulphate crystal for example, its density can be found by totally immersing it in a liquid in which it is insoluble. Copper sulphate can be weighed in paraffin oil, for example. Suppose the apparent weight is m_1, and the weight in air is m_0. Then

$$m_0 - m_1 = \text{upthrust in liquid} = V\rho,$$

where V is the volume of the solid and ρ is the density of the liquid.

$$\therefore V = \frac{m_0 - m_1}{\rho}$$

$$\therefore \text{density of solid} = \frac{\text{mass}}{\text{volume}} = \frac{m_0}{V} = \frac{m_0}{m_0 - m_1} \cdot \rho.$$

The density, ρ, of the liquid can be found by means of a specific gravity bottle, for example. Thus knowing m_0 and m_1, the density of the solid can be calculated.

9. Density of Cork.

If a solid floats in water, cork for example, its density can be found by attaching a brass weight or "sinker" to it so that both solids become totally immersed in water. The apparent weight (m_1) of the sinker and cork together is then obtained. Suppose m_2 is the weight of the sinker in air, m_3 is the weight of the sinker alone in water, and m_0 is the weight of the cork in air.

Then $m_2 - m_3 = \text{upthrust on sinker in water.}$

$$\therefore m_0 + m_2 - m_1 - (m_2 - m_3) = \text{upthrust on cork in water}$$

$$= m_0 - m_1 + m_3$$

$$\therefore \text{density of cork} = \frac{m_0}{m_0 - m_1 + m_3}.$$

10. Density of Liquid.

The density or specific gravity of a *liquid* can be found by weighing a solid in air (m_0), then weighing it totally immersed in the liquid (m_1), and then when it is totally immersed in water (m_2).

Now $m_0 - m_2 = \text{upthrust in water} = \text{weight of water displaced,}$

and $m_0 - m_1 = \text{upthrust in liquid} = \text{weight of liquid displaced.}$

$$\therefore \frac{m_0 - m_1}{m_0 - m_2} = \text{specific gravity of liquid,}$$

or $\quad \dfrac{m_0 - m_1}{m_0 - m_2} = \text{density of liquid in grams per c.c.}$

11. The Simple (Constant Weight) Hydrometer.

A *hydrometer* is an instrument used for measuring the specific gravity or density of a liquid. Hydrometers are used for testing the specific gravities of milk, spirits, and acid in accumulators.

A simple hydrometer can be made by attaching a piece of lead to the bottom, C, of a length of wood D of uniform cross-sectional area, Fig. 59. The wood then floats upright in a liquid, and if h is the length DC of wood immersed,

upthrust on wood = weight of liquid displaced

$$= ha\rho,$$

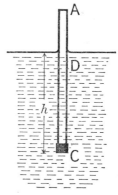

Fig. 59.
Simple hydrometer.

where a is the cross-sectional area and ρ is the density of the liquid. But if the wood floats, the upthrust is equal to its weight, w.

$$\therefore ha\rho = w.$$

$$\therefore \rho = \frac{w}{ah}$$

$$\therefore \rho \propto \frac{1}{h}.$$

If the depth h immersed in water of density 1 gram per c.c. is noted, the length of the wood can be labelled with density values, since $\rho \propto 1/h$. The wood then acts as a simple hydrometer.

12. Practical Hydrometer.

In practice a hydrometer has a narrow stem, BL, of uniform cross-sectional area, a wide bulb below the stem, and lead shot or other heavy substances at the bottom M, Fig. 60. Suppose y is the length of stem *not* immersed when the hydrometer floats in a liquid of density ρ. Then if a is the cross-sectional area of the stem, and V is the volume of the whole hydrometer, the volume of liquid displaced $= V - ay$. By Archimedes principle, it follows that

$$(V - ay)\, \rho = w,$$

where w is the weight of the hydrometer.

$$\therefore V - ay = \frac{w}{\rho}$$

$$\therefore y = \frac{1}{a}\left(V - \frac{w}{\rho}\right) = \frac{V}{a} - \frac{w}{a} \cdot \frac{1}{\rho}.$$

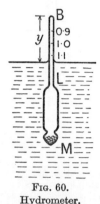

FIG. 60.
Hydrometer.

Since w/a and V/a are constants for a given hydrometer, the relation between y and $1/\rho$ is a linear one. To calibrate the stem in terms of density, ρ, the hydrometer is immersed in two liquids of known density, the corresponding distances y are observed, and the values of y are then plotted against $1/\rho$. The two points thus obtained are joined. From this straight line graph, the values of $1/\rho$ corresponding to a particular value of y can be read off, and thus the stem can be calibrated in terms of density.

In general a hydrometer is not as accurate as a specific gravity bottle for determining the density of a liquid, owing to the downward pull on the hydrometer due to the surface tension of the liquid in which it is placed.

13. Nicholson's (Constant Volume) Hydrometer.

NICHOLSON designed a hydrometer which had a hollow metal cylindrical body X, a "basket" B, a thin upper stem M, and a scale-pan S above M. When the hydrometer is placed in a liquid, weights are placed in the pan S,

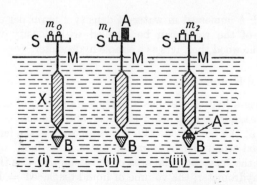

FIG. 61. Nicholson's hydrometer.

or taken from it, until the instrument sinks to a fixed mark on M. *The volume of the hydrometer immersed is thus kept constant each time.*

The weight m_0 required to sink the hydrometer in water to the fixed mark is first found, Fig. 61 (i). An object A whose density is required is placed on S, and the reduced weight m_1 to restore the hydrometer level is obtained, Fig. 61 (ii). Then $m_0 - m_1 =$ the weight of A. The object A is then placed in the basket B, and the new weight m_2 on S to restore the level is noted, Fig. 61 (iii). Then $m_2 - m_1 =$ the upthrust on A in water = the weight of water displaced by A.

$$\therefore \text{ specific gravity of A } = \frac{m_0 - m_1}{m_2 - m_1}.$$

If the object A floats in water, it can be tied to B and the procedure repeated.

The density or specific gravity of a *liquid* can easily be found by the Nicholson hydrometer. Suppose m_3, m_4 are the respective weights on the scale-pan S required to sink the hydrometer to the fixed mark when it is placed first in water and then in the liquid. Then, if m is the weight of the hydrometer,

upthrust on hydrometer in liquid $= m + m_4$,

and upthrust on hydrometer in water $= m + m_3$.

From Archimedes principle, the upthrust in each case is equal to the weight of liquid displaced. Thus, since the volumes of the liquids are the same in each case,

$$\text{specific gravity of liquid } = \frac{m + m_4}{m + m_3}.$$

It should be noted that Nicholson's hydrometer is a constant volume hydrometer, whereas the common hydrometer (p. 100) is a constant weight hydrometer. The surface tension of the liquid reduces the accuracy of the hydrometer.

14. Pressure in a Liquid.

The *pressure* at a place in a liquid is defined as the *force per unit area* there. Observation shows that the pressure increases with the depth, h, below the liquid surface and with its density ρ, and acts in all directions at a given place in the liquid.

To obtain a formula for the pressure, p, suppose that a horizontal plate X of area A is placed at a depth h below the liquid surface, Fig. 62. By drawing vertical lines from points on the perimeter of X, we can see that the force on X due to the liquid is equal to the weight of liquid of height h and uniform cross-section A. Since the volume of this liquid is Ah, the mass of the liquid $= Ah \times \rho$.

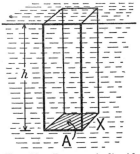

FIG. 62. Pressure in liquid.

$$\therefore \text{weight} = Ah\rho g \text{ dynes,}$$

where g is 980, h is in cm., A is in sq. cm., and ρ is in grams per c.c.

$$\therefore \text{pressure, } p, \text{ on } X = \frac{\text{force}}{\text{area}} = \frac{Ah\rho g}{A}$$

$$\therefore \mathbf{p} = \mathbf{h}\rho\mathbf{g} \quad . \quad . \quad . \quad . \quad (49)$$

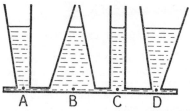

FIG. 63.   Pressure constant at same horizontal level.

When h, ρ, g have the units already mentioned, the pressure p is in dynes per sq. cm. Thus suppose the atmospheric pressure corresponds to a column of mercury 76 cm. high (called *one atmosphere*). Since the density of mercury, ρ, is 13·6 grams per c.c., the atmospheric pressure $p = 76 \times 13\cdot6 \times 980 = 1\cdot01 \times 10^6$ dynes per sq. cm.

The student is advised to commit the expression for pressure, $p = h\rho g$, to memory; it is required in many branches of Physics. From the formula, it follows that *the pressure in a liquid is the same at all points on the same horizontal level in it.* Experiment also gives the same result. Thus a liquid filling the vessel shown in Fig. 63 rises to the same height in each section if ABCD is horizontal. The cross-sectional area of B is greater than that of D; but the force on B is the sum of the weight of water above it together with the (downward) reaction of the sides of the vessel, whereas the force on D is the weight of water above it *minus* the (upward) reaction of the sides of the vessel. It will thus be noted that the pressure in a vessel is independent of the cross-sectional area of the vessel.

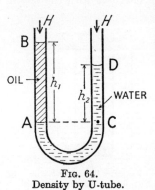

FIG. 64.
Density by U-tube.

15. Measurement of Density of Liquid.

U-tube method. Suppose a U-tube is partly filled with water, and oil is then poured into the left side of the tube. The oil will then reach some level B at a height h_1 above the surface of separation, A, of the water and oil, while the water on the right side of the tube will then reach some level D at a height h_2 above the level of A, Fig. 64.

Since the pressure in the water at A is equal to the pressure at C on the same horizontal level, it follows that

$$H + h_1 \rho_1 g = H + h_2 \rho_2 g,$$

where H is the atmospheric pressure, and ρ_1, ρ_2 are the respective densities of oil and water. Simplifying,

$$h_1 \rho_1 = h_2 \rho_2$$

$$\therefore \qquad \rho_1 = \rho_2 \times \frac{h_2}{h_1}.$$

Since $\rho_2 = 1$ gram per c.c., and h_2, h_1 are known, the density ρ_1 of the oil can be calculated. Mercury can be used as the liquid originally in the U-tube, for liquids much denser than water.

Hare's apparatus. The densities of dilute and concentrated copper sulphate solution, for example, cannot be compared by the U-tube method, as the two liquids would mix. HARE used two vertical connected tubes to compare the densities of liquids, and placed them in beakers B, C respectively which contained the two liquids. By means of a tap at A, some of the liquids were drawn up the two tubes, as shown in Fig. 65.

Suppose h_1, h_2 are then the respective heights of the two liquids above the surface of the liquids in each beaker; ρ_1, ρ_2 are the respective densities; p, H are the respective pressures of the air above the liquid in the tube and the atmospheric pressure.

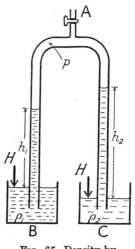

FIG. 65. Density by Hare's apparatus.

Then

$$H = p + h_1 \rho_1 g = p + h_2 \rho_2 g.$$

$$\therefore \qquad h_1 \rho_1 g = h_2 \rho_2 g$$

$$\therefore \qquad \frac{\rho_1}{\rho_2} = \frac{h_2}{h_1}.$$

The densities are thus inversely proportional to the heights in the tubes. Hare's apparatus can also be used to find the actual densities of liquids such as oil, in which case the beaker B is filled with the oil and the beaker C is filled with water, of known density 1.

16. Atmospheric Pressure.

The pressure of the atmosphere was first measured by Galileo, who observed the height of a water column in a tube placed in a deep well. About 1640 TORRICELLI thought of the idea of using mercury instead of water, to obtain a much shorter column. He completely filled a glass tube about a metre long with mercury, and then inverted it in a vessel D containing the liquid, taking care that no air entered the tube. He observed that the mercury in the tube fell to a level A about 76 cm. (or 30 in.) above the level of the mercury in D, Fig. 66. Since there was

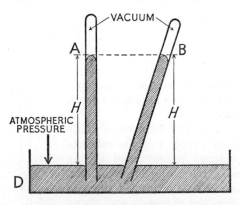

FIG. 66.   Simple barometer.

no air originally in the tube, there must be a vacuum above the mercury at A, and it is called a *Torricellian vacuum*. This was the first occasion in the history of science that a vacuum had been created.

If the tube in Fig. 66 is inclined to the vertical, the mercury ascends the tube to a level B at the same vertical height H above the level of the mercury in D as A.

The pressure on the surface of the mercury in D is atmospheric pressure; and since the pressure is transmitted through the liquid, the atmospheric pressure supports the column of mercury in the tube. Suppose A is at a height H above the level of the mercury in D. Now the pressure, p, at the bottom of a column of liquid of height H cm. and density ρ gm. per c.c. is given by $p = H\rho g$ dynes per sq. cm., where g is 980 (p. 102). Thus if H is 76 cm.,

$$p = H\rho g = 76 \times 13 \cdot 6 \times 980 = 1 \cdot 012 \times 10^6 \text{ dynes per sq. cm.,}$$

since the density of mercury is 13·6 gm. per c.c. The pressure at the bottom of a column of mercury 76 cm. high is known as *standard pressure* or *one atmosphere*, and *standard temperature and pressure* (*S.T.P.* or *N.T.P.*) is 0° C. and 76 cm. pressure.

A *bar* is the name given to a pressure of one million (10^6) dynes per sq. cm., and is thus very nearly equal to one atmosphere.

17. Fortin's Barometer.

A *barometer* is an instrument for measuring the pressure of the atmosphere, which is required in weather-forecasting, for example. The most accurate form of barometer is due to FORTIN, and like the simple arrangement already described, it consists basically of a barometer tube containing mercury, with a vacuum at the top, Fig. 67. One end of the tube dips into a pool of mercury contained in a washleather bag B. A brass scale graduated in centimetres (C) or inches (I) is fixed at the top of the barometer. The zero of the scale correspondings to the tip of an ivory tooth P, and hence, before the level of the top of the mercury is read from the scales, the screw S is adjusted until the level of the mercury in B just reaches the tip of P. A vernier scale V can be moved by a screw D until the bottom of it just reaches the top of the mercury in the tube, and the reading of the height of the mercury is taken from C and V or from I and V. Torricelli was the first person to observe the variation of the barometric height as the weather changed.

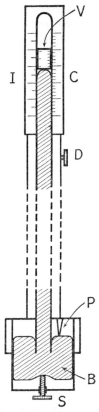

FIG. 67.
Fortin's barometer.

18. "Correction" to the Barometric Height.

For comparison purposes, the pressure read on a barometer is often "reduced" or "corrected" to the magnitude the pressure would have at 0° C. and at sea-level, latitude 45°. Suppose the "reduced" pressure is H_o cm. of mercury, and the observed pressure is H_t cm. of mercury, corresponding to a temperature of $t°$ C. Then, since pressure $= h\rho g$ (p. 102),

$$H_o \rho_o g = H_t \rho_t g',$$

where g is the acceleration due to gravity at sea-level, latitude 45°, and g' is the acceleration at the latitude of the place where the barometer was read.

$$\therefore H_o = H_t \times \frac{\rho_t}{\rho_o} \times \frac{g}{g'}.$$

The magnitude of g'/g can be obtained from standard tables. The ratio ρ_t/ρ_o of the densities $= 1/(1 + \gamma t)$, where γ is the absolute coefficient of cubical expansion of mercury. Further, the observed height, H_t, on the brass scale requires correction for the expansion of brass from the temperature at which it was correctly calibrated. If the latter is $0°$ C., then the corrected height is $H_t(1 + at)$, where a is the linear coefficient of brass. Thus, finally, the "corrected" height H_o is given by

$$H_o = H_t \cdot \frac{1 + at}{1 + \gamma t} \cdot \frac{g'}{g}.$$

For further accuracy, a correction must be made for the surface tension of mercury (p. 115).

19. Aneroid Barometer.

The aneroid barometer is one which does not use any liquid. It consists of a corrugated metal box B from which nearly all the air has been evacuated, with a spring S attached to the top to prevent the box from collapsing, Fig. 68. When the atmospheric pressure varies, the

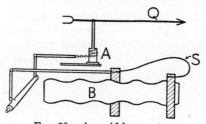

FIG. 68.   Aneroid barometer.

top and bottom of the box move in or out. The slight movement is magnified by a system of jointed levers, which pull a chain wound round a spindle A. A pointer Q then rotates over a scale (not shown), which is calibrated in centimetres of mercury by noting the corresponding pressure from a Fortin barometer.

The pressure of the atmosphere decreases approximately by one centimetre of mercury for every 1,000 ft. ascended. The aneroid barometer is therefore used as an *altimeter* (height-measurer) in aeroplanes, and it is also used for the same purpose by mountain climbers.

20. Pressure of a Gas.

The pressure of a gas can be measured by connecting it to a U-tube, M, containing water or mercury, Fig. 69. The liquid in the two sides

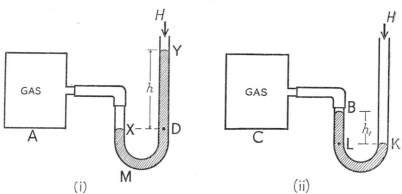

FIG. 69. Measurement of pressure.

of the *manometer*, as M is called, then registers a difference in levels. Suppose the level, Y, in the open side of M is higher than the level, X, in the other side, Fig. 69 (i). Then the pressure at X, p, = the pressure at the same level, D, on the other side.

$$\therefore p = H + h\rho g,$$

where H is the atmospheric pressure, h is the difference in levels of the liquid, and ρ is the density of the liquid. If the level, K, of the liquid in the open side of the manometer is lower than the level, B, of the other side, the pressure at K = the pressure at $L = p + h_1\rho g$, where p is the pressure of the gas and h_1 is the difference in levels of the liquid, Fig. 69 (ii). But the pressure at K = the atmospheric pressure = H.

$$\therefore \quad p + h_1\rho g = H$$

$$\therefore \quad p = H - h_1\rho g.$$

The pressure of the gas is thus *less* than the atmospheric pressure in this case.

EXAMPLES

1. Describe a hydrometer suitable for the determination of the specific gravity of spirits. How would you test the graduation of a hydrometer?

A mixture of alcohol (s.g. 0·84) and water has a specific gravity of 0·90. What is the proportion of the constituents (a) by weight, (b) by volume (neglecting any change of volume which occurs on mixing)? (*C.*)

First part. See text. The graduation would be tested by placing the hydrometer in turn in water and other liquids whose specific gravities are found accurately by the specific gravity bottle method.

Second part. For convenience, consider 100 c.c. of the mixture. Suppose
x c.c. is the volume of alcohol; then $(100 - x)$ c.c. is the volume of water.

$$\therefore 0\cdot84x \text{ gm. wt.} = \text{weight of alcohol,}$$

$$(100 - x) \text{ gm. wt.} = \text{weight of water.}$$

$$\therefore 0\cdot84x + 100 - x = \text{weight of mixture in gm. wt.}$$

$$\text{Now specific gravity} = \frac{\text{weight of mixture}}{100 \text{ gm. wt.}},$$

since 100 gm. wt. is the weight of an equal volume of water.

$$\therefore \quad 0\cdot90 = \frac{0\cdot84x + 100 - x}{100}$$

$$\therefore \quad 90 = 100 - 0\cdot16x$$

$$\therefore 0\cdot16x = 10$$

$$\therefore \quad x = \frac{10}{0\cdot16} = 62\cdot5 = \text{volume of alcohol in c.c.}$$

$$\therefore \quad 100 - 62\cdot5 = 37\cdot5 = \text{volume of water in c.c.}$$

(b) $\therefore$ proportion of constituents by volume $= 62\cdot5 : 37\cdot5 = 5 : 3$.

(a)   Weight of alcohol in 100 c.c. of mixture

$$= 62\cdot5 \times 0\cdot84 = 52\cdot5 \text{ gm. wt.}$$

Also, weight of water in 100 c.c. of mixture $= 37\cdot5$ gm. wt.

$\therefore$ proportion by weight $= 52\cdot5 : 37\cdot5 = 7 : 5$.

2. A hydrometer consists of a bulb of volume V and a uniform stem of
volume v per cm. of its length. It floats upright in water so that the bulb
is just completely immersed. Explain for what density range this hydrometer may be used and how you would determine the density of such
liquids. Describe the graph which would be obtained by plotting the
reciprocal of the density against the length of the stem immersed.
A hydrometer such as that described sinks to the mark 3 on the stem,
which is graduated in cm., when it is placed in a liquid of density 0·95
gm./c.c. If the volume per cm. of the stem is 0·1 c.c., find the volume of
the bulb. (*L.*)

First part. (i) When the hydrometer is placed in liquids less dense than
water, it sinks more than in water (p. 99). Consequently the hydrometer
can be used for liquids whose density is less than 1. The density of the
liquids can be determined by using a specific gravity bottle. (ii) The graph
obtained is a straight line (see p. 100).

Second part. Let $V =$ volume of bulb in c.c.
Then upthrust in water $= V \times 1 =$ wt. of hydrometer.
In the liquid of density 0·95 gm./c.c., the volume immersed $= (V + 3 \times 0\cdot1)$

$$\therefore \text{upthrust} = (V + 0\cdot3)\, 0\cdot95 = \text{wt. of hydrometer.}$$

$$\therefore V \times 1 = (V + 0\cdot3)\, 0\cdot95$$

$$\therefore 0\cdot05V = 0\cdot3 \times 0\cdot95$$

$$\therefore V = 5\cdot7 \text{ c.c.}$$

3. State the principle of Archimedes. A body of mass 100 gm. and of specific gravity 2·00 is suspended by a thread so as to be completely immersed in a liquid of specific gravity 0·92. Find the tension in the thread. If the thread is cut, what will be the initial acceleration of the body? Why will this acceleration not be maintained as the body falls in the liquid? (*W*.)

First part. See text.

Second part. The volume of the body $= \dfrac{100}{2\cdot00} = 50$ c.c.

$\therefore$ upthrust on body $=$ weight of liquid displaced.

$$= 50 \times 0\cdot92 = 46 \text{ gm. wt.}$$

$\therefore$ tension in thread $= 100 - 46 = 54$ gm. wt.

The net downward force on the body $=$ weight $-$ upthrust $= 54$ gm. wt.

$$= 54 \times 980 \text{ dynes}$$

$\therefore$ initial acceleration f if thread cut $= \dfrac{54 \times 980}{100}$,

since $f = P/m$.

$$\therefore f = 529\cdot2 \text{ cm. per sec.}^2$$

This acceleration is not maintained as the body falls through the liquid, owing to the friction or viscosity of the liquid. The frictional force diminishes the acceleration, and a constant (terminal) velocity is reached (p. 165).

EXERCISES V

1. An alloy of mass 588 gm. and volume 100 c.c. is made of iron of specific gravity 8·0 and aluminium of specific gravity 2·7. Calculate the proportion (i) by volume, (ii) by weight of the constituents of the alloy.

2. A string supports a solid iron object of mass 180 grams totally immersed in a liquid of density 0·8 gm. per c.c. Calculate the tension in the string if the density of iron is 8·0 gm. per c.c.

3. Describe how you would measure (i) the density of sand, (ii) the density of copper sulphate crystals. Give imaginary measurements, and calculate the result, for each case.

4. A hydrometer floats in water with 6·0 cm. of its graduated stem unimmersed, and in oil of specific gravity 0·8 with 4·0 cm. of the stem unimmersed. What is the length of stem unimmersed when the hydrometer is placed in a liquid of specific gravity 0·9?

5. State *Archimedes' Principle.* Describe how you would measure the density of cork, giving numerical values in illustration and calculating the result.

6. An alloy of mass 170 gm. has an apparent weight of 95 gm. in a liquid of density 1·5 gm. per c.c. If the two constituents of the alloy have specific gravities of 4·0 and 3·0 respectively, calculate the proportion by volume of the constituents in the alloy.

7. Distinguish between *mass* and *weight.* Define *density.*

Describe and explain how you would proceed to find an accurate value for the density of gold, the specimen available being a wedding ring of pure gold.

What will be the reading of (a) a mercury barometer, (b) a water barometer, when the atmospheric pressure is 10^6 dyne cm.$^{-2}$? The density of mercury may be taken as 13·6 gm. cm.$^{-3}$ and the pressure of saturated water vapour at room temperature as 1·3 cm. of mercury. (L.)

8. Describe an accurate form of barometer and illustrate your description with a sketch. Indicate how a vernier may be used to obtain an accurate reading. Explain the corrections which have to be applied to the reading observed to make it suitable for meteorological purposes. (N.)

9. State the principle of Archimedes, and discuss its application to the determination of specific gravities by means of a common hydrometer. Why is this method essentially less accurate than the specific gravity bottle?

A common hydrometer is graduated to read specific gravities from 0·8 to 1·0. In order to extend its range a small weight is attached to the stem, above the liquid, so that the instrument reads 0·8 when floating in water. What will be the specific gravity of the liquid corresponding to the graduation 1·0? (O. & C.)

10. State Archimedes' principle. A measuring jar containing 200 c.c. of water at 0° C. A lump of ice at 0° C. is added, which brings the level of the water up to 240 c.c. mark. Deduce the mass of the lump of ice. If the ice is allowed to melt, the contents of the jar being maintained at 0° C., deduce the final level of the water surface. (You may assume that the density of water at 0° C. is 1 gm./cm.^{3})

Brass "weights" of density 8·4 gm./cm.^{3} are employed in the determination of the weight of a given quantity of water. Show that, if the air buoyancy correction is applied, a correction of about 0·1 per cent. will be necessary to obtain the true weight from the recorded weight. (Density of air = 0·00125 gm./cm.^{3}) (W.)

11. Describe two methods by which you could measure the density of ice. Calculate the mass of lead which must be attached to 90 gm. of wax in order that the whole may float totally immersed in a solution of density 1·04 gm. per c.c. The densities of lead and wax respectively are 11·3 and 0·86 gm. per c.c. (L.)

12. A variable immersion hydrometer has a range from 1·00 to 1·02 gm./cm.^{3} marked on its stem, which is of uniform cross-section. The distance between these extreme markings is 30 cm. Find the distance between the 1·02 mark and the 1·01 mark on the hydrometer stem. (W.)

13. Describe some form of barometer used for the accurate measurement of atmospheric pressure, and point out the corrections to be applied to the observation.

Obtain an expression for the correction to be applied to the reading of a mercurial barometer when the reading is made at a temperature other than 0° C. (L.)

14. Define *hydrostatic pressure* at a point, and state the units in which it may be measured. Obtain an expression for the pressure at a point h cm. below the surface of the sea, if d_1 is the density of sea-water, P_0 is the height of the mercury barometer, and d_2 is the density of mercury, all in c.g.s. units.

A hollow metal ball, with a small hole at the bottom and an eyelet at the top, is lowered into a fresh-water lake by means of a wire attached to the eyelet. Find the tension at the upper end of the wire when the ball has been lowered 50 metres, given that ball and 50 metres of wire together weigh 780 gm. and have a common density of 7·8 gm./cm.³, volume of hollow interior of ball is 500 cm.³, atmospheric pressure is 760 mm. of mercury of density 13·6 gm./cm.³, and temperature everywhere is 18° C. Show that the tension might be used to indicate the temperature of the water at 50 metres depth, and calculate the amount by which the tension would alter per deg. C. in the neighbourhood of 18° C. (*W.*)

15. State Archimedes principle, and describe how you would verify it experimentally.

A hydrometer of mass 50 gm. floats in water with a mark X on its stem level with the water. If a mass of 5 gm. is placed on top of the hydrometer, it sinks again to the mark X when placed in brine. Calculate the specific gravity of the brine.

16. State the principle of Archimedes and use it to derive an expression for the resultant force experienced by a body of weight W and density σ when it is totally immersed in a fluid of density ρ.

A solid weighs 237·5 gm. in air and 12·5 gm. when totally immersed in a liquid of specific gravity 0·9. Calculate (*a*) the specific gravity of the solid, (*b*) the specific gravity of a liquid in which the solid would float with one-fifth of its volume exposed above the liquid surface. (*L.*)

CHAPTER VI

SURFACE TENSION

It is a well-known fact that some insects, for example a water-carrier, are able to walk across a water surface; that a drop of water may remain suspended for some time from a tap before falling, as if the water particles were held together in a bag; that mercury gathers into small droplets when spilt; and that a dry steel needle S may be made, with care, to float on water, Fig. 70 (i). These observations suggest that *the surface of a liquid acts like an elastic skin covering the liquid.*

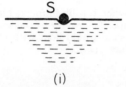

(i)

FIG. 70.   Needle on water.

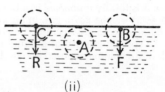

(ii)

Molecular explanation of surface tension.

1. The Force on Molecules in the Liquid Surface.

We can understand why the surface of a liquid acts like a skin if we consider firstly molecules such as A in the interior of the liquid, Fig. 70 (ii). All the molecules which have an appreciable attraction on A are those contained in a sphere of centre A which has a very small but finite radius, known as the *sphere of molecular activity*. This is represented by an exaggerated dotted circle round A in Fig. 70 (ii). Since there are as many molecules attracting A in one direction as attract it in the opposite direction, the resultant force on A in *any* direction is zero. Now consider a molecule B of the liquid very close to the surface. If the sphere of molecular activity is drawn round it, part of the sphere will be in the air above the liquid, as shown. The horizontal attractive forces on B in any direction will still cancel out; but there is now a resultant force F on B acting towards the interior of the liquid, because there are more liquid molecules in the hemisphere below B than above B. If we draw the sphere of molecular activity round a molecule C in the surface, half the sphere is in air and half is in liquid; with the result that the force R on C is inwards towards the liquid. (It must be emphasised here that B is very close to the surface, and that Fig. 70 (ii) is exaggerated for clarity.)

112

2. The Shape of Liquids.

The inward forces on the molecules in the liquid surface will tend to make the molecules move towards the interior. As a result, the liquid surface tends to contract and become as small as possible, which implies that (i) the surface acts like a skin covering the liquid, (ii) the *area of the surface is a minimum* for a given volume of liquid. Now a *sphere* is that shape which has a minimum surface area for a given volume. We can therefore expect that liquids assume a spherical shape when care is taken to neutralise forces, such as gravity, other than those just discussed. PLATEAU placed a drop of oil in a mixture of alcohol and water of the same density, in which case the weight of oil was exactly balanced by the upthrust of the mixture and the effect of gravity on the drop was neutralised. He then observed that the drop was a perfect sphere.

Observations also show that a small drop of mercury is spherical; that a rain-drop falling through air is spherical; and that a soap-bubble is spherical. Lead shot is made by pouring a fine stream of molten lead from a tall tower, when the stream breaks up into small spherical drops owing to surface tension forces.

3. Surface Tension.

Since the surface of a liquid acts like an elastic skin, the surface is in a state of tension. As a very rough analogy we can think of a blown-up football bladder, whose surface is in a condition of tension. Any line in the surface is then acted on by two equal and opposite forces, and if the bladder is cut with a knife the rubber draws away from the incision under the action of the two forces.

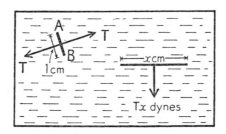

FIG. 71. Surface tension forces.

The surface tension, T, of a liquid is defined *as numerically equal to the force in the surface acting at right angles to one side of a line AB one centimetre long drawn in the surface*, Fig. 71. The unit of T is thus *dynes per cm.* or *dyne cm.*$^{-1}$

The magnitude of T depends on the temperature of the liquid and on the medium on the other side of the surface. For water at 20° C. in contact with air, $T = 72\cdot6$ dynes per cm. (dyne cm.$^{-1}$). For mercury at 20° C. in contact with air, $T = 465$ dynes per cm. The surface tension of a water-oil (olive-oil) boundary is 20·6 dynes per cm., and for a mercury-water boundary it is 427 dynes per cm.

4. Dimensions of Surface Tension.

Since surface tension is a "force per unit length", the dimensions of

$$\text{surface tension} = \frac{\text{dimensions of force}}{\text{dimension of length}}$$

$$= \frac{[M]\,[L]\,[T]^{-2}}{[L]} \text{ (p. 25).}$$

$$= [M]\,[T]^{-2}$$

5. Phenomena Concerning Surface Tension.

The effect of surface tension forces in a soap film can be demonstrated by placing a thread B carefully on a soap film formed in a metal ring A, Fig. 72 (i). If the film enclosed by the thread is pierced, the thread

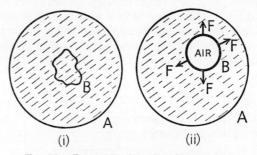

FIG. 72.   Demonstration of surface tension.

is pulled out into a circle by the surface tension forces F at the junction of the air and soap-film, Fig. 72 (ii).

Another demonstration of surface tension forces can be made by sprinkling light dust or lycopoduim powder over the surface of water contained in a dish. If the middle of the water is touched with the end of a glass rod which had previously been dipped into soap solution, the powder is carried away to the sides by the water. The explanation lies in the fact that the surface tension of water is greater than that of a soap-film (p. 121). The resultant force at the place where the rod touched the water is hence *away from* the rod, and thus the powder moves away from the centre towards the sides of the vessel.

A toy duck moves by itself across the surface of water when it has a small bag of camphor attached to its base. The camphor lowers the surface tension of the water in contact with it, and the duck is urged across the water by the resultant force on it.

6. Capillarity.

When a capillary tube is immersed in water, and then placed vertically with one end in the liquid, observation shows that the water rises in the tube to a height above the surface. The narrower the tube, the greater is the height to which the water rises, Fig. 73 (i). See also

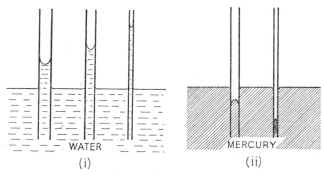

(i)   (ii)

FIG. 73.   Capillarity.

p. 125. This phenomenon is known as *capillarity*, and it occurs when blotting-paper is used to dry ink. The liquid rises up the pores of the paper when it is pressed on the ink.

When a capillary tube is placed inside mercury, however, the liquid is depressed *below* the outside level, Fig. 73 (ii). The depression increases as the diameter of the capillary tube decreases. See also p. 126.

7. Angle of Contact.

In the case of water in a glass capillary tube, observation of the meniscus shows that it is hemispherical if the glass is clean, that is, the glass surface is tangential to the meniscus where the water touches it. In other cases where liquids rise in a capillary tube, the tangent BN to the liquid surface where it touches the glass may make an acute angle θ with the glass, Fig. 74 (i). The angle θ is known as the *angle of contact* between the liquid and the glass, and is always measured *through the liquid*. The angle of contact between two given surfaces varies largely with their freshness and cleanliness. The angle of contact between

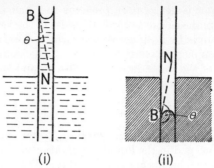

(i)   (ii)

Fig. 74.   Angle of contact.

water and very clean glass is zero, but when the glass is not clean the
angle of contact may be about 8°. The angle of contact between
alcohol and very clean glass is zero.

When a capillary tube is placed inside mercury, observation shows
that the surface of the depressed liquid in the tube is convex upwards.
Fig. 74 (ii). The tangent BN to the mercury at the point B where the
liquid touches the glass thus makes an obtuse angle, θ, with the glass
when measured through the liquid. We shall see later (p. 124) that a
liquid will rise in a capillary tube if the angle of contact is acute, and
that a liquid will be depressed in the tube if the angle of contact is
obtuse. For the same reason, water spreads over, or "wets", a clean
glass surface when spilt on it, Fig. 75 (i), whereas mercury gathers

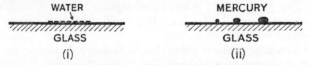

WATER   MERCURY

GLASS   GLASS
(i)   (ii)

Fig. 75.   Water and mercury on clean glass.

itself into small pools or globules when spilt on glass, and does not
"wet' glass, Fig. 75 (ii).

The difference in behaviour of water and mercury on clean glass can
be explained in terms of the attraction between the molecules of these
substances. It appears that the force of *cohesion* between two molecules
of water is less than the force of *adhesion* between a molecule of water
and a molecule of glass; and thus water spreads over glass. On the
other hand, the force of cohesion between two molecules of mercury
is greater than the force of adhesion between a molecule of mercury
and a molecule of glass; and thus mercury gathers in pools when
spilt on glass.

8. The Angle of Contact of Mercury with Glass can be measured by placing mercury in an inverted flask, and connecting a movable column M of mercury to it, Fig. 76. When M is moved vertically, the mercury surface in the flask appears horizontal right up to the edges of the glass at some position AB. In this case the tangent DAC to the flask at A is also a tangent to the liquid where the latter meets the glass. Thus angle BAC is the angle of contact between mercury and glass. By measuring the diameter of AB, and knowing the radius AO of the sphere, the angle AOB subtended at the centre, O, can be calculated by simple trigonometry.

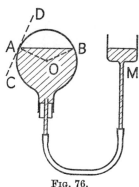

FIG. 76.
Angle of contact of mercury

Angle DAB is half the angle AOB, by geometry; and hence the supplementary angle BAC, the angle of contact, is easily obtained. For a freshly-formed mercury drop in contact with a clean glass plate, the angle of contact is 137°.

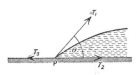

FIG. 77.   Angle of contact.

Spreading and Wetting. We have already seen that the surface boundary between a liquid and air has a surface tension (p. 112). By analogous reasoning, it follows that the surface boundary between a solid and air, or between a solid and liquid, has a surface tension.

Consider a drop of liquid in equilibrium on a solid P, with an angle of contact θ, Fig. 77. Suppose T_1, T_2, T_3 denote the respective surface-tensions of the air-liquid, liquid-solid, and air-solid boundaries. If we consider the horizontal forces on a line 1 cm. long through P into the paper, we must have, for equilibrium,

$$T_1 \cos \theta + T_2 = T_3.$$

$$\therefore \cos \theta = \frac{T_3 - T_2}{T_1}.$$

If T_3 is greater than T_2, $\cos \theta$ is positive and θ is less than 90°. In this case (an acute angle of contact), "wetting" of the surface takes place. If T_3 is less than T_2, $\cos \theta$ is negative and θ must be an obtuse angle; in this case there is no "wetting". "Wetting" is the result of a relatively high degree of attraction between the molecules of the solid and liquid concerned.

9. Surface Tension and Surface Energy.

We come now to a relation between the surface energy of a liquid and its surface tension T. Consider a film of liquid stretched across a horizontal frame ABCD, Fig. 78. If T is the surface tension of the liquid in dynes per centimetre, the force on the rod BC due to surface tension

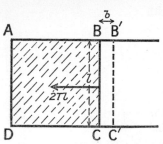

FIG. 78.   Surface energy.

forces $= 2T \times l$ dynes, where BC is l cm. long, since there are two surfaces to the film.

Suppose the rod is now moved a distance b cm. from BC to B'C' against the surface tension forces, so that the surface area of the film increases. The temperature of the film then usually decreases, in which case the surface tension alters (p. 129). If the surface area increases under *isothermal* (constant temperature) conditions, however, the surface tension is consant; and we can then say that, if T is the surface tension at that temperature,

work done in enlarging surface area $=$ force $\times$ distance

$$= 2Tl \times b = T \times 2lb.$$

But $2lb$ is the total increase in surface area of the film.

∴ work done per sq. cm. in enlarging area $= T$.

Thus the surface tension, T, can be defined as *the work done in increasing the surface area of a liquid by one square centimetre under isothermal conditions*, which is also called the *free surface energy*. See also p. 200.

It is a well-known principle in Mechanics that an object is in stable equilibrium when its potential energy is a minimum. From our discussion, this implies that a given volume of liquid, under surface tension forces, will assume a minimum surface area, which is the shape of a sphere (see p. 113).

EXAMPLES

1. (i) Calculate the work done against surface tension forces in blowing a soap bubble of 1 cm. diameter if the surface tension of soap solution is 25 dynes per cm. (ii) Find the work required to break up a drop of water of radius 0·5 cm. into drops of water each of radii 1 mm. (Surface tension of water $= 70$ dynes per cm.)

(i) The original surface area of the bubble is zero, and the final surface area $= 2 \times 4\pi r^2$ (two surfaces of bubble) $= 2 \times 4\pi \times 0.5^2 = 2\pi$ sq. cm.

∴ work done $= T \times$ increase in surface area in sq. cm.

$$= 25 \times 2\pi = 157 \text{ ergs.}$$

(ii) Since volume of a drop $= \frac{4}{3}\pi r^3$,

$$\text{number of drops formed} = \frac{\frac{4}{3}\pi \times 0.5^3}{\frac{4}{3}\pi \times 0.1^3} = 125.$$

∴ final total surface area of drops

$$= 125 \times 4\pi r^2 = 125 \times 4\pi \times 0\cdot1^2$$
$$= 5\pi \text{ sq. cm.}$$

But original surface area of drop $= 4\pi \times 0\cdot5^2 = \pi$ sq. cm.

∴ work done $= T \times$ change in surface area

$$= 70 \times (5\pi - \pi) = 879 \text{ ergs.}$$

2. A soap bubble in a vacuum has a radius of 3 cm. and another soap bubble in the vacuum has a radius of 6 cm. If the two bubbles coalesce under isothermal conditions, calculate the radius of the bubble formed.

Since the bubbles coalesce under isothermal conditions, the surface tension T is constant. Suppose R is the radius in cm. of the bubble formed.

Then   work done $= T \times$ surface area $= T \times 8\pi R^2$.

But   original work done $= T \times 8\pi \cdot 3^2 + T \times 8\pi \cdot 6^2$.

$$\therefore T \times 8\pi R^2 = T \times 8\pi \cdot 3^2 + T \cdot 8\pi \cdot 6^2.$$

$$\therefore R^2 = 3^2 + 6^2$$

$$\therefore R = \sqrt{3^2 + 6^2} = 6\cdot7 \text{ cm.}$$

10. Measurement of Surface Tension by Capillary Tube Method.

Theory. Suppose T is the magnitude of the surface tension of a liquid such as water, which rises up a clean glass capillary tube and has an angle of contact zero. Fig. 79 shows a section of the meniscus M at B, which is a hemisphere. Since the glass AB is a tangent to the

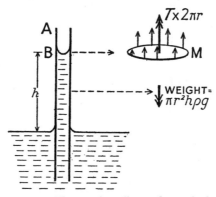

FIG. 79. Theory of capillary tube method.

liquid, the surface tension forces, which act along the boundary of the liquid with the air, act vertically downwards on the glass. By the law of action and reaction, the glass exerts an equal force in an upward direction on the liquid. Now surface tension, T, is the force per unit length acting in the surface of the liquid, and the length of liquid in contact with the glass is $2\pi r$, where r is the radius of the capillary tube.

$$\therefore 2\pi r \times T = \text{upward force on liquid.}$$

This force supports the weight of a column of height h above the outside level of liquid. The volume of the liquid $= \pi r^2 h$, and thus the mass, m, of the liquid column $=$ volume $\times$ density $= \pi r^2 h \rho$, where ρ is the density. The *weight* of the liquid $= mg = \pi r^2 h \rho g$ dynes, where r and h are in centimetres, ρ is in grams per c.c., and $g = 980$ cm. sec.$^{-2}$.

$$\therefore 2\pi r T = \pi r^2 h \rho g$$

$$\therefore T = \frac{rh\rho g}{2} \quad . \quad . \quad . \quad . \quad . \quad (50)$$

In deriving this formula for T it should be noted that we have (i) assumed the glass to be a tangent to the liquid surface meeting it, (ii) neglected the weight of the small amount of liquid above the bottom of the meniscus at B, Fig. 79.

Experiment. In the experiment, the capillary tube C is supported in a beaker Y, and a pin P, bent at right angles at two places, is attached to C by a rubber band, Fig. 80. P is adjusted until its point just touches

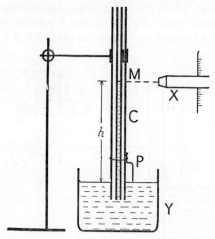

Fig. 80.   Surface tension by capillary tube method.

the horizontal level of the liquid in the beaker. A travelling microscope is now focussed on to the meniscus M in C, and then it is focussed on to the point of P, the beaker being removed for this observation. In this way the height h of M above the level in the beaker is determined. The radius of the capillary at M can be found by cutting the tube at this place and measuring the diameter by the travelling microscope; or by measuring the length, l cm., and mass, m grams, of a mercury thread drawn into the tube, and calculating the radius, r cm., from the relation $r = \sqrt{m/\pi l \rho}$, where ρ is the density of mercury, 13·6 gm. per c.c. The surface tension T is then calculated from the formula $T = rh\rho g/2$. Its magnitude for water at 15° C. is 73·3 dynes per cm.; for alcohol at 20° C. it is 23·0 dynes per cm.; for paraffin oil at 25° C. it is 26·4 dynes per cm.

11. Measurement of Surface Tension by Microscope Slide.

Besides the capillary tube method, the surface tension of water can be measured by weighing a microscope slide in air, and then lowering it until it just meets the surface of water, Fig. 81. The surface tension

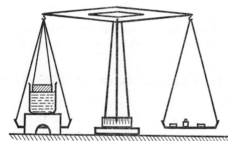

Fig. 81.   Surface tension by microscope slide method.

force acts vertically downward round the boundary of the slide, and pulls the slide down. Thus the apparent increase, m grams, in the weight is equal to $T(2a + 2b)$ where a, b are the length and thickness of the slide in cm., since, by definition, T is the force per unit length acting in the liquid surface.

$$\therefore T(2a + 2b) = mg,$$

where g is 980. cm. sec.$^{-2}$

$$\therefore T = \frac{mg}{2a + 2b},$$

Thus T can be calculated in dynes per cm.

12. The Surface Tension of a Soap Solution can be found by a similar method. A soap-film is formed in a three-sided metal frame ABCD, and the apparent weight is found, Fig. 82. When the film is broken by piercing it, the decrease in the apparent weight, m grams, is equal to the surface tension force acting downwards when the film existed. This is equal to $2Tb$, where $b = $ BC cm., since the film has *two* sides.

E

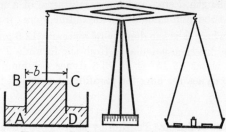

FIG. 82.   Surface tension of soap film.

$$\therefore 2Tb = mg$$

$$\therefore T = \frac{mg}{2b}.$$

It will be noted that the surface tension forces on the sides AB, CD of the frame act horizontally, and their resultant is zero.

13.   Pressure Difference in a Bubble or Curved Liquid Surface.

As we shall see presently, the magnitude of the curvature of a liquid, or of a bubble formed in a liquid, is related to the surface tension of the liquid.

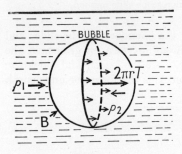

FIG. 83.
Excess pressure in a bubble.

Consider a bubble formed inside a liquid, Fig. 83. If we consider the equilibrium of *one half*, B, of the bubble, we can see that the surface tension force on B plus the force on B due to the external pressure p_1 = the force on B due to the internal pressure p_2 inside the bubble. The force on B due to the pressure p_1 is given by $\pi r^2 \times p_1$, since πr^2 is the area of the circular face of B and pressure is "force per unit area"; the force on B due to the pressure p_2 is given similarly by $\pi r^2 \times p_2$. The surface tension force acts round the *circumference* of the bubble, which has a length $2\pi r$; thus the force is $2\pi rT$. It follows that

$$2\pi rT + \pi r^2 p_1 = \pi r^2 p_2$$

Simplifying, $$\therefore 2T = r(p_2 - p_1),$$

or $$p_2 - p_1 = \frac{2T}{r}.$$

Now $(p_2 - p_1)$ is the excess pressure, p, in the bubble over the outside pressure.

$$\therefore excess\ pressure,\ p,\ = \frac{2T}{r} \qquad . \qquad . \qquad . \qquad . \quad (51)$$

Although we considered a bubble, the same formula for the excess pressure holds for any curved liquid surface or meniscus, where r is its radius of curvature and T is its surface tension, provided the angle of contact is zero. If the angle of contact is θ, the formula is modified by replacing T by $T \cos \theta$. Thus, in general,

$$excess\ pressure,\ p,\ = \frac{2T \cos \theta}{r} \qquad . \qquad . \qquad . \quad (52)$$

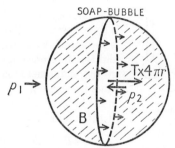

FIG. 84.   Excess pressure in a soap bubble.

14. Excess Pressure in Soap Bubble.

A soap bubble has two liquid surfaces in contact with air, one inside the bubble and the other outside the bubble. The force on one half, B, of the bubble due to surface tension forces is thus $T \times 2\pi r \times 2$, i.e., $T \times 4\pi r$, Fig. 84. For the equilibrium of B, it follows that

$$4\pi r T + \pi r^2 p_1 = \pi r^2 p_2,$$

where p_2, p_1 are the pressures inside and outside the bubble respectively. Simplifying,

$$\therefore p_2 - p_1 = \frac{4T}{r}$$

$$\therefore excess\ pressure = \frac{4T}{r} \qquad . \qquad . \qquad . \qquad . \quad (53)$$

The result for the excess pressure should now be compared with the result obtained for a bubble formed inside a liquid, equation (51).

Two soap-bubbles of unequal size can be blown on the ends of a tube, communication between them being prevented by a closed tap in the middle. If the tap is opened, the *smaller* bubble is observed to collapse gradually and the size of the larger bubble increases. This can be explained from our formula $p = 4T/r$, which shows that the pressure of air inside the smaller bubble is greater than that inside the larger bubble. Consequently air flows from the smaller to the larger bubble when communication is made between the bubbles, and the smaller bubble thus gradually collapses.

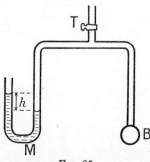

FIG. 85.
Surface tension of soap bubble.

15. Surface Tension of Soap-Bubble.

The surface tension of a soap solution can be measured by blowing a small soap-bubble at the end B of a tube connected to a manometer M, Fig. 85. The tap T is then closed, the diameter d of the bubble is measured by a travelling microscope, and the difference in levels h of the liquid in the manometer is observed with the same instrument. The excess pressure, p, in the bubble $= h\rho g$, where ρ is the density of the liquid in M.

$$\therefore h\rho g = \frac{4T}{r} = \frac{4T}{d/2}.$$

$$\therefore \quad T = \frac{h\rho gd}{8}.$$

16. Rise or Fall of Liquids in Capillary Tubes.

From our knowledge of the angle of contact and the excess pressure on one side of a curved liquid surface, we can deduce that some liquids will rise in a capillary tube, whereas others will be depressed.

Suppose the tube A is placed in water, for example, Fig. 86 (i). At first the liquid surface becomes concave upwards in the tube, because the angle of contact with the glass is zero. Consequently the pressure on the air side, X, of the curved surface is greater than the pressure on the liquid side Y by $2T/r$, where T is the surface tension and r is the radius of curvature of the tube. But the pressure at X is atmospheric, H. Hence the pressure at Y must be less than atmospheric by $2T/r$. Fig. 86 (i) is therefore impossible because it shows the pressure at Y equal to the atmospheric pressure. Thus, as shown in Fig. 86 (ii), the liquid ascends the tube to a height h such that the pressure at N is less than at M by $2T/r$, Fig. 86 (ii). A similar argument shows that a liquid rises in a capillary tube when the angle of contact is acute.

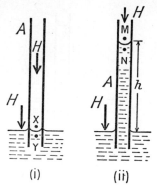

The angle of contact between mercury and glass is obtuse (p. 116). Thus when a capillary tube is placed in mercury the liquid first curves downwards. The pressure inside the liquid just below the curved surface is now greater than the pressure on the other side, which is atmospheric, and the mercury therefore moves down the tube until the excess pressure $= 2T\cos\theta/r$, with the usual notation. A liquid thus falls in a capillary tube if the angle of contact is obtuse.

Fig. 86. Rise of liquid in capillary tube.

17. Capillary Rise and Fall by Pressure Method.

We shall now calculate the capillary rise of water by the excess pressure formula $p = 2T/r$, or $p = 2T\cos\theta/r$.

In the case of a capillary tube dipping into water, the angle of contact is practically zero, Fig. 87 (i). Thus if p_2 is the pressure of the atmosphere, and p_1 is the pressure in the liquid, we have

$$p_2 - p_1 = \frac{2T}{r}.$$

Now if H is the atmospheric pressure in dynes per sq. cm., h is the height of the liquid in the tube and ρ its density,

$$p_2 = H \text{ and } p_1 = H - h\rho g$$

$$\therefore \ H - (H - h\rho g) = \frac{2T}{r}$$

$$\therefore \ h\rho g = \frac{2T}{r}$$

$$\therefore \ h = \frac{2T}{r\rho g} \qquad . \qquad . \qquad . \qquad . \qquad \text{(i)}$$

The formula shows that h increases as r decreases, i.e., the narrower the tube, the greater is the height to which the water rises (see Fig. 73 (i), p. 115).

If the height l of the tube above the water is less than the calculated value of h in the above formula, the water surface at the top of the tube now meets it at an acute angle of contact θ. Its radius is therefore $r/\cos\theta$, and $l\rho g = 2T/(r/\cos\theta)$, or

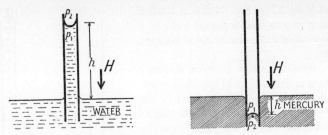

FIG. 87.   Rise and fall of liquids by excess pressure method.

$$l = \frac{2T \cos \theta}{r \rho g} \quad . \quad . \quad . \quad . \quad \text{(ii)}$$

Dividing (ii) by (i), it follows that

$$\cos \theta = \frac{l}{h}.$$

18. With Mercury in Glass.

Suppose that the depression of the mercury inside a tube of radius r is h, Fig. 87 (ii). The pressure p_2 in the curved surface of the mercury is then greater than the (atmospheric) pressure p_1 outside the curved surface; and, from our general result,

$$p_2 - p_1 = \frac{2T \cos \theta}{r},$$

where θ is the supplement of the obtuse angle of contact of mercury with glass (about $137°$). But $p_1 = H$ and $p_2 = H + h \rho g$, where H is the atmospheric pressure in dynes per sq. cm.

$$\therefore \ (H + h\rho g) - H = \frac{2T \cos \theta}{r}.$$

$$\therefore \ h\rho g = \frac{2T \cos \theta}{r}.$$

$$\therefore \quad h = \frac{2T \cos \theta}{r \rho g} \quad . \quad . \quad . \quad \text{(54)}$$

The height of depression, h, thus increases as the radius r of the tube decreases. See Fig. 73 (ii), p. 115.

19. Effect of Surface Tension in Hare's Apparatus.

When we discussed the measurement of the specific gravity or density of a liquid by an inverted U-tube or Hare's apparatus, the effect of

surface tension was not considered. If the tubes are wide, the surface
tension effect can be neglected. If the tubes are narrow, we can take
surface tension into account in the following way.

With the notation on p. 103, and referring to Fig. 65,

$$p - p_1 = \frac{2T_1}{r_1},$$

where p_1 is the pressure in the liquid near the meniscus of the tube in
B, T_1 is the surface tension of the liquid, and r_1 is the radius of B. But,
from hydrostatics, $p_1 = H - h_1 \rho_1 g$.

$$\therefore p - (H - h_1 \rho_1 g) = \frac{2T_1}{r_1}$$

$$\therefore H - p = h_1 \rho_1 g - \frac{2T_1}{r_1} \qquad . \quad . \quad . \quad \text{(i)}$$

If T_2 is the surface tension of the liquid in C, and r_2 is the radius of
the tube in the liquid, then, by similar reasoning,

$$H - p = h_2 \rho_2 g - \frac{2T_2}{r_2} \qquad . \quad . \quad . \quad . \quad \text{(ii)}$$

From (i) and (ii),

$$\therefore h_2 \rho_2 g - \frac{2T_2}{r_2} = h_1 \rho_1 g - \frac{2T_1}{r_1}$$

Re-arranging,

$$\therefore h_2 = \frac{\rho_1}{\rho_2} h_1 - \frac{2}{\rho_2 g}\left(\frac{T_1}{r_1} - \frac{T_2}{r_2}\right)$$

Suppose the liquid in C is water, that is, $\rho_2 = 1$ gm. per c.c. Then

$$h_2 = \rho_1 h_1 - \frac{2}{g}\left(\frac{T_1}{r_1} - \frac{T_2}{r_2}\right),$$

which is an equation of the form $y = mx + c$, where c is a constant,
$h_2 = y$, $h_1 = x$, and $\rho_1 = m$. Thus by taking different values of h_2 and
h_1, and plotting h_2 against h_1, a straight-line graph is obtained whose
slope is equal to ρ_1, the density. In this way the effect of the surface
tension can be eliminated.

20. Variation of Surface Tension with Temperature. Jaeger's Method.

By forming a bubble inside a liquid, and measuring the excess
pressure, JAEGER was able to determine the variation of the surface

tension of a liquid with temperature. One form of the apparatus is shown in Fig. 88. A capillary or drawn-out tubing A is connected to a

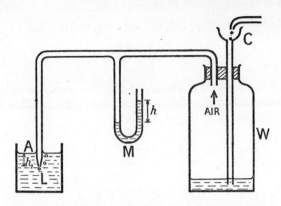

FIG. 88. Variation of surface tension with temperature.

vessel W containing a funnel C, so that air is driven slowly through A when water enters W through C. The capillary A is placed inside a beaker containing the liquid L, and a bubble forms slowly at the end of A when air is passed through at it a slow rate. *The bubble becomes unstable and breaks away from A when its radius is the same as that of A.* Thus as the bubble grows the pressure in it increases to a maximum, and then decreases as the bubble breaks away. The maximum pressure is observed from a manometer M containing a light oil of density ρ, and a series of observations are taken as several bubbles grow.

The maximum pressure inside the bubble $= H + h\rho g$ where h is the maximum difference in levels in the manometer M, and H is the atmospheric pressure. The pressure outside the bubble $= H + h_1\rho_1 g$, where h_1 is the depth of the orifice of A below the level of the liquid L, and ρ_1 is the latter's density.

$\therefore$ excess pressure $= (H + h\rho g) - (H + h_1\rho_1 g) = h\rho g - h_1\rho_1 g$

But   excess pressure $= \dfrac{2T}{r}$,

where r is the radius of the orifice of A (p. 123).

$$\therefore \frac{2T}{r} = h\rho g - h_1\rho_1 g$$

$$\therefore T = \frac{rg}{2}(h\rho - h_1\rho_1)$$

By adding warm liquid to the vessel containing L, the variation of the surface tension with temperature can be determined. Experiment shows that the surface tension of liquids, and water in particular, decreases with increasing temperature, as the table below indicates. Various formulæ relating the surface tension to temperature have been proposed, but none has been found to be completely satisfactory.

SURFACE TENSION OF WATER

TEMPERATURE ° C.	T (DYNES/CM.)
0	75·5
10	74·0
15	73·3
20	72·6
30	71·1
40	69·4
50	67·8
60	66·0
70	64·2

EXAMPLES

1. Define surface tension of a liquid and describe a method of finding this quantity for alcohol.

If water rises in a capillary tube 5·8 cm. above the free surface of the outer liquid, what will happen to the mercury level in the same tube when it is placed in a dish of mercury? Illustrate this by the aid of a diagram. Calculate the difference in level between the mercury surfaces inside the tube and outside. (S.T. of water = 75 dynes/cm. S.T. of mercury = 547 dynes per cm. Angle of contact of mercury with clean glass = 130°. Density of mercury = 13·6 gm./c.c.) (*L.*)

First part. "Surface tension" is defined in the text. The surface tension of alcohol can be found by measuring the rise in a capillary tube, p. 120.

Second part. The mercury is depressed a distance h below the outside level, and is convex upward, Fig. 89. Suppose r is the capillary tube radius. Then, since $T = rh\rho g/2$ for the case of the water (p. 120),

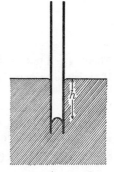

FIG. 89.

$$\frac{r \times 5\cdot8 \times 1 \times 980}{2} = 75.$$

$$\therefore r = \frac{150}{5 \cdot 8 \times 980}.$$

In the case of the mercury, the equation which applies is

$$T \cos 50° = \frac{rh\rho g}{2},$$

since $180° - 130° = 50°$. See p. 126.

$$\therefore h = \frac{2T \cos 50°}{r\rho g}$$

$$= \frac{2 \times 547 \cos 50° \times 5\cdot8 \times 980}{13\cdot6 \times 980 \times 150},$$

substituting for r from above.

$$\therefore h = 2\cdot0 \text{ cm.}$$

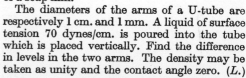

FIG. 90.

2. Explain how to measure the surface tension of a soap film.

The diameters of the arms of a U-tube are respectively 1 cm. and 1 mm. A liquid of surface tension 70 dynes/cm. is poured into the tube which is placed vertically. Find the difference in levels in the two arms. The density may be taken as unity and the contact angle zero. (*L.*)

First part. The surface tension of a soap film can be measured by the "framework film" method, described on p. 121.

Second part. The liquid in the narrower tube reaches a greater height than that in the wider tube, Fig. 90. Suppose H is the atmospheric pressure and p_2 is the pressure in the liquid below the meniscus. Then, since excess pressure $= 2T/r$,

$$H - p_2 = \frac{2T}{r_2}, \qquad \cdot \qquad \cdot \qquad \text{(i)}$$

where $r_2 = \frac{1}{2}$ mm. $= 0\cdot05$ cm.

If p_1 is the pressure in the liquid below the meniscus in the wider tube, we have, similarly,

$$H - p_1 = \frac{2T}{r_1}, \qquad \cdot \qquad \cdot \qquad \cdot \qquad \text{(ii)}$$

where $r_1 = \frac{1}{2}$ cm. $= 0\cdot5$ cm.

Subtracting (ii) from (i),

$$\therefore p_1 - p_2 = \frac{2T}{r_2} - \frac{2T}{r_1}$$

But $p_1 - p_2 = h\rho g$,

where h is the difference in levels of the liquid.

$$\therefore h\rho g = \frac{2T}{r_2} - \frac{2T}{r_1}$$

$$\therefore h \times 1 \times 980 = \frac{2 \times 70}{0 \cdot 05} - \frac{2 \times 70}{0 \cdot 5}$$

$$\therefore h = 2 \cdot 6 \text{ cm.}$$

3. Define *surface tension* and derive an expression for the rise of a liquid in a vertical capillary tube whose lower end is immersed in the liquid. The lower ends of two vertical glass tubes, each 1 mm. internal diameter, are immersed in two beakers containing water and chloroform respectively, and the upper ends are joined by a T-piece. Air is withdrawn through the T-piece until the top of the water column is 20 cm. above the level in the beaker. Find the height of the chloroform column above the level in the beaker, assuming that the surface tensions of water and chloroform are 73 dyne cm.$^{-1}$ and 27 dyne cm.$^{-1}$ respectively, the specific gravity of chloroform is 1·5, and the angle of contact is zero for each liquid. (*L.*)

First part. See text.

Second part. Suppose h cm. is the height of the chloroform in cm., p is the pressure of the air inside the T-piece, H is the atmospheric pressure, Fig. 91.

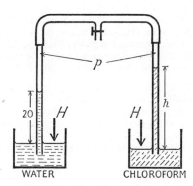

Fɪɢ. 91.

For the water, the pressure in the liquid on one side of the meniscus is $(H - 20g)$ if H is in dynes per sq. cm. Since the pressure of the air in the T-piece is p, the excess pressure $= p - (H - 20g) = p - H + 20g$.

$$\therefore p - H + 20g = \frac{2T}{r} = \frac{2 \times 73}{0 \cdot 05}, \qquad \cdot \quad \cdot \quad \cdot \quad \text{(i)}$$

since $r = 0 \cdot 5$ mm. $= 0 \cdot 05$ cm.

By similar reasoning, the excess pressure for the chloroform meniscus $= p - (H - h\rho g) = p - H + h \times 1 \cdot 5g$, since $\rho = 1 \cdot 5$ for chloroform.

$$\therefore p - H + h \times 1 \cdot 5g = \frac{2T}{r} = \frac{2 \times 27}{0 \cdot 05} \qquad \cdot \quad \cdot \quad \cdot \quad \cdot \quad \text{ii)}$$

From (i), $p - H = \dfrac{2 \times 73}{0 \cdot 05} - 20g.$

From (ii), $p - H = \dfrac{2 \times 27}{0 \cdot 05} - h \times 1 \cdot 5g.$

$$\therefore \frac{2 \times 73}{0\cdot05} - 20g = \frac{2 \times 27}{0\cdot05} - h \times 1\cdot5g$$

$$\therefore 1\cdot5\,hg = \frac{54}{0\cdot05} - \frac{146}{0\cdot05} + 20g.$$

$$\therefore h = \frac{54}{0\cdot05 \times 980 \times 1\cdot5} - \frac{146}{0\cdot05 \times 980 \times 1\cdot5} + \frac{20}{1\cdot5}$$

$$= 12\cdot1 \text{ cm}$$

EXERCISES VI

1. Define *surface tension*. A rectangular plate of dimensions 6 cm. by 4 cm. and thickness 2 mm. is placed with its largest face flat on the surface of water. Calculate the force due to surface tension on the plate. What is the downward force due to surface tension if the plate is placed vertical and its longest side just touches the water? (Surface tension of water = 70 dynes per cm.)

2. What are the *dimensions* of surface tension? A capillary tube of 0·4 mm. diameter is placed vertically inside (i) water of surface tension 65 dynes per cm. and zero angle of contact, (ii) a liquid of density 0·8 gm. per c.c. surface tension 50 dynes per cm. and angle of contact 30°. Calculate the height to which the liquid rises in the capillary in each case.

3. Define the *angle of contact*. What do you know about the angle of contact of a liquid which (i) wets glass, (ii) does not wet glass?
A capillary tube is immersed in water of surface tension 70 dynes per cm. and rises 6·2 cm. By what depth will mercury be depressed if the same capillary is immersed in it? (Surface tension of mercury = 540 dynes per cm.; angle of contact between mercury and glass = 140°; density of mercury = 13·6 gm. per c.c.)

4. (i) A soap-bubble has a diameter of 4 mm. Calculate the pressure inside it if the atmospheric pressure is 10^6 dynes per sq. cm. (Surface tension of soap solution = 28 dynes per cm.) (ii). Calculate the radius of a bubble formed in water if the pressure outside it is 10^6 dynes per sq. cm. and the pressure inside it is $1\cdot001 \times 10^6$ dynes per sq. cm. (Surface tension of water = 70 dynes per cm.)

5. Define *surface tension* of a liquid. State the units in which it is usually expressed and give its dimensions in mass, length, and time.
Derive an expression for the difference between the pressures inside and outside a spherical soap bubble. Describe a method of determining surface tension, based on the difference of pressure on the two sides of a curved liquid surface or film. (*L.*)

6. Explain briefly (a) the approximately spherical shape of a rain drop, (b) the movement of tiny particles of camphor on water, (c) the possibility of floating a needle on water, (d) why a column of water will remain in an open vertical capillary tube after the lower end has been dipped in water and withdrawn. (*N.*)

7. Explain what is meant by surface tension, and show how its existence is accounted for by molecular theory.

SURFACE TENSION 133

Find an expression for the excess pressure inside a soap-bubble of radius R and surface tension T. Hence find the work done by the pressure in increasing the radius of the bubble from a to b. Find also the increase in surface area of the bubble, and in the light of this discuss the significance of your result. (*C.*)

8. A clean glass capillary tube, of internal diameter 0·04 cm., is held vertically with its lower end below the surface of clean water in a beaker, and with 10 cm. of the tube above the surface. To what height will the water rise in the tube? What will happen if the tube is now depressed until only 5 cm. of its length is above the surface? The surface tension of water is 72 dynes per cm.

Describe, and give the theory of some method, other than that of the rise in a capillary tube, of measuring surface tension. (*O. & C.*)

9. Define *surface tension* and derive an expression for the pressure difference for equilibrium between the two sides of a spherical liquid surface.

Describe how you would determine the surface tension of soap solution by measurements made on *either* (*a*) a soap-bubble, *or* (*b*) a soap film.

Two bubbles of unequal size are blown on the two ends of a tube, communication between the bubbles being prevented by means of a closed tap in the tube. Describe and explain what happens when the tap is opened. (*N.*)

10. Describe the capillary tube method of measuring the surface tension of a liquid.

An inverted U-tube (Hare's apparatus) for measuring the specific gravity of a liquid was constructed of glass tubing of internal diameter about 2 mm. The following observations of the heights of balanced columns of water and another liquid were obtained:

Height of water (cm.)	2·8	4·2	5·4	6·9	8·5	9·8	11·6
Height of liquid (cm.)	2·0	3·8	5·3	7·0	9·1	10·7	13·0

Plot the above results, explain why the graph does not pass through the origin, and deduce from the graph an accurate value for the specific gravity of the liquid. (*N.*)

11. How does simple molecular theory account for surface tension? Illustrate your account by explaining the rise of water up a glass capillary.

A light wire frame in the form of a square of side 5 cm. hangs vertically in water with one side in the water-surface. What additional force is necessary to pull the frame clear of the water? Explain why, if the experiment is performed with soap-solution, as the force is increased a vertical film is formed, whereas with pure water no such effect occurs. (Surface tension of water is 74 dynes per cm.) (*O. & C.*)

12. Derive an expression for the excess pressure inside a spherical drop of liquid in terms of its radius and surface tension. Describe a method of finding the surface tension of a liquid in which this expression is utilized.

Would you expect the pressure inside (*a*) a soap-bubble, (*b*) a rubber balloon, to increase as the bubble or balloon is inflated? Give your reasons. (*O. & C.*)

13. What is meant by surface tension? Give **three** examples of simple demonstrations which demonstrate its existence.

The lower end of a vertical tube 2 mm. in diameter dips into soap-solution, and on the upper end is a soap-bubble 20 mm. in diameter. How much is the level of the liquid above that of the surrounding soap-solution? [Surface tension of soap-solution 27 dynes per cm.; the density of soap-solution may be assumed to be 1.] (*C.*)

14. What is meant by the dimensions of a physical quantity? Explain, with examples, how the method of dimensions can be used to test the validity of an equation.

Find how the period of vibration of a drop of liquid depends upon the radius, the density, and the surface tension, assuming no other quantities involved. (*C.*)

15. Describe how you would measure the variation with temperature of surface tension of a liquid.

A capillary U-tube contains a liquid of surface tension 75 dyne cm.$^{-1}$ One limb of the tube has internal diameter 2 mm. and the other 0·4 mm., and the tube contains a liquid of density 1·2 gm. cm.$^{-3}$ which wets the glass. What is the difference of level of meniscus in the two limbs? (*L.*)

16. Deduce an expression for the excess pressure inside a spherical soap-bubble due to surface tension.

Calculate the work done against surface tension in blowing a bubble of 8 cm. diameter. If the bubble is blown on the end of a capillary tube and the air is then allowed to escape through this tube compare the times it will take for the bubble diameter to shrink by the same small amount (*a*) when the diameter is 8 cm., (*b*) when it has decreased to 4 cm. (Surface tension of soap-solution = 25 dynes per cm.) (*L.*)

17. Describe in detail the experiments you would make, using a capillary tube method, to find the surface tension of a liquid which wets glass.

A circular ring of thin wire of 2 cm. mean radius, suspended horizontally by a thread passing through the 5 cm. mark on a metre rule pivoted at its centre, is balanced by a 5 gm. weight suspended from the 70 cm. mark. A beaker of liquid is then arranged so that the ring is just attached to the liquid surface when the rule is horizontal. It is found necessary to move the 5 gm. to the 80 cm. mark in order to detach the ring from the liquid surface. Find the surface tension of the liquid. (*N.*)

18. Show, arguing from molecular theory, that the surface of a liquid must be in a state of tension. Define the quantity known as the *surface tension*, and state the units in which it is measured.

Describe in detail how you would determine the surface tension of water by observing the rise of water in a capillary tube. Emphasise the precautions which are necessary, and explain how the result is calculated.

How, if at all, does the result of this experiment depend on the material of the tube? (*W.*)

19. Give some explanation of each of the following observations: (*a*) A small drop of mercury resting on a table is nearly spherical, a larger drop is flattened. (*b*) Water gathers itself into drops on a dusty surface. (*c*) Small pieces of camphor move about on a clean water surface, but not on one contaminated with oil or grease. (*L.*)

20. Define *surface tension* and describe in detail a method, involving the use of a capillary tube, of determining the surface tension of alcohol.

The vertical limbs A and B of a Hare's apparatus consists of capillary tubing 0·5 mm. in diameter. Their lower ends dip into alcohol and water respectively and the liquids are sucked up the tubes so that the height of water in B is 20 cm. above the free surface. Find the height of the alcohol in A above the free surface. The surface tensions of water and alcohol are 73 and 22 dynes/cm. respectively, and the specific gravity of alcohol is 0·80. Assume that the angle of contact of alcohol and glass is zero. (*L.*)

21. Derive an expression for the difference in pressure between the inside and outside of a spherical soap-bubble in terms of the surface tension S and radius r. Describe briefly any experiment, depending on this pressure difference, for the determination of surface tension.

Two soap-bubbles, of radii r_1 and r_2 are situated in a vacuum and coalesce under isothermal conditions. What is the radius of the resulting bubble? (*C.*)

22. Distinguish between *surface energy* and *surface tension*. Derive an expression for the excess pressure inside a spherical soap-bubble. A vertical U-tube contains liquid. One limb of this tube is open to the atmosphere while a soap film is formed across the end of the other limb, to which there is attached a side-tube so that, by blowing, the soap-film may be distended. Show that for different-sized bubbles the product of the radius of the bubble and the difference in height of the liquid levels in the U-tube is constant.

If the liquid in the U-tube is water and the above constant is 0·125 cm.^{2}, calculate a value for the surface tension of the soap solution. (*L.*)

CHAPTER VII

ELASTICITY. MODULUS OF ELASTICITY

1. Elasticity.

A bridge, when used by traffic during the day, is subjected to loads of varying magnitude. Before a steel bridge is erected, therefore, samples of the steel are sent to a research laboratory, where they undergo tests to find out whether the steel can withstand the loads to which it is likely to be subjected.

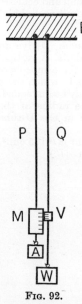

Fig. 92 illustrates a simple laboratory method of discovering useful information about the property of steel we are discussing. Two long thin steel wires, P, Q, are suspended beside each other from a rigid support B, such as a girder at the top of the ceiling. The wire P is kept taut by a weight A attached to its end and carries a scale M graduated in centimetres. The wire Q carries a vernier scale V which is alongside the scale M.

When a load W such as 1 kilogram is attached to the end of Q, the wire increases in length by an amount which can be read from the change in the reading on the vernier V. If the load is taken off and the reading on V returns to its original value, the wire is said to be **elastic** for loads from zero to 1 kilogram, a term adopted by analogy with an elastic thread. When the load W is increased to 2 kilograms the extension (increase in length) is obtained from V again; and if the reading on V returns to original value when the load is removed the wire is said to be elastic at least for loads from zero to 2 kilograms.

FIG. 92.
Measurement of
Young's modulus.

2. Elastic Limit.

The extension of a thin wire such as Q for increasing loads may be found by experiment to be as follows:

W (kilograms)	0	1	2	3	4	5	6	7	8
Extension (mm.)	0	0·14	0·28	0·42	0·56	0·70	0·85	0·91	1·09

When the extension, e, is plotted against the load, W, a graph is

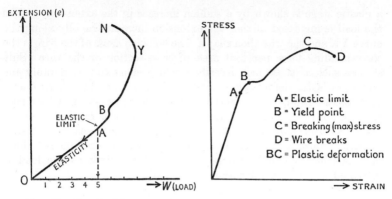

FIG. 93.   Graph of (i) extension v. load (*not to scale*) (ii) stress v. strain.

obtained which is a *straight line* OA, followed by a curve ABY rising slowly at first and then very sharply, Fig. 93. Up to 5 kilograms, then, the results in the table show that the extension increased by 0·14 mm. for every kilogram added to the wire. Further, the wire returned to its original length when the load was removed. For loads greater than 5 kilograms, however, the extension increases relatively more and more, and the wire now no longer returns to its original length when it is unloaded. The wire is thus permanently strained, and A corresponds to its *elastic limit*.

3. Hooke's Law.

From the straight line graph OA, we deduce that *the extension is proportional to the load or tension in the wire when the elastic limit is not exceeded*. This is known as *Hooke's law*, after ROBERT HOOKE, founder of the Royal Society, who discovered the relation in 1676.

The measurements also show that it would be dangerous to load the wire with weights greater than 5 kilograms, the elastic limit, because the wire then suffers a permanent strain. Similar experiments in the research laboratory enable scientists to find the maximum load in tons weight a steel bridge, for example, should carry for safety. Rubber samples are also subjected to similar experiments, to find the maximum safe tension in rubber belts used in machinery.

4. Yield Point.   Ductile and Brittle Substances.   Breaking Stress.

Careful experiments show that, for mild steel and iron for example, the molecules of the wire begin to "slide" across each other soon after the load exceeds the elastic limit, that is, the material becomes *plastic*. This is indicated by the slight "kink" at B beyond A in Fig. 93 (i), and it is called the *yield point* of the wire. The change from an elastic to a plastic stage is shown by a sudden increase in the extension, and as the load is increased further the extension increases rapidly along the curve YN and the wire then snaps. The *breaking stress* of the wire is the corresponding force per unit area of cross-section of the wire. Substances such as those just described, which elongate considerably and undergo plastic deformation until they break, are known as *ductile* substances. Lead, copper and wrought iron are ductile. Other substances, however, break just after the elastic limit is reached; they are known as *brittle* substances. Glass and high carbon steels are brittle.

Brass, bronze, and many alloys appear to have no yield point. These materials increase in length beyond the elastic limit as the load is increased without the appearance of a plastic stage.

5. Tensile Stress and Tensile Strain.   Young's Modulus.

We have now to consider the technical terms used in the subject of elasticity of wires. When a force or tension F is applied to the end of a wire of cross-sectional area A, Fig. 94,

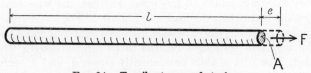

Fig. 94.   Tensile stress and strain.

$$\text{the } \textit{tensile stress} = \textit{force per unit area} = \frac{F}{A} \quad . \quad . \quad (55)$$

If the extension of the wire is e, and its original length is l,

$$\text{the } \textit{tensile strain} = \textit{extension per unit length} = \frac{e}{l} \quad . \quad (56).$$

Thus if 2 kgm. is attached to the end of a wire of length 200 cm. of diameter 0·64 mm., and the extension is 0·60 mm., then, with tensile understood,

$$\text{stress} = \frac{\text{force}}{\text{area}} = \frac{2{,}000 \times 980 \text{ dynes}}{\pi \times (0{\cdot}032)^2 \text{ sq. cm}}.$$

$$= \frac{2000 \times 980}{\pi \times (0{\cdot}032)^2} \text{ dynes per sq. cm.,}$$

and $$\text{strain} = \frac{0{\cdot}060}{200}.$$

It will be noted that "stress" has units such as "dynes per sq. cm."; "strain" has no units because it is the ratio of two lengths.

A *modulus of elasticity* of the wire, called **Young's modulus (E)**, is defined as the ratio

$$E = \frac{\text{stress}}{\text{strain}} \qquad \cdots \cdots \qquad (57)$$

Thus
$$E = \frac{F/A}{e/l}.$$

Using the above figures,
$$E = \frac{2000 \times 980/[\pi \times (0\cdot032)^2]}{0\cdot060/200}$$

$$= \frac{2000 \times 200 \times 980}{\pi \times (0\cdot032)^2 \times 0\cdot060}$$

$$= 2\cdot0 \times 10^{12} \text{ dynes per sq. cm.}$$

It should be noted that Young's modulus, E, is calculated from the ratio stress: strain only when the wire is under "elastic" conditions, that is, the load does not then exceed the elastic limit (p. 137). Fig. 93 (ii) shows the general stress-strain diagram for a ductile material.

6. Dimensions of Young's Modulus.

As stated before, the "strain" of a wire has no dimensions of mass, length, or time, since, by definition, it is the ratio of two lengths. Now

$$\text{dimensions of stress} = \frac{\text{dimensions of force}}{\text{dimension of area}}$$

$$= \frac{[M]\,[L]\,[T]^{-2}}{[L]^2}$$

$$= [M]\,[L]^{-1}\,[T]^{-2}$$

$\therefore$ dimensions of Young's modulus, E,

$$= \frac{\text{dimensions of stress}}{\text{dimensions of strain}}$$

$$= [M]\,[L]^{-1}\,[T]^{-2}$$

7. Determination of Young's Modulus.

The magnitude of Young's modulus for a material in the form of a wire can be found with the apparatus illustrated in Fig. 92, p. 136, to which the reader should now refer. The following practical points should be specially noted:

(1) The use of two wires, P, Q, of the same material and length, eliminates the correction for (i) the yielding of the support when loads are added to Q, (ii) changes of temperature.

(2) Both wires should be free of kinks, otherwise the increase in length cannot be accurately measured. The wires are straightened by attaching weights to their ends, as shown in Fig. 92.

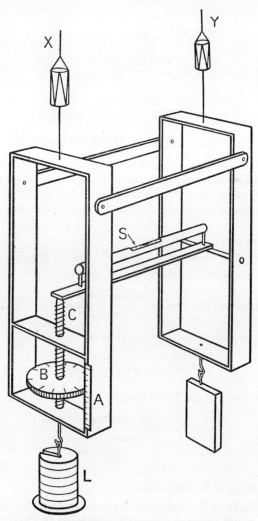

FIG. 95.   Searle's apparatus for Young's modulus.

(3) A vernier scale is necessary to measure the extension of the wire since this is always small. The "original length" of the wire is measured from the top B *to the vernier V* by a ruler, since an error of 1 millimetre is negligible compared with an original length of several metres. For

very accurate work, the extension can be measured by an arrangement due to G. F. C. SEARLE. The two wires, X, Y, are attached to two frames connected by a spirit level S, one end of which rests on a screw C operated by a graduated wheel B, Fig. 95. The movement of B can be measured on a fixed scale A graduated in millimetres. The load is placed on L.

(4) The diameter of the wire must be found by a micrometer screw gauge at several places, and the average value then calculated. The area of cross-section, A, $= \pi r^2$, where r is the radius.

(5) The readings on the vernier are also taken when the load is gradually removed in steps of 1 kilogram; they should be very nearly the same as the readings on the vernier when the weights were added, showing that the elastic limit was not exceeded. Suppose the readings on V for loads, W, of 1 to 6 kilograms are a, b, c, d, e, f, as follows:

W (kg.)	1	2	3	4	5	6
Reading on V	a	b	c	d	e	f

The average extension for 3 kilograms is found by taking the average of $(d - a)$, $(e - b)$, and $(f - c)$. Young's modulus can then be calculated from the relation stress/strain, where the stress $= 3000 \times 980/\pi r^2$, and the strain $=$ average extension/original length of wire (p. 139).

8. Some Magnitudes of Young's Modulus are shown below:

	YOUNG'S MODULUS (dynes per sq. cm.)
Steel	$19 \cdot 5 \times 10^{11}$
Wrought iron	$19 \ \times 10^{11}$
Cast iron	$11 \cdot 5 \times 10^{11}$
Copper	$12 \cdot 4 \times 10^{11}$
Brass	$10 \ \times 10^{11}$
Silver	$7 \cdot 9 \times 10^{11}$
Ice	$0 \cdot 28 \times 10^{11}$
Oak	$1 \cdot 3 \ \times 10^{11}$

The breaking stress of cast-iron is about 10 tons per sq. in.; the breaking stress of mild steel (0.2% C.) is about 30 tons per sq. in.

At Royal Ordnance and other Ministry of Supply factories, tensile testing is carried out by placing a sample of the material in a machine known as an *extensometer*, which applies stresses of increasing value along the length of the sample and automatically measures the slight increase in length. When the elastic limit is reached, the pointer on the dial of the machine flickers, and soon after the yield point is reached the sample becomes thin at some point and then breaks. A graph showing the load *vs.* extension is recorded automatically by a moving pen while the sample is undergoing test.

9. Force in Bar Due to Contraction or Expansion.

When a bar is heated, and then prevented from contracting as it cools, a considerable force is exerted at the ends of the bar. We can derive a formula for the force if we consider a bar of Young's modulus E, a cross-sectional area A, a linear coefficient of expansion a, and a decrease in temperature of $t°$ C. Then, if the original length of the bar is l, the decrease in length e if the bar were free to contract $= alt$.

Now
$$E = \frac{F/A}{e/l}.$$

$$\therefore F = \frac{EAe}{l} = \frac{EAalt}{l}.$$

$$\therefore F = EAat.$$

As an illustration, suppose a steel rod of cross-sectional area 2·0 sq. cm. is heated to 100° C., and then prevented from contracting when it is cooled to 10° C. Since the linear coefficient of steel $= 0·000012$ per ° C., and Young's modulus $= 2·0 \times 10^{12}$ dynes per sq. cm.,

$$\therefore F = EA \, a \, t = 2·0 \times 10^{12} \times 2·0 \times 0·000012 \times 90 \text{ dynes.}$$

$$\therefore F = 43·2 \times 10^8 \text{ dynes}$$

$$= \frac{43·2 \times 10^8}{980 \times 1000} = 4,400 \text{ kilogram wt.}$$

10. Energy Stored in a Wire.

Suppose that a wire has an original length l and is stretched by a length e when a force F is applied at one end. If the elastic limit is not exceeded, the extension is directly proportional to the applied load (p. 137). Consequently the force *in the wire* has increased in magnitude from zero to F, and hence the average force in the wire while stretching was $F/2$. Now

$$\text{work done} = \text{force} \times \text{distance.}$$

$$\therefore \text{work} = \text{average force} \times \text{extension}$$

$$= \tfrac{1}{2}Fe \quad . \quad . \quad . \quad . \quad . \quad . \quad 58\text{(i)}$$

This is the amount of energy stored in the wire. The formula $\tfrac{1}{2}Fe$ gives the energy in ergs when F is in dynes and e is in centimetres.

Further, since $F = EAe/l$,

$$\text{energy} = \tfrac{1}{2} EA \frac{e^2}{l}.$$

From 58 (i), the energy per c.c. $= \tfrac{1}{2} Fe \div Al$, since Al is the volume of the wire. But $F/A = $ stress, and $e/l = $ strain.

$$\therefore \text{energy per c.c.} = \tfrac{1}{2} \text{ stress} \times \text{strain} \quad . \quad . \quad . \quad . \quad 58 \text{ (ii)}$$

Suppose that the wire has a load F_1 on it which produces an extension e_1, and that the load is increased to F_2, producing an extension e_2. If the elastic limit is not exceeded the graph of extension, e, against load,

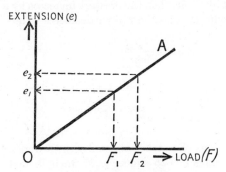

FIG. 96.   Energy in wire.

F, is a straight line OA, Fig. 96. Thus the extra energy, W, stored in the wire when the load is increased is given by

$$W = \text{average force} \times \text{extension}$$

$$= \tfrac{1}{2}(F_1 + F_2) \times (e_2 - e_1)$$

$$= \tfrac{1}{2}\left(\frac{EAe_1}{l} + \frac{EAe_2}{l}\right) \times (e_2 - e_1)$$

$$= \tfrac{1}{2}\frac{EA}{l}(e_1 + e_2)(e_2 - e_1)$$

$$= \tfrac{1}{2}\frac{EA}{l}(e_2{}^2 - e_1{}^2)$$

11. Bulk Modulus of Elasticity.

When a gas or a liquid is subjected to an increased pressure the substance contracts. A change in bulk thus occurs, and the *bulk strain* is defined by

$$\text{strain} = \frac{\text{change in volume}}{\text{original volume}}.$$

The *stress* on the substance is the force per unit area, by definition, and the bulk modulus, k,

$$= \frac{\text{stress}}{\text{strain}}$$

$$= \frac{\text{force per unit area}}{\text{change in volume/original volume}}.$$

If the original volume of the substance is v, the change in volume may be denoted by $-\delta v$ when the pressure increases by a small amount δp; the minus indicates that the volume decreases. Thus

$$k = -\frac{\delta p}{\delta v/v}.$$

When δp and δv become very small, then, in the limit,

$$k = -v\frac{dp}{dv} \quad . \quad . \quad . \quad . \quad . \quad (59)$$

The bulk modulus of water is about 2×10^{10} dynes per sq. cm. for pressures in the range $1 - 25$ atmospheres; the bulk modulus of mercury is about 27×10^{10} dynes per sq. cm. The bulk modulus of gases depends on the pressure, as we shall now explain.

12. Bulk Modulus of a Gas.

If the pressure, p, and volume, v, of a gas change under conditions such that

$$pv = \text{constant},$$

which is Boyle's law, the changes are said to be *isothermal* ones. In this case, by differentiating the product pv with respect to v, we have

$$p + v\frac{dp}{dv} = 0.$$

$$\therefore p = -v\frac{dp}{dv}.$$

But the bulk modulus, k, of the gas is equal to $-v\dfrac{dp}{dv}$ by definition (see p. 144).

$$\therefore k = p \qquad \qquad (60)$$

Thus the *isothermal bulk modulus is equal to the pressure.*

When the pressure, p, and volume, v, of a gas change under conditions such that

$$pv^\gamma = \text{constant},$$

where $\gamma = c_p/c_v =$ the ratio of the principal specific heats of the gas, the changes are said to be *adiabatic* ones. This equation is the one obeyed by local values of pressure and volume in air when a sound wave travels through it. Differentiating both sides with respect to v,

$$\therefore p \times \gamma v^{\gamma-1} + v^\gamma \frac{dp}{dv} = 0$$

$$\therefore \gamma p = -v\frac{dp}{dv}$$

$$\therefore \text{adiabatic bulk modulus} = \gamma p \qquad \qquad (61)$$

13. Velocity of Sound.

The velocity of sound waves through any material depends on (i) its density ρ, (ii) its modulus of elasticity, E. Thus if V is the velocity, we may say that

$$V = k\,E^x\rho^y \qquad \qquad \text{(i)},$$

where k is a constant and x, y are indices we can find by the theory of dimensions (p. 25).

The units of velocity, V, are $[L][T]^{-1}$; the units of density ρ are $[M][L]^{-3}$; and the units of modulus of elasticity, E, are $[M][L]^{-1}[T]^{-2}$ (see p. 139). Equating the dimensions on both sides of (i),

$$\therefore [L][T]^{-1} = [M]^x[L]^{-x}[T]^{-2x} \times [M]^y[L]^{-3y}$$

Equating the indices of $[M]$, $[L]$, $[T]$ on both sides, we have

$$0 = x + y,$$
$$1 = -x - 3y,$$
$$-1 = -2x.$$

Solving, we find $x = \tfrac{1}{2}, y = -\tfrac{1}{2}$. Thus $V = kE^{\frac{1}{2}}\rho^{-\frac{1}{2}}$. A rigid investigation shows $k = 1$, and thus

$$V = E^{\frac{1}{2}}\rho^{-\frac{1}{2}} = \sqrt{\frac{E}{\rho}}.$$

In the case of a solid, E is Young's modulus. In the case of air and other gases, and of liquids, E is the bulk modulus. Laplace showed that the adiabatic bulk modulus must be used in the case of a gas, and since this is γp, the velocity of sound in a gas is given by the expression

$$V = \sqrt{\frac{\gamma p}{\rho}}.$$

14. Torsion Wire. Rigidity.

If a phosphor-bronze wire is fixed at one end and twisted through a small angle at the other end, the wire will unwind when left to itself and regain its initial appearance in a very short time. Phosphor-bronze has thus torsional elastic properties. Quartz fibre has a small torsion; it will twist to a considerable extent when a small force acts at one end. Silk thread is inelastic from this point of view.

When a phosphor-bronze wire or quartz fibre is twisted at one end through a small angle θ, the other end being fixed, *the material sets up an opposing couple whose magnitude is proportional to* θ. Thus

opposing couple $= c\theta$,

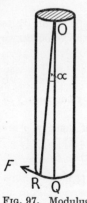

FIG. 97. Modulus of rigidity.

where c is a constant of the wire. If $\theta = 1$ radian, or 1 degree, the opposing couple $= c$. Thus c is the opposing couple per unit radian of twist (or per unit degree of twist), and it may therefore be expressed in "dyne cm. per radian (or per degree)". Phosphor-bronze wire is used in sensitive moving-coil electrical instruments to control the rotation of a coil of wire and the elastic constant, c, of the wire in one make of instrument is 200 dyne cm. per degree.

Suppose a wire of cross-sectional area A is fixed at one end O and twisted by applying a force F at the other end, Fig. 97. A line OQ on the wire is then displaced or sheared to the position OR through an angle a. The **modulus of rigidity**, n, of the wire is defined by the ratio "shearing stress/shearing strain", or

$$n = \frac{F/A}{a} \qquad \cdot \qquad \cdot \qquad \cdot \qquad \cdot \qquad (62)$$

The modulus of rigidity of quartz fibre is $3 \cdot 0 \times 10^{11}$ dynes per sq. cm.; for phosphor-bronze it is $4 \cdot 4 \times 10^{11}$ dynes per sq. cm.; for rubber it is $0 \cdot 00016 \times 10^{11}$ dynes per sq. cm. See also p. 192.

15. Poisson's Ratio.

When a rubber cord is extended its diameter usually decreases at the same time. *Poisson's ratio*, σ, is the name given to the ratio

$$\frac{\text{lateral contraction/original diameter}}{\text{longitudinal extension/original length}}, \qquad . \quad . \quad . \quad (63)$$

and is a constant for a given material. If the original length of a rubber strip is 100 cm. and it is stretched to 102 cm., the fractional longitudinal extension = 2/100. If the original diameter of the cord is 0·5 cm. and it decreases to 0·495 cm., the fractional lateral contraction = 0·005/0·5 = 1/100. Thus, from the definition of Poisson's ratio,

$$\sigma = \frac{1/100}{2/100} = \tfrac{1}{2}.$$

When the *volume* of a strip of material remains *constant* while an extension and a lateral contraction takes place, it can easily be shown that Poisson's ratio is 0·5 in this case. Thus suppose that the length of the strip is l and the radius is r.

Then   volume, $V, = \pi r^2 l.$

By differentiating both sides, noting that V is a constant and that we have a product of variables on the right side,

$$\therefore 0 = \pi r^2 \times \delta l + l \times 2\pi r\, \delta r$$

$$\therefore r\, \delta l = -2l\, \delta r$$

$$\therefore -\frac{\delta r/r}{\delta l/l} = \tfrac{1}{2}.$$

But $-\delta r/r$ is the lateral contraction in radius/original radius, and $\delta l/l$ is the longitudinal extension/original length.

$$\therefore \text{Poisson's ratio, } \sigma, = \tfrac{1}{2}.$$

Experiments show that σ is 0·48 for rubber, 0·29 for steel, 0·27 for iron, and 0·26 for copper. Thus the three metals increase in volume when stretched, whereas rubber remains almost unchanged in volume.

EXAMPLES

1. Define *stress, strain, Young's modulus.* Give a brief account of an experimental method for determining the value of Young's modulus for the material of a wire.

A weight of 20 kgm. hangs by a support 5 metres long compounded of two wires, respectively of brass and steel, each 5 metres long, joined at both ends. If the cross-sectional area of each wire is 0·01 sq. cm., by how much will the wires stretch when the weight is applied? [Young's modulus for steel = 20 × 10¹¹ c.g.s. units; for brass = 10 × 10¹¹ c.g.s. units.] (*C.*)

First part. See text.

Second part. The two wires stretch by the same amount, *e* cm. say.

Thus for the brass wire, from the formula $E = \dfrac{F/A}{e/l}$ (p. 138), we have

$$F = \frac{EAe}{l} = \frac{10 \times 10^{11} \times 0\cdot01 \times e}{500}, \quad . \quad \text{(i)}$$

where F is the applied force and $l = 5$ metres = 500 cm. Similarly, for the steel wire,

$$F_1 = \frac{EAe}{l} = \frac{20 \times 10^{11} \times 0\cdot01 \times e}{500}, \quad . \quad \text{(ii)}$$

where F_1 is the applied force on the steel wire. From (i) and (ii), it follows that

$$F_1 = 2F.$$

Also, $$F + F_1 = 20 \text{ kgm. wt.}$$

$$\therefore F + 2F = 20 \text{ kgm. wt., or } F = 6\tfrac{2}{3} \text{ kgm. wt.}$$

Substituting for F in dynes in (i),

$$\therefore 6\tfrac{2}{3} \times 1000 \times 980 = \frac{10 \times 10^{11} \times 0\cdot01 \times e}{500}.$$

$$\therefore e = \frac{20 \times 1000 \times 980 \times 500}{3 \times 10 \times 10^{11} \times 0\cdot01} = 0\cdot327 \text{ cm.}$$

2. Define *tensile stress, tensile strain, Young's modulus of elasticity.* Describe a method of measuring Young's modulus for a wire.

A mass of 10 kg. hangs from the lower end of a vertical steel wire whose upper end is fixed. Calculate the energy stored in the wire, the diameter of which is 1 mm. and the length 4 metres. (Young's modulus for steel = 2×10^{12} dyne cm.⁻²) (*L.*)

First part. For definitions and method of measurement, see text.

Second part. The energy stored in the wire = average force in wire × extension = $\tfrac{1}{2}Fe$.
With the usual notation,

$$\text{Young's modulus, } E = \frac{F/A}{e/l},$$

where *e* is the extension.

$$\therefore e = \frac{F \times l}{A \times E}$$

$$= \frac{10{,}000 \times 980 \times 400}{\pi(0\cdot05)^2 \times 2 \times 10^{12}} \text{ cm.,}$$

since $F = 10{,}000$ gm. wt. = $10{,}000 \times 980$ dynes.

$$\therefore \text{ energy stored } = \tfrac{1}{2}Fe$$

$$= \frac{10,000^2 \times 980^2 \times 400}{2 \times \pi(0.05)^2 \times 2 \times 10^{12}} \text{ ergs}$$

$$= 1.22 \times 10^6 \text{ ergs.}$$

3. State Hooke's law, and describe in detail how it may be verified experimentally for copper wire. A copper wire, 200 cm. long and 1·22 mm. diameter, is fixed horizontally to two rigid supports 200 cm. long. Find the mass in grams of the load which, when suspended at the mid-point of the wire, produces a sag of 2 cm. at that point. Young's modulus for copper $= 12.3 \times 10^{11}$ dyne cm.$^{-2}$ (L.)

First part. See text.

Second part. Suppose m is the mass in grams of the load at the mid-point O of the stretched wire AOC, Fig. 98. If T is the tension in the wire then, for vertical equilibrium,

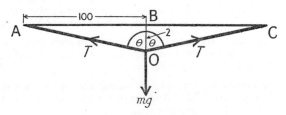

FIG. 98. (Not to scale.)

$$2T \cos \theta = mg, \quad \cdot \quad \cdot \quad \cdot \quad \cdot \quad \cdot \quad \text{(i)}$$

where θ = angle AOB. Now OB = 2 cm., AB = 100 cm. Thus

$$AO = \sqrt{100^2 + 2^2} = 100 \text{ cm.}$$

to a good approximation. Hence $\cos \theta = OB/OA = 2/100$. From (i),

$$\therefore 2T \times \frac{2}{100} = mg.$$

$$\therefore T = 25 \, mg \quad \cdot \quad \quad \text{(ii)}$$

Now Young's Modulus, E, is given by

$$E = \frac{T/A}{e/l},$$

or

$$T = EAe/l.$$

The extension $e = AOC - 200 = 2AO - 200$, and

$$AO = \sqrt{100^2 + 2^2} = 100 \left[1 + \left(\frac{2}{100} \right)^2 \right]^{\frac{1}{2}}.$$

$$= 100 \, [1 + 0.0004 \,]^{\frac{1}{2}} = 100 \, (1 + 0.0002).$$

$$= 100.02 \text{ cm.}$$

$$\therefore e = 200.04 - 200 = 0.04 \text{ cm.}$$

$$\therefore T = EA \times \frac{0.04}{200}$$

$$= 12 \cdot 3 \times 10^{11} \times \pi (0 \cdot 061)^2 \times \frac{0 \cdot 04}{200} \text{ dynes,}$$

since $r = 0 \cdot 061$ cm. From (ii), $T = 25 \times 980 \times m$.

$$\therefore m = \frac{12 \cdot 3 \times 10^{11} \times \pi (0 \cdot 061)^2 \times 0 \cdot 04}{25 \times 980 \times 200}.$$

$$= 117 \text{ gram wt.}$$

EXERCISES VII

1. Define *tensile stress, tensile strain, Young's modulus*. What are the units and dimensions of each?

A load of 2 kilograms is applied to the ends of a wire 4 metres long, and produces an extension of 0·24 mm. If the diameter of the wire is 2 mm., calculate the stress on the wire, its strain, and the value of Young's modulus.

2. What load in kilograms must be applied to a steel wire 6 metres long and diameter 1·6 mm. to produce an extension of 1 mm.? (Young's modulus for steel $= 2 \cdot 0 \times 10^{12}$ dynes per sq. cm.)

3. Find the extension produced in a copper wire of length 2 metres and diameter 3 mm. when a load of 3 kilograms is applied. (Young's modulus for copper $= 1 \cdot 1 \times 10^{12}$ dynes per cm.)

4. What is meant by (i) elastic limit, (ii) Hooke's law, (iii) yield point (iv) perfectly elastic? Draw sketches of stress v. strain to illustrate your answers.

5. Describe an experimental method for the determination of (a) Young's modulus, (b) the elastic limit, of a metal in the form of a thin wire.

A steel rod of mass 97·5 gm. and of length 50 cm. is heated to 200° C. and its ends securely clamped. Calculate the tension in the rod when its temperature is reduced to 0° C., explaining how the calculation is made. (Young's modulus for steel $= 2 \cdot 0 \times 10^{12}$ dyne cm.$^{-2}$; coefficient of linear expansion of steel $= 1 \cdot 1 \times 10^{-5}$ deg.$^{-1}$ C.; density of steel $= 7 \cdot 80$ gm. cm.$^{-3}$) (*L.*)

6. What do you understand by Hooke's law of elasticity? Describe how you would verify it in any particular case.

A wire of radius 0·2 mm. is extended by 0·1 per cent of its length when it supports a load of 1 kgm.; calculate Young's modulus for the material of the wire. (*L.*)

7. Explain in some detail how you would determine Young's modulus for a copper wire. Describe the behaviour of a copper wire as it is gradually loaded to just beyond the elastic limit and then gradually unloaded and reloaded to breaking point.

A steel rod of 1 in. diameter is heated to 200° C. and its ends are then fastened firmly to two rigid supports. Find, in tons wt., the tension in the rod when the temperature falls to 15° C. Assume that Young's modulus for steel is $1 \cdot 3 \times 10^4$ tons wt. per sq. in. and that the coefficient of linear expansion of steel is 12×10^{-6} per deg. C. (*N.*)

8. What is meant by saying that a substance is "elastic"?

A vertical brass rod of circular section is loaded by placing a 5 kilogramme weight on top of it. If its length is 50 cm., its radius of cross-section 1 cm., and the Young's modulus of the material $3 \cdot 5 \times 10^{11}$ dynes per sq. cm., find (a) the contraction of the rod, (b) the energy stored in it. (C.)

9. Give a short account of what happens when a copper wire is stretched under a gradually increasing load. What is meant by *modulus of elasticity, elastic limit, perfectly elastic?*
When a rubber cord is stretched the change in volume is very small compared with the change in shape. What will be the numerical value of Poisson's ratio for rubber, i.e., the ratio of the fractional decrease in diameter of the stretched cord to its fractional increase in length? (L.)

10. Describe an accurate method of determining Young's modulus for a wire. Detail the precautions necessary to avoid error, and estimate the accuracy attainable.
A steel tyre is heated and slipped on to a wheel of radius 40 cm. which it fits exactly at a temperature t° C. What is the maximum value of t if the tyre is not to be stretched beyond its elastic limit when it has cooled to air temperature (17° C.)? What will then be the tension in the tyre, assuming it to be 4 cm. wide and 3 mm. thick? The value of Young's modulus for steel is 2×10^4 kg. per sq. mm., its coefficient of linear expansion is $1 \cdot 1 \times 10^{-5}$ per ° C., and its elastic limit occurs for a tension of 28 kg. per sq. mm. The wheel may be assumed to be at air temperature throughout, and to be incompressible. (O. & C.)

11. Define *elastic limit, Young's modulus.*
What geometrical changes occur in a uniform wire when it is stretched within the limits in which Hooke's law is obeyed? Derive an expression for the energy stored in unit volume of a wire when stretched in this way.
If Young's modulus for steel is $2 \cdot 0 \times 10^{12}$ dyne cm.$^{-2}$, calculate its value in ton-wt. in.$^{-2}$ (Assume 1 ft. = $30 \cdot 5$ cm., 1 kgm. = $2 \cdot 20$ lb.) (L.)

12. Define *Young's modulus.* How would you measure it for the material of a wire? A stretched wire, 35 cm. long between bridges, vibrates with a frequency of 500 cycles per sec. when struck. By how much will this part of the wire contract if the stretching force is removed? The density of steel is $7 \cdot 9$ gm. cm.$^{-3}$; Young's modulus for steel is 2×10^{12} dyne cm.$^{-2}$ (L.)

13. Define Young's modulus of elasticity. Describe an accurate method of determining it. The rubber cord of a catapult is pulled back until its original length has been doubled. Assuming that the cross-section of the cord is 2 mm. square, and that Young's modulus for rubber is 10^8 c.g.s. calculate the tension in the cord. If the two arms of the catapult are 6 cm. apart, and the unstretched length of the cord is 8 cm. what is the stretching force? (O. & C.)

14. Define *Young's modulus.* Calculate Young's modulus for rubber if a rubber tube 40 cm. long, whose external and internal diameters are $1 \cdot 0$ cm. and $0 \cdot 40$ cm. respectively, extends $0 \cdot 60$ mm. when stretched by a force of 5 kgm. wt. Indicate how the data given in the problem may be obtained. (L.)

15. Define *Young's modulus of elasticity* and *coefficient of linear expansion.* State units in which each may be expressed and describe an experimental determination of Young's modulus.
For steel, Young's modulus is $1 \cdot 8 \times 10^{12}$ and the coefficient of expansion

$1 \cdot 1 \times 10^{-5}$, the units being based on cm., gm., sec. and ° C. A steel wire 1 mm. in diameter is stretched between two supports when its temperature is 200° C. By how much will the force the wire exerts on the supports increase when it cools to 20° C., if they do not yield? Express the answer in terms of the weight of a kilogram. (*L.*)

16. Define *elastic limit* and *Young's modulus* and describe how you would find their values for a copper wire.

What stress would cause a wire to increase in length by one-tenth of one per cent if Young's modulus for the wire is 12×10^{11} dynes per sq. cm.? What load in kgm. wt. would produce this stress if the diameter of the wire is 0·56 mm.? (*L.*)

17. Define *Young's modulus*. How would you measure its value for a specimen of steel wire?

A copper wire of diameter 2 mm. is suspended vertically, a light load being attached to the lower end. If the temperature of the wire falls from 20° C. to 0° C., calculate in grams weight the additional load that must be added to prevent alteration in the length of wire. (Young's modulus for copper = $1 \cdot 1 \times 10^{12}$ c.g.s.; coefficient of linear expansion of copper = 0·000018 per ° C.) (*L.*)

18. State Hooke's law and describe, with the help of a rough graph, the behaviour of a copper wire which hangs vertically and is loaded with a gradually increasing load until it finally breaks. Describe the effect of gradually reducing the load to zero (*a*) before, (*b*) after the elastic limit has been reached.

A uniform steel wire of density 7·8 gm. per c.c. weighs 16 gm. and is 250 cm. long. It lengthens by 1·2 mm. when stretched by a force of 8 kg. weight. Calculate (*a*) the value of Young's modulus for the steel, (*b*) the energy stored in the wire. (*N.*)

19. You are provided with a length of elastic cord, a set of known masses, a stop clock and the usual facilities of a physical laboratory. Describe how you would use them to find a value for the acceleration due to gravity and give the theory of the method.

The ends of a light elastic cord of natural length 200 cm. and diameter 2 mm. are attached to two points 200 cm. apart in a horizontal plane. Find to the nearest gram the mass which, when suspended in equilibrium from the mid-point of the cord, produces a depression of 10 cm. at this point and calculate the energy which would then be stored in the strained cord. Young's modulus for the material of the cord is $5 \cdot 0 \times 10^{8}$ dynes cm.$^{-2}$ (*N.*)

CHAPTER VIII

FRICTION IN SOLIDS AND LIQUIDS

OSMOSIS, DIFFUSION

1. Static Friction.

When a person walks along a road, he or she is prevented from slipping by the force of friction at the ground. In the absence of friction, for example on an icy surface, the person's shoe would slip backwards when placed on the ground. The frictional force, however, always *opposes* the motion.

The frictional force between the surface of a table and a block of wood A can be investigated by attaching one end of a string to A and the other to a scale-pan S, Fig. 99. The string passes over a fixed

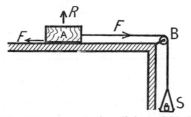

Fig. 99. Measurement of coefficient of friction.

grooved wheel B. When small weights are added to S, the block does not move. The frictional force between the block and table is thus equal to the total weight on S together with the weight of S. When more weights are added, A does not move, showing that the frictional force has increased, but as the weight is increased further, A suddenly begins to slip. The frictional force now present between the surfaces is called the *limiting frictional force*, and we are said to have reached *limiting friction*. The limiting frictional force is the maximum frictional force between the surfaces.

2. Coefficient of Static Friction.

The normal reaction, R, of the table on A is equal to the weight of A. By placing various weights on A to alter the magnitude of R, we can

F

find how the limiting frictional force F varies with R by the experiment just described. The results show that, approximately,

$$\frac{\text{limiting frictional force } (F)}{\text{normal reaction } (R)} = \mu, \text{ a constant,}$$

and μ is known as the *coefficient of static friction* between the two surfaces. The magnitude of μ depends on the nature of the two surfaces; for example, it is about 0·2 to 0·5 for wood on wood, and about 0·2 to 0·6 for wood on metals. Experiment also shows that the limiting frictional force is the same if the block A in Fig. 99 is turned on one side so that its surface area of contact with the table decreases, and thus the limiting frictional force is independent of the area of contact when the normal reaction is the same.

The coefficient of static friction, μ, can also be found by placing the block A on the surface S, and then gently tilting S until A is on the point of slipping down the plane, Fig. 100. The static frictional force F

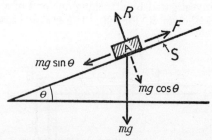

FIG. 100.   Coefficient of friction by inclined plane.

is then equal to $mg \sin \theta$, where θ is the angle of inclination of the plane to the horizontal; the normal reaction R is equal to $mg \cos \theta$.

$$\therefore \mu = \frac{F}{R} = \frac{mg \sin \theta}{mg \cos \theta} = \tan \theta,$$

and hence μ can be found by measuring θ.

3. Kinetic Friction.   Coefficient of Kinetic (Dynamic) Friction.

When the brakes are applied to the wheels of a train in motion, a frictional force is exerted between the brake block and the wheel which gradually slows the wheel down. While this happens, the frictional force between the two surfaces concerned is called a *kinetic (or dynamic) frictional force*. Generally kinetic friction occurs between two surfaces which have relative motion.

The *coefficient of kinetic (dynamic) friction*, μ', between two surface is defined by the relation

$$\mu' = \frac{F'}{R},$$

where F' is the frictional force when the object moves with a uniform velocity and R is the normal reaction between the surfaces. The coefficient of kinetic friction between a block A and a table can be found by the apparatus shown in Fig. 99.   Weights are added to the scale-pan, and each time A is given a slight push. At one stage A continues to move with a constant velocity, and the kinetic frictional force F' is then equal to the total weight in the scale-pan together with the latter's weight. On dividing F' by the weight of A, the coefficient can be calculated. Experiment shows that, when weights are placed on A to vary the normal reaction R, the magnitude of the ratio F'/R is approximately constant. Results also show that the cofficient of kinetic friction between two given surfaces is less than the coefficient of static friction between the same surfaces, and that the coefficient of kinetic friction between two given surfaces is approximately independent of their relative velocity.

4. Laws of Solid Friction.

Experimental results on solid friction are summarised in the *laws of friction*, which state:

(1) The frictional force between two surfaces opposes their relative motion.

(2) The frictional force is independent of the area of contact of the given surfaces when the normal reaction is constant.

(3) The limiting frictional force is proportional to the normal reaction for the case of static friction. The frictional force is proportional to the normal reaction for the case of kinetic (dynamic) friction, and is independent of the relative velocity of the surfaces.

These results are explained on p. 194.

5. Rope-Brake.

It is common knowledge that a rope wound several times round a cylindrical drum, for example, can sustain a powerful pull at one end by the application of a small force at the other end.

Suppose the rope is wound round a drum so that one end leaves it at X and the other end leaves it at Y, Fig. 101. If the tension T_1 at X is small and the tension T_2 at Y is large, the tension along the rope

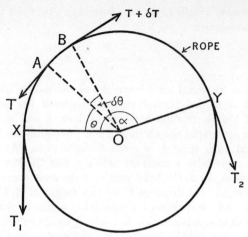

FIG. 101.   The rope-brake.

increases gradually from X to Y. Suppose AB is a small element of the rope subtending an angle $\delta\theta$ at the centre O, T is the tension at A, and $T + \delta T$ is the tension at B. Then the normal pressure R on the drum due to AB, which passes through O,

$$= (T + \delta T) \sin\frac{\delta\theta}{2} + T \sin\frac{\delta\theta}{2}$$

$$= T\frac{\delta\theta}{2} + T\frac{\delta\theta}{2} = T\delta\theta,$$

since $\delta\theta$ and δT are both very small.

If the rope is just on the point of slipping, the frictional force $F = \mu R$, where μ is the coefficient of static friction.

$$\therefore F = \mu T\delta\theta.$$

But $$F = (T + \delta T) \cos \delta\theta - T = \delta T,$$

considering equilibrium along the tangent at A.

$$\therefore \delta T = \mu T\delta\theta$$

$$\therefore \int_{T_1}^{T_2}\frac{dT}{T} = \mu \int_{o}^{} d\theta,$$

where a is the angle XOY.

$$\therefore \log_e\frac{T_2}{T_1} = \mu a$$

$$\therefore T_2 = T_1 e^{\mu a}$$

As an illustration, suppose the pull at X is 20 lb. wt., the frictional coefficient between the rope and drum is 0·3, and the rope is wound three times round the drum, so that $a = 6\pi$ radians.

$$\therefore T_2 = 20e^{\,1·8\pi} = 5700 \text{ lb. wt.}$$

Thus a pull of 5700 lb. wt. could be sustained by a pull of 20 lb. wt.

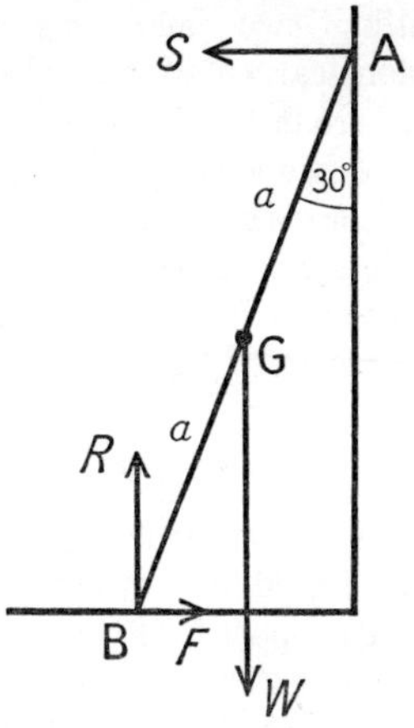

EXAMPLE

A uniform heavy ladder rests with its upper end against a smooth vertical wall. The bottom rests on rough horizontal ground, and is on the point of slipping when the ladder is 30° to the vertical. Calculate the coefficient of static friction between the bottom of the ladder and the ground.

FIG. 102.

Suppose F is the frictional force at the ground, R is the normal reaction there, S is the reaction at the wall acting perpendicular to the wall, W is the weight of the ladder acting at its mid-point G, and AB is the ladder of length $2a$, Fig. 102. Then, for vertical equilibrium,

$$R = W \qquad . \qquad . \qquad . \qquad . \qquad . \qquad \text{(i)}.$$

For horizontal equilibrium, $F = S$ . . . . .   ii).

Taking moments about B to find S in terms of W, we have

$$S \,.\, 2a \cos 30° = W \,.\, a \sin 30°.$$

$$\therefore S = \frac{W}{2}\tan 30°.$$

$$\therefore F = \frac{W}{2}\tan 30°, \text{ from (ii).}$$

But coefficient of friction, μ, $= \dfrac{F}{R}.$

$$\therefore \mu = \frac{W}{2}\tan 30°/W = \tfrac{1}{2}\tan 30°.$$

$$\therefore \mu = 0·29.$$

VISCOSITY OF LIQUIDS

If we move through a pool of water we experience a resistance to our motion. This shows that there is a *frictional force* in liquids, and in this connection we refer to the **viscosity** of the liquid. If the frictional force is comparatively low, as in water, the viscosity of the liquid is low; if the frictional force is large, as in glue or glycerine, the viscosity of the liquid is high. We can compare roughly the viscosity of two liquids by filling two measuring cylinders with each of them, and allowing identical small steel ball-bearings to fall through each liquid. The sphere falls more slowly through the liquid of higher viscosity.

As we shall see later, the viscosity of a lubricating oil is one of the factors which decide whether it is suitable for use in an engine. The Ministry of Aircraft Production, for example, listed viscosity values to which lubricating oils for aero-engines must conform. The subject of viscosity has thus considerable practical importance.

6. Newton's Formula. Coefficient of Viscosity.

When water flows slowly and steadily through a pipe, the layer A of the liquid in contact with the pipe is practically stationary, but the central part C of the water is moving relatively fast, Fig. 103. At other

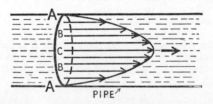

FIG. 103.   Velocity of layers of liquid in pipe.

layers between A and C, such as B, the water has a velocity less than at C, the magnitude of the velocities being represented by the length of the arrowed lines in Fig. 103. Now as in the case of two solid surfaces moving over each other, a frictional force is exerted between two liquid layers when they move over each other. Thus because the velocities of neighbouring layers are different, as shown in Fig. 103, a frictional force occurs between the various layers of a liquid when flowing through a pipe.

The basic formula for the frictional force, F, in a liquid was first suggested by NEWTON. He saw that the larger the *area* of the surface of liquid considered, the greater was the frictional force F. He also stated that F was directly proportional to the *velocity gradient* at the part of the liquid considered. If v_1, v_2 are the velocities of C, B respectively in Fig. 103, and h is their distance apart, the velocity gradient between the liquids is defined as $(v_1 - v_2)/h$. The velocity gradient can thus be expressed in (cm. per sec.)/cm., or as "sec.$^{-1}$"

Thus if A is the area of the liquid surface considered, the frictional force F on the surface is given by

$$F \propto A \times \text{velocity gradient},$$

or $$F = \eta A \times \text{velocity gradient}, \quad . \quad . \quad . \quad (64)$$

where η is a constant of the liquid known as the *coefficient of viscosity*. This expression for the frictional force in a liquid should be contrasted with the case of solid friction, in which the frictional force is independent of the area of contact and of the relative velocity between the solid surfaces concerned (p. 155).

7. Definition, Units, and Dimensions of Coefficient of Viscosity.

The magnitude of η is given by

$$\eta = \frac{F}{A \times \text{velocity gradient}}.$$

The unit of F is a dyne, the unit of A is a sq. cm., and the unit of velocity gradient is (1 cm. per sec.)/cm. Thus η may be defined as *the frictional force in dynes exerted on 1 square centimetre of a liquid when it is in a region of unit velocity gradient.*

From above, the unit of η is "dynes per sq. cm. per unit velocity gradient", or briefly "c.g.s. unit"; this unit is called a *poise*. The coefficient of viscosity of water at 10° C. is 0·013 poises, at 10° C. mercury has a coefficient of 0·016 poises, at 10° C. glycerine has a coefficient of 21·0 poises, and black treacle has a coefficient of 400 poises at 12·3° C. Since $F = \eta A \times$ velocity gradient, the frictional force over an area of 10 sq. cm. in water at 10° C. between two layers of water 0·1 cm. apart which move with a relative velocity of 2 cm. per sec. is given by

$$F = 0{\cdot}013 \times 10 \times \frac{2}{0{\cdot}1} = 2{\cdot}6 \text{ dynes.}$$

Dimensions. The dimensions of a force, F, (= mass $\times$ acceleration = mass $\times$ velocity change/time) are $[M] [L] [T]^{-2}$. See p. 25. The dimensions of an area, A, are $[L]^2$. The dimensions of velocity gradient

$$= \frac{\text{velocity change}}{\text{distance}} = \frac{[L]}{[T]} \div [L] = \frac{1}{[T]}$$

Now $$\eta = \frac{F}{A \times \text{velocity gradient}}$$

$$\therefore \text{dimensions of } \eta = \frac{[M] [L] [T]^{-2}}{[L]^2 \times 1/[T]}$$

$$= [M] [L]^{-1} [T]^{-1}$$

8. Steady Flow of Liquid Through Pipe. Poiseuille's Formula.

The steady flow of liquid through a pipe was first investigated thoroughly by POISEUILLE in 1844, who derived an expression for the volume of liquid issuing per second from the pipe. The proof of the formula is given on p. 162, but we can derive most of the formula by the *method of dimensions* (p. 25).

The volume of liquid issuing per second from the pipe depends on (i) the coefficient of viscosity, η, (ii) the radius, a, of the pipe, (iii) the *pressure gradient*, g, set up along the pipe. The pressure gradient $= p/l$, where p is the pressure difference between the ends of the pipe and l is its length. Thus x, y, z being indices which require to be found, suppose

$$\text{volume per sec.} = k\eta^x a^y g^z \quad . \quad . \quad . \quad . \quad (i)$$

Now the dimensions of volume per sec. are $[L]^3/[T]$; the dimensions of η are $[M]/[L]\,[T]$, see p. 159; the dimension of a is $[L]$; and the dimensions of g are

$$\frac{[\text{pressure}]}{[\text{length}]}, \text{ or } \frac{[\text{force}]}{[\text{area}]\,[\text{length}]}, \text{or } \frac{[M]\,[L]}{[T^2]\,[L]^2\,[L]}.$$

Thus from (i), equating dimensions on both sides,

$$\frac{[L]^3}{[T]} = \frac{[M]^x}{[L]^x[T]^x}\,[L]^y\,\frac{[M]^z.}{[L]^{2z}[T]^{2z}}$$

Equating the respective indices of $[M]$, $[L]$, $[T]$ on both sides, we have

$$x + z = 0,$$
$$- x + y - 2z = 3$$
$$x + 2z = 1$$

Solving, we obtain $x = -1$, $z = 1$, $y = 4$. Hence, from (i),

$$\text{volume per sec.} = k\,\frac{a^4 g}{\eta} = k\frac{pa^4}{l\eta}.$$

We cannot obtain the numerical factor k from the method of dimensions. As shown on p. 162, the factor of $\pi/8$ enters into the formula, which is:

$$\textbf{Volume per second} = \frac{\pi p a^4}{8\eta l} \quad . \quad . \quad . \quad . \quad . \quad (65)$$

9. Turbulent Motion.

Poiseuille's formula holds as long as the velocity of each layer of the liquid is parallel to the axis of the pipe and the flow pattern has been developed. As the pressure difference between the ends of the pipe is increased, a critical velocity is reached at some stage, and the motion of the liquid changes from an orderly to a *turbulent* one. Poiseuille's formula does not apply to turbulent motion.

The onset of turbulence was first demonstrated by O. REYNOLDS in 1883, and was shown by placing a horizontal tube T, about 0·5 cm. in diameter, at the bottom of a tank W of water, Fig. 104 (i). The flow of water along T is controlled by a clip C on rubber tubing connected to T. A drawn-out glass jet B, attached to a reservoir A containing coloured

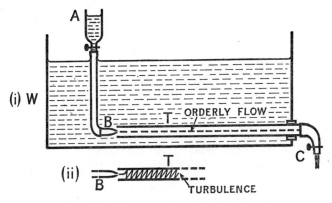

FIG. 104.   Demonstration of turbulent motion.

water, is placed at one end of T, and at low velocities of flow a thin coloured stream of water is observed flowing along the middle of T. As the rate of flow of the water along T is increased, a stage is reached when the colouring in T begins to spread out and fill the whole of the tube, Fig. 104 (ii). The critical velocity has now been exceeded, and turbulence has begun.

10. Analogy with Ohm's Law.

For orderly flow along a pipe, Poiseuille's formula in equation (65) states:

$$\text{Volume per second flowing} = \frac{\pi p a^4}{8 \eta l}$$

$$= \frac{p \times \pi a^2}{8 \pi \eta \times \dfrac{l}{\pi a^2}}.$$

Now $p \times \pi a^2 =$ excess pressure $\times$ area of cross-section of liquid $=$

excess force F on liquid, and $l/\pi a^2 = l/A$, where A is the area of cross-section.

$$\therefore \text{ volume per second flowing} = \frac{F}{8\pi\eta \times \dfrac{l}{A}} \qquad \cdot \qquad \cdot \qquad \cdot \qquad \text{(i)}$$

The volume of liquid per second is analogous to electric current (I) if we compare the case of electricity flowing along a conductor, and the excess force F is analogous to the potential difference (V) along the conductor. Also, the resistance R of the conductor $= \rho l/A$, where ρ is its resistivity, l is its length, and A is the cross-sectional area. Since, from Ohm's law, $I = V/R$, it follows from (i) that

$$8\pi\eta \text{ is analogous to } \rho, \text{ the resistivity;}$$

that is, the coefficient of viscosity η is a measure of the "resistivity" of a liquid in orderly flow.

11. Proof of Poiseuille's Formula. Suppose a pipe of radius a has a liquid flowing steadily along it. Consider a cylinder of the liquid of radius r having the same axis as the pipe, where r is less than a. Then the force on this cylinder due to the excess pressure $p = p \times \pi r^2$. We can imagine the cylinder to be made up of cylindrical *shells*; the force on the cylinder due to viscosity is the algebraic sum of the viscous forces on these shells. The force on one shell is given by $\eta A dv/dr$, where dv/dr is the corresponding velocity gradient and A is the surface area of the shell. And although dv/dr changes as we proceed from the narrowest shell outwards, the forces on the neighbouring shells cancel each other out, by the law of action and reaction, leaving a net force of $\eta A dv/dr$, where dv/dr is the velocity gradient at the surface of the cylinder. The viscous force on the cylinder, and the force on it due to the excess pressure p, are together zero since there is no acceleration of the liquid, i.e., we have orderly flow.

$$\therefore \eta A \frac{dv}{dr} + \pi r^2 p = 0$$

$$\therefore \eta \cdot 2\pi r l \frac{dv}{dr} + \pi r^2 p = 0,$$

since $A = 2\pi r l$.

$$\therefore \frac{dv}{dr} = -\frac{pr}{2\eta l}$$

$$\therefore v = -\frac{p}{4\eta l} r^2 + c,$$

where c is a constant. Since $v = 0$ when $r = a$, at the surface of the tube, $c = pa^2/4\eta l$.

$$\therefore v = \frac{p}{4\eta l} (a^2 - r^2) \qquad \cdot \qquad \cdot \qquad \cdot \qquad \text{(i)}$$

Consider a cylindrical shell of the liquid between radii r and $(r + \delta r)$.

The liquid in this shell has a velocity v given by the expression in (i), and the volume per second of liquid flowing along this shell $= v \times$ cross-sectional area of shell, since v is the distance travelled in one second, $= v \times 2\pi r \,.\, \delta r$.

∴ total volume of liquid per second along tube

$$= \int_{o}^{a} v \,.\, 2\pi r \,.\, dr$$

$$= \int \frac{p}{4\eta l} \,(a^2 - r^2)\,.\,2\pi r\,.\,dr$$

$$= \frac{\pi p a^4}{8\eta l}.$$

12. Determination of Viscosity by Poiseuille's Formula.

The viscosity of a liquid such as water can be measured by connecting one end of a capillary tube T to a constant pressure apparatus A, which provides a *steady* flow of liquid, Fig. 105. By means of a beaker B

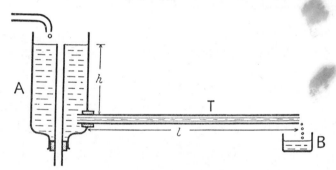

Fig. 105.   Viscosity by Poiseuille's method.

and a stop-clock, the volume of water per second flowing through the tube can be measured. The pressure difference between the ends of T is $h \rho g$ dynes per sq. cm., where h is the pressure head, ρ is the density of the liquid, and g is 980.

$$\therefore \text{ volume per second} = \frac{\pi p a^4}{8\eta l} = \frac{\pi h \rho g a^4}{8\eta l},$$

where l is the length of T and a is its radius. The radius of the tube can be measured by means of a mercury thread or by a microscope. The coefficient of viscosity η can then be calculated, since all the other quantities in the above equation are known.

13. Comparison of Viscosities.   Ostwald Viscometer.

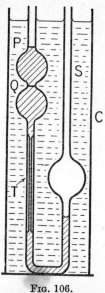

An Ostwald viscometer, which contains a vertical capillary tube T, is widely used for comparing the viscosities of two liquids, Fig. 106. The liquid is introduced at S, drawn by suction above P, and the time t_1 taken for the liquid level to fall between the fixed marks P, Q is observed. The experiment is then repeated with the *same volume* of a second liquid, and the time t_2 for the liquid level to fall from P to Q is noted.

Suppose the liquids have respective densities ρ_1, ρ_2. Then, since the average head h of liquid forcing it through T is the same in each case, the pressure excess between the ends of T $=$ $h\rho_1 g$, $h\rho_2 g$ respectively. If the volume between the marks P, Q is V, then, from Poiseuille's formula, we have

$$\frac{V}{t_1} = \frac{\pi(h\rho_1 g)a^4}{8\eta_1 l} \qquad \cdots \qquad \text{(i)},$$

FIG. 106.
Ostwald viscometer.

where a is the radius of T, η_1 is the coefficient of viscosity of the liquid, and l is the length of T. Similarly, for the second liquid,

$$\frac{V}{t_2} = \frac{\pi(h\rho_2 g)a^4}{8\eta_2 l} \qquad \cdots \qquad \text{(ii)}$$

Dividing (ii) by (i),

$$\therefore \ \frac{t_1}{t_2} = \frac{\eta_1 \rho_2}{\eta_2 \rho_1}.$$

$$\therefore \ \frac{\eta_1}{\eta_2} = \frac{t_1}{t_2} \cdot \frac{\rho_1}{\rho_2} \qquad \cdots \qquad \text{(iii)}$$

Thus knowing t_1, t_2 and the densities ρ_1, ρ_2, the coefficients of viscosity can be compared. Further, if a pure liquid of a known viscosity is used, the viscometer can be used to measure the coefficient of viscosity of a liquid. Since the viscosity varies with temperature, the viscometer should be used in a cylinder C and surrounded by water at a constant temperature, Fig. 106. The arrangement can then also be used to investigate the variation of viscosity with temperature. In very accurate work a small correction is required in equation (iii). BARR, an authority on viscosity, estimates that nearly 90% of petroleum oil is tested by an Ostwald viscometer.

Experiment shows that the viscosity coefficient of a liquid diminishes as its temperature rises. The table shows some results for the viscosity coefficient of water at various temperatures.

TEMPERATURE ° C.	η (POISES)
0	0·179
10	0·013
15	0·011
30	0·008
50	0·006

14. Stokes' Law.   Terminal Velocity.

When a small object, such as a steel ball-bearing, is dropped into a viscous liquid like glycerine it accelerates at first, but its velocity soon reaches a steady value known as the *terminal velocity*. In this case the viscous force acting upwards, and the upthrust due to the liquid on the object, are together equal to its weight acting downwards, so that the resultant force on the object is zero. An object dropped from an aeroplane at first increases its speed, but soon reaches its terminal speed.

Suppose a sphere of radius a is dropped into a viscous liquid of coefficient of viscosity η, and its velocity at an instant is v. The frictional force, F, can be partly found by the method of dimensions. Thus suppose $F = ka^x \eta^y v^z$, where k is a constant. The dimensions of F are [M] [L] [T]$^{-2}$; the dimension of a is [L]; the dimensions of η are [M] [L]$^{-1}$ [T]$^{-1}$; and the dimensions of v are [L] [T]$^{-1}$.

$$\therefore [M] [L] [T]^{-2} = [L]^x \times [M]^y [L]^{-y} [T]^{-y} \times [L]^z [T]^{-z}.$$

Equating indices of [M], [L], [T] on both sides,

$$\therefore y = 1,$$
$$x - y + z = 1,$$
$$- y - z = - 2.$$

Hence $z = 1$, $x = 1$, $y = 1$. Consequently $F = k\eta av$. In 1850 STOKES showed mathematically that the constant k was 6π, and he arrived at the formula

$$F = 6\pi a \eta v \qquad . \qquad . \qquad . \qquad (66)$$

15. Comparison of Viscosities of Viscous Liquids.

Stokes' formula can be used to compare the coefficients of viscosity

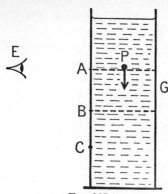

Fig. 107.
Viscosity by falling sphere.

of very viscous liquids such as glycerine or treacle. A tall glass vessel G is filled with the liquid, and a small ball-bearing P is dropped gently into the liquid so that it falls along the axis of G, Fig. 107. Towards the middle of the liquid P reaches its terminal velocity v_0, which is measured by timing its fall through a distance AB or BC.

The upthrust on P due to the liquid $= \frac{4}{3}\pi a^3 \sigma g$, where a is the radius of P and σ is the density of the liquid. The weight of P is $\frac{4}{3}\pi a^3 \rho g$, where ρ is the density of the bearing's material. Since the resultant force is zero when the terminal velocity v_0 is reached,

$$\therefore \frac{4}{3}\pi a^3 \sigma g + 6\pi a \eta v_0 = \frac{4}{3}\pi a^3 \rho g$$

Solving for η,
$$\therefore \eta = \frac{2ga^2(\rho - \sigma)}{9v_0} \qquad . \quad . \quad \text{(i)}$$

When the experiment is repeated with a liquid of coefficient of viscosity η_1 and density σ_1, using the same ball-bearing, then

$$\eta_1 = \frac{2ga^2(\rho - \sigma_1)}{9v_1} \qquad . \quad . \quad \text{(ii)}$$

where v_1 is the new terminal velocity. Dividing (i) by (ii),

$$\therefore \frac{\eta}{\eta_1} = \frac{v_1(\rho - \sigma)}{v_0(\rho - \sigma_1)} \qquad . \quad . \quad \text{(iii)}$$

Thus knowing v_1, v, ρ, σ_1, σ, the coefficients of viscosity can be compared. In very accurate work a correction to (iii) is required for the effect of the walls of the vessel containing the liquid.

16. Viscosity and Lubrication.

When two metal surfaces slide over each other, a considerable wear and tear of metal occurs. Lubricating oil separates the moving metal parts and reduces the frictional force considerably. Thus when a shaft rotates in a lubricated bearing, for example, a very thin film of oil exists between the metal surfaces; the layer of oil in contact with the stationary bearing is then at rest, the layer in contact with the moving shaft travels at the same speed, while intermediate layers have intermediate speeds. The force on the shaft, and the efficiency of the engine, will thus be affected by the *viscosity* of the oil, among other factors.

The viscosity of a lubricating oil must generally be low when it is cold, so that the engine can start easily. When the engine has been running for a time it becomes hot, and as the oil temperature then rises the viscosity of the oil diminishes (p. 165). If the oil viscosity is suitable at a low temperature, but decreases *rapidly* with temperature, the oil becomes unsuitable as the engine is running. Consequently a good lubricating oil is one whose viscosity decreases very slightly with temperature. It can now be seen that measurements of viscosity, and of the variation of viscosity with temperature, are essential in judging whether a lubricating oil is suitable for an engine. The variation of viscosity with pressure is also measured, as the oil is subjected to considerable pressure when the machine is moving.

Viscosity measurements are also used by chemists to find the molecular weight and shape of large organic molecules such as proteins and cellulose.

OSMOSIS

17. Semi-Permeable Membranes.

If a sugar solution contained inside an inverted funnel F by a parchment sheet P is placed in a vessel of pure water at the same temperature, the level of the liquid in F rises to some height h above the level of the water in the vessel, Fig. 108. The water has thus passed through the

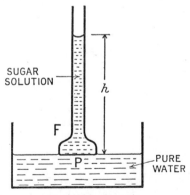

SUGAR
SOLUTION

h

F

P

PURE
WATER

FIG. 108. Osmosis.

parchment; but no sugar can be detected in the water in the vessel, so that the parchment only allows water molecules to pass through it and not sugar molecules. The parchment is called a *semi-permeable membrane* because it allows the solvent (water) to pass through it but not the solute (sugar). This phenomenon is known as **osmosis** after the greek word for "push", and the pressure $h\rho g$, where ρ is the density of the sugar solution, measures the **osmotic pressure** of the solution. The osmotic pressure may be defined as that pressure required to stop the passage of the solvent through a semi-permeable membrane into the solution.

Dried fruit swells when placed in water; this is an example of osmosis, the skin of the fruit acting as a semi-permeable membrane. For a similar reason, the skin of the fingers crinkle if they are placed in a strong soda solution. The cells of living plants and animals have semi-permeable membranes which allow water to pass through them; these membranes play an important part in maintaining the required concentration of salt solution in their systems, for example. The theory of osmosis is still not clearly understood.

18. Laws of Osmotic Pressure.

The first accurate investigations into osmotic pressure were carried out by PFEFFER about 1877. He placed a porous pot containing copper sulphate solution in potassium ferrocyanide solution, so that a strong semi-permeable membrane of copper ferrocyanide was formed in the pores of the pot. After filling the pot, P, with a known concentration of sugar solution he connected it to a uniform capillary tube containing nitrogen, sealed by a mercury column in a U-tube M, Fig. 109.

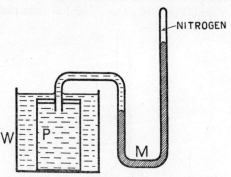

FIG. 109.   Measurement of osmotic pressure.

When the pot is placed in a vessel, W, of pure water at the same temperature, the nitrogen is compressed to a volume depending on the magnitude of the osmotic pressure. Having found the volume of nitrogen under atmospheric pressure, Pfeffer was easily able to calculate the osmotic pressure from Boyle's law. In this way he found that the osmotic pressure p increased as the concentration C increased. The following table shows some results obtained later for cane-sugar:

CONCENTRATION (C)	OSMOTIC PRESSURE (p)	VOLUME (V) OF GRAM-MOL.	PRODUCT pV
Gm./litre	Atm.	Litres	
2·02	0·134	169·3	22·7
10·0	0·66	34·2	22·6
20·0	1·32	17·1	22·6
45·0	2·97	7·60	22·6
93·75	6·18	3·65	22·5

19. Van't Hoff's Deductions.

Van't Hoff, in 1887, studied Pfeffer's results, and saw that *the osmotic pressure (p) is proportional to the concentration (C)* of the solute. From the above results, for example, $p/C = 0.066$ in each of the five cases. Now the concentration, C, $\propto 1/V$, where V is the volume of the solution. Hence, since p/C is a constant for the solution, it follows that

$$pV = \text{constant} \quad . \quad . \quad . \quad (67)$$

This result is similar to Boyle's law for gases. Van't Hoff, who first deduced the relation, then proposed the theory that the molecules of the solute (sugar for example) could be considered to move about in the solution and exert a pressure (osmotic pressure), just as the molecules of a gas exert a pressure.

Some years later, experiments were carried out on the variation of the osmotic pressure, p, with temperature for a given sugar concentration. For this purpose the solution in Fig. 109 was warmed to different temperatures, and the experiment described on p. 168 was carried out each time. Some results are shown below for the osmotic pressure variation with temperature of a solution containing 0·3 gram-molecule of sugar per litre of water:

OSMOTIC PRESSURE (p)	TEMPERATURE	$\dfrac{p}{\text{ABSOLUTE TEMP.}}$ (T)
Atm.		
7·085	0° C.	0·026
7·334	10° C.	0·026
7·605	20° C.	0·026
7·729	25° C.	0·026

Van't Hoff showed that, for dilute solutions,

$$p \propto T, \quad . \quad . \quad . \quad . \quad . \quad (68)$$

where T is the absolute temperature. This is exactly analogous to the law obeyed by the pressure of a given gas at constant volume when its temperature is altered.

20. Volume of Gram-Molecular Weight of Solute.

From the results given in the table on p. 169, 102·6 grams of cane-sugar in 1,000 c.c. of water at 10° C. has an osmotic pressure of 7·33 atmospheres. Now the gram-molecular weight of cane-sugar is 342 grams. Thus 1 gram-molecular weight of sugar in 1,000 c.c. of water at 10° C. has an osmotic pressure of 7·33 × 342/102·6 atmospheres. Hence the volume occupied by the gram-molecular weight at S.T.P. (0° C. and 1 atmosphere pressure)

$$= 1 \times \frac{7 \cdot 33 \times 342}{102 \cdot 6} \times \frac{273}{283} = 22 \cdot 4 \text{ litres.}$$

But 22·4 litres is the volume occupied by 1 gram-molecular weight of any *gas* at S.T.P. *Thus the osmotic pressure of a dilute solution is equal to the pressure which the dissolved substance would exert if it were a gas,* and we can therefore apply all the gas laws to the dilute solution. The molecular weights of compounds of very high molecular weight, such as proteins or synthetic and natural rubber, have been determined by measuring the osmotic pressure of a solution of known concentration, and then calculating the weight which would exert a pressure of 1 atmosphere at 0° C. when the volume of the solution is 22·4 litres.

Experiments by Van't Hoff also showed that the osmotic pressures of dilute salt and mineral acid solutions were two or three times as great as that expected. This lent support to the *theory of dissociation* proposed by Arrhenius, which stated that acids and salts produce electrified particles (*ions*) in solution. Each molecule produces two or three ions, and thus the osmotic pressure is two or three times as great as that exerted if only molecules were present in the solution. Further discussion of Osmosis is outside the scope of this book, and the interested reader should refer to text-books such as Glasstone's *Physical Chemistry.*

DIFFUSION

21 Diffusion of Liquids.

If pure water is poured carefully on to a concentrated solution of copper sulphate in a beaker, a line of demarcation between the blue and the colourless liquids can be seen. When the beaker is left for a week the liquid becomes almost uniformly blue, showing that the copper sulphate molecules had intermingled with the water molecules. We say that the copper sulphate *diffused* into the water, and the phenomenon is known as *diffusion*. It is due to the mobility of the molecules of a liquid.

22. Graham's Experiments.

GRAHAM was one of the first to investigate the phenomenon of diffusion. In 1851 he placed a jar P containing a salt solution inside a wide beaker Q containing pure water, Fig. 110. The cover over P was than slid off, and after known intervals of time samples of the liquid in Q were drawn off by a pipette and analysed. In this way Graham found that (i) solutions of different salts diffuse at a different rate, (ii) salt solutions of different strengths diffuse at a rate proportional to their strength, (iii) the rate of diffusion of a solution increases with the temperature.

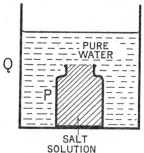

FIG. 110. Graham's experiment on diffusion.

Graham also found that substances could be divided into two classes. Albumen and gelatine solutions, for example, diffuse at a much slower rate than salt and acid solutions, and are known as **colloids**; salt and acid solutions are known as **crystalloids**.

23. Fick's Law of Diffusion.

In 1855 FICK proposed a law of diffusion, now generally accepted. This states:

The quantity per second (Q/sec.) of a solute flowing between two liquids is proportional to the area, the time, and the gradient of the concentration.

Thus

$$Q/\text{sec.} = kA\frac{c_1 - c_2}{x}, \quad . \quad . \quad . \quad . \quad (69)$$

where A is the area in sq. cm., c_1, c_2 are the concentrations in gm. per c.c. at planes a distance x cm. apart, and k is a constant known as the *coefficient of diffusion*. Since the "concentration gradient" can be written as dc/dx, the quantity per second, Q/sec., $= kAdc/dx$ from (69). Fick was led to propose this law after a study of the work of Fourier on the conduction of heat some years before, in which it was stated that the quantity of heat per second flowing through a section of a conductor in the steady state was proportional to the area of the section and to the temperature gradient. On the molecular theory, however, we now recognise that conduction of heat is a transfer of energy of the molecules, whereas diffusion is a transfer of the mass of the molecules.

The determination of the coefficient of diffusion cannot be performed by drawing off samples of the liquid at different places, because this would disturb the concentration gradient. Lord Kelvin got over the difficulty by using floating balls of known density, and observing their positions. In this way it was poss ble to determine the concentration gradient and the quantity of solute iflowing in the given time. The most accurate method, however, is an optical method, in which it is possible to measure the refractive index of the liquid while diffusion takes place, without disturbing the liquid. The concentration can be deduced from a knowledge of the refractive index by a previous calibration experiment. Modern technique utilises very thin layers of liquids so that the concentration gradient is high, and the concentration gradient and quantity of solute at points are determined by means of a photometric method.

24. Diffusion and Effusion of Gases.

A gas-jar of air, inverted over a jar of carbon dioxide, soon shows the presence of carbon dioxide, although the latter is heavier than air. Diffusion has thus taken place.

The term *effusion* refers to the passage of a gas through a hole whose diameter is less than the mean free path (average distance between successive collisions) of the molecules. Effusion can be studied by connecting a sealed pot P containing air to a manometer M containing oil, Fig. 111. When P is surrounded by a vessel Q containing carbon dioxide gas, the level of the oil on the left side of M rises, showing that the rate of effusion of air from P is greater than the rate of effusion of carbon dioxide into P. When P

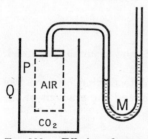

Fig. 111.   Effusion of gases.

is surrounded by a vessel containing hydrogen, in place of carbon dioxide, the liquid level on the left of M falls, showing that the rate of effusion of hydrogen into P is greater than the rate of effusion of air out of P. By testing samples of the gases at various times Graham found that:

The rate of effusion of a gas is inversely proportional to the square root of its density. This is known as *Graham's law.*

The relative densities of hydrogen and carbon dioxide are $1 : 22$. Thus if a porous pot with hydrogen is placed in a vessel with carbon dioxide, the rates of effusion of the two gases initially are $\sqrt{22} : \sqrt{1}$; the hydrogen thus effuses into the carbon dioxide about 4·3 times as fast as the carbon dioxide effuses into the hydrogen. The concentration of hydrogen in the upper jar thus diminishes, whilst that in the lower jar increases. After a time there is a uniform concentration of the mixture of gases in both jars.

25. Separation of Gases by Effusion.

Graham saw that a mixture of gases could be separated by an effusion method. He surrounded a clay (porous) pipe P by a tube Q which was sealed, and then passed a mixture of air, carbon dioxide and oxygen through P, Fig. 112. As oxygen is the lighter gas it effuses faster

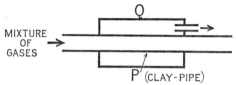

FIG. 112.   Separation of gases by effusion method.

through P into Q. In this way Graham obtained in Q air which had a relatively higher percentage of oxygen than ordinary air. This process of separating gases is known as **atmolysis**, and it was used by Ramsey in 1899 in his early attempt to isolate helium from the air. Having eliminated the oxygen from a sample of air, he passed the nitrogen and helium remaining along a porous pipe stem. Helium passed through the pipe at a rate of $\sqrt{28/4}$ or 2·6 times as fast as the nitrogen, and the process was repeated with the issuing gas, thus obtaining a mixture richer in helium than at the outset.

"Heavy hydrogen" or **deuterium** is an isotope of hydrogen which has a mass of two, and is present in hydrogen with the much more plentiful hydrogen of mass one. UREY first isolated heavy hydrogen in 1931, using an effusion method; the relative rates of effusion of the two isotopes are $\sqrt{2} : \sqrt{1}$, or 1·4 : 1, from Graham's law. The separation of isotopes by effusion is a slow process, but an electrolytic method is quicker. The mobility of heavy hydrogen ions in dilute acid solutions is less than those of mass one as the former are larger and heavier, and thus the concentration of heavy hydrogen in the solution increases as electrolysis takes place.

EXERCISES VIII

Friction. Viscosity

1. Define *coefficient of sliding friction, coefficient of viscosity.* Contrast the laws of solid friction with those which govern the flow of liquids through tubes.

Sketch the apparatus you would employ to determine the coefficient of sliding friction between a wood block and a board and show how you would deduce the coefficient from a suitable graph. (*L.*)

2. A friction band is wrapped round a pulley (radius 10 cm.) attached to an electric motor. One end of the band supports a 2 kgm. weight, and the other is fastened to the hook of a spring dynamometer which is anchored to the floor. When the motor is running the band supports the weight in a stationary position and the dynamometer reads 200 gm. wt. If the motor makes 1,200 revolutions per minute what is its power output in watts? Give a diagram of the arrangement showing the direction of rotation. (*L.*)

3. Explain what is meant by the *dimensions* of a physical quantity in mass, length and time. Find the dimensions of *weight, velocity gradient, coefficient of viscosity.*

A small sphere of radius *r*, falling under gravity through a fluid of coefficient of viscosity η, ultimately attains a steady or terminal velocity *v*. Apply the method of dimensions to determine how *v* depends upon *r*, η, and *w*, where *w* is the effective weight of the sphere in the fluid, i.e., the difference between the true weight and the upward thrust due to the displaced fluid. (*O. & C.*)

4. Define *coefficient of viscosity.* For orderly flow of a given liquid through a capillary tube of length *l*, radius *r*, the volume of liquid issuing per sec. is proportional to pr^4/l where *p* is the pressure difference between the ends of the tube. How would you verify this relation experimentally for water at room temperature? How would you detect the onset of turbulence? (*N.*)

5. State the laws of friction between dry solid surfaces, and define *coefficient of friction.* Describe very briefly one method for finding this coefficient for two given surfaces, for example, a cardboard surface and the surface of a table.

A mass projected along the surface of a horizontal table, 3·2 ft. above floor-level, with an initial speed of 9 ft./sec., travels 4 ft. on the table surface and a further horizontal distance of 18 ins. beyond the edge of the table before striking the floor. At what inclination of the table would the same mass slide without acceleration? (*W.*)

6. Define *coefficient of viscosity.* What are its dimensions?

By the method of dimensions, deduce how the rate of flow of a viscous liquid through a narrow tube depends upon the viscosity, the radius of the tube, and the pressure difference per unit length. Explain how you would use your results to compare the coefficients of viscosity of glycerine and water. (*C.*)

7. Distinguish between *static* and *sliding* (kinetic) friction and define the *coefficient of sliding friction.*

How would you investigate the laws of sliding friction between wood and iron?

An iron block, of mass 10 lb., rests on a wooden plane inclined at 30° to the horizontal. It is found that the least force parallel to the plane which causes the block to slide *up* the plane is 10 lb. wt. Calculate the coefficient of sliding friction between wood and iron. (*N*.)

8. Explain the meaning of *terminal velocity* as applied to the motion of a small sphere falling through a viscous liquid. Describe an experiment to show how the terminal velocity of a ball-bearing falling under gravity in a viscous oil varies with the diameter.

An oil drop carrying a charge of 144×10^{-10} e.s.u. is balanced in air by an electric field of 5,000 volt cm.$^{-1}$ Determine (*a*) the radius of the drop, (*b*) the terminal velocity acquired after removal of the field. (Densities of the oil and of air are 0·9200 and 0·0013 gm. cm.$^{-3}$ respectively. 300 volt = 1 e.s.u. of potential. Viscosity of air, $1·824 \times 10^{-4}$ gm. cm.$^{-1}$ sec.$^{-1}$ (*N*.)

9. Give an account of the factors which determine the force of friction (i) between solids, (ii) in liquids.

A block weighing 12 kilograms is drawn along a horizontal surface by a steadily applied force of 4 kg. weight acting in the direction of motion. Find the kinetic energy acquired by the block at the end of 10 secs. and compare it with the total work done on the block in the same time. (Coefficient of friction = 0·28.) (*L*.)

10. Define *coefficient of viscosity*. Distinguish between orderly and turbulent flow of a liquid through a tube. Describe a method to determine for a given tube and liquid the pressure head at which the transition from orderly to turbulent flow occurs.

A horizontal capillary tube, 50 cm. long and 0·20 mm. internal radius, is inserted into the lower end of a tall cylindrical vessel of cross-sectional area 10 sq. cm. The vessel is filled with water which is allowed to flow out through the tube. Calculate the time taken for the level of the water in the vessel to fall from a height of 100 cm. to 50 cm. above the axis of the tube. Assume that the volume of water passing per sec. through a horizontal tube is $\pi a^4 (p_1 - p_2)/8l\eta$, where a = tube radius, l = tube length, η = coefficient of viscosity of water, and $(p_1 - p_2)$ = difference in the pressures at the ends of the tube. Take the viscosity of water as 0·010 gm. cm.$^{-1}$ sec.$^{-1}$ and $\log_e 10 = 2·30.$ (*N*.)

11. State the laws of sliding friction between solid surfaces and explain briefly how you would proceed to verify them.

Masses of 9 lb. and 12 lb. are connected by a tight cord and placed on a line of greatest slope of a rough plane which is slowly tilted. If the 9 lb. mass is the lower, find the inclination at which slipping will take place. The coefficient of friction between the plane and the 9 lb. mass is 1/3; between the plane and the 12 lb. mass, 1/2. (*W*.)

12. Define *coefficient of friction* and *coefficient of viscosity*.

Describe how you would (*a*) measure the coefficient of sliding friction between iron and wood, and (*b*) compare the viscosities of water and paraffin oil. (*L*.)

13. Define *coefficient of viscosity* and deduce its dimensions.

The annular space between an outer fixed cylinder of radius a_1 and an inner coaxial rotatable cylinder of radius a_2 is filled with a liquid of coefficient of viscosity η. If $a_1 - a_2$ is small compared with a_1, find the couple required to cause the inner cylinder to rotate with angular velocity ω

when immersed to a depth *l*. Explain how the effects of the ends of the cylinders can be eliminated in practice. (*C*.)

Osmosis. Diffusion.

14. What is meant by osmotic pressure? How does this pressure, in a dilute solution, depend on (*a*) the concentration of the solution used, and (*b*) the temperature of the solution?

Give a simple theoretical basis to account for all the phenomena you have described.

How would you measure the osmotic pressure of a solution? (*L*.)

15. Distinguish between *diffusion* and *osmosis*. What laws do you know concerning (*a*) the relative rates of diffusion of gases, and (*b*) the osmotic pressure of solutions? By whom were these laws discovered? Describe one experiment on gaseous diffusion and one on osmotic pressure. (*L*.)

16. Write an essay on osmosis and explain how the osmotic pressure of a dilute aqueous sugar solution may be measured. (*L*.)

17. What is meant by *osmosis* and by *osmotic pressure?* Describe how the osmotic pressure of a solution can be measured.

State the quantitative laws of osmotic pressure. (*L*.)

18. Write a brief account of the phenomenon of diffusion in liquids and in gases. (*L*.)

19. Calculate the osmotic pressure at 0° C. of a solution of sugar containing 10 gm. of sugar per litre, if the molecular weight of the sugar is 342 and the gram-molecular weight of a gas at S.T.P. occupies 22·4 litres.

20. An osmotic pressure of 35·4 cm. mercury is exerted by a sugar solution at 10° C. containing 8 gm. of sugar per litre. Calculate the concentration of sugar solution which has an osmotic pressure of 26·0 cm. mercury at 30° C.

21. State *Graham's law of effusion*. Describe an experiment (i) to demonstrate effusion, (ii) to verify Graham's law.

CHAPTER IX

SOME VERNIER AND SCREW INSTRUMENTS

1. The Vernier.

In order to measure lengths to a higher degree of accuracy than one millimetre, for example, VERNIER designed a scale V known as a *vernier*, which is placed alongside the millimetre scale, M, Fig. 113. The vernier scale has a length of 0·9 cm. and 10 divisions, and hence

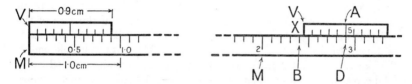

FIG. 113. Vernier scale.

each division on the vernier is 0·09 cm. long. Thus each division on the vernier scale is (0·1 − 0·09) or 0·01 cm. less than each division on the millimetre scale.

When a vernier scale is used, we look along this scale, V, and the millimetre scale, M, and *we note the division on V which coincides with one of the divisions on M*. In Fig. 113, for example, the fifth division, A, on the vernier coincides with a division D on the scale M. From above, it follows that the division on the vernier on the immediate left of A is 0·01 cm. in front of the division on the left of D. Now we move five divisions from A on the vernier until the zero division of it, X, is reached; hence we conclude that X is 5 × 0·01 cm. in front of the division B on the millimetre scale M. The reading corresponding to X on the scale M is therefore 2·4 + 0·05, or 2·45 cm.

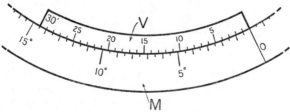

FIG. 114. Circular vernier scale.

Circular vernier scales are used on instruments which measure angles, such as the spectrometer or the sextant. In Fig. 114, the main circular scale M is graduated from 0 – 360 degrees in half-degrees, and the circular vernier scale V occupies a length equivalent to 14·5° on M. Since the vernier is divided into 30 equal divisions, the difference between a division on M and a division on V

$$= \frac{1}{30} (15° - 14·5°) = \frac{1}{30} \times 0·5° = 1 \text{ minute of arc.}$$

The vernier thus enables the reading on M to be found to an accuracy of one minute.

2. Zero Error.

On occasions, the "zeros" of a vernier and the accompanying main scale may not originally coincide. For example, the vernier zero in Fig. 113 may be a little distance *c* say to the right of the zero of the straight main scale M before the instrument is used. If the vernier V is moved to the position X shown in Fig. 113, for example, the length 2·45 cm. recorded is slightly greater than the true distance moved by V. The error in the reading is *c*, which is called the *zero error* of the ruler. The zero error of an instrument must always be searched for and determined before the instrument is used.

3. Vernier Callipers.

Another instrument for measuring linear dimensions is the vernier callipers. This consists of a straight metal scale M graduated in millimetres (or inches), with a movable vernier scale V engraved on a metal B, Fig. 115. When the movable jaw on B is in contact with the

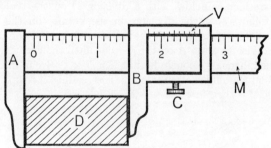

FIG. 115.   Vernier callipers.

fixed jaw A of the instrument, the readings on A and V should be zero; if it is not, the "zero error" is noted. The object D is then placed between the jaws by moving B, and its length is read from the scales M and V, allowing for any "zero error".

4. The Micrometer Screw Gauge.

When a *screw* is rotated through one revolution its point advances through a distance known as the *pitch*, *p*, of the screw, which is the distance between corresponding points on consecutive threads of the screw, Fig. 116 (i).

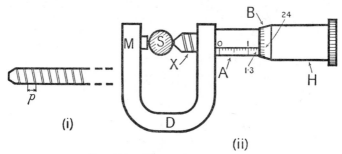

FIG. 116.   Micrometer screw gauge.

The micrometer screw gauge is an instrument used for measuring the diameters of wires or ball-bearings, or the thickness of a thin plate, and consists of a screw X moving in a fixed curved metal frame D, Fig. 116 (ii). The screw moves inside a nut on which a linear scale A in millimetres is engraved, and it is operated by a head H which has a circular scale B engraved on it. When the screw X makes contact with the projection at M, the reading on A and on B should be zero; if not, the zero error is noted.

The pitch of the screw is found by turning the screw through one revolution and noting the advance of the screw from the scale A. Suppose the pitch is ½ millimetre, and the number of divisions on B is 100. Then each division on B corresponds to a distance of $\frac{1}{200}$ or 0·005 mm. If the diameter of a ball-bearing S is required it is placed between the jaws of the gauge, and the screw is adjusted until it touches S gently. The readings on A and on B are then noted. Suppose the reading on A is 1·3 cm. and the reading on B corresponds to the 24th division and there is no zero error. Then

$$\text{diameter of S} = 1\!\cdot\!3 + 24 \times 0\!\cdot\!0005 = 1\!\cdot\!312 \text{ cm.}$$

5. The Spherometer.

The spherometer is an instrument used for measuring the radii of curvature of surfaces, such as those of a lens or a curved mirror. It consists of a screw S which moves through a fixed nut by turning the head H, with three fixed legs A, B, C situated round S, Fig. 117 (i). The distances between the points of the legs are equal. A fixed vertical

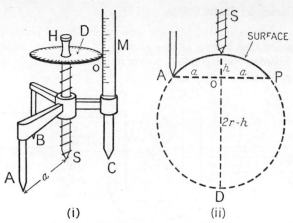

FIG. 117.   Spherometer.

scale M, graduated in millimetres, is attached to the instrument as shown, and a circular scale D, containing 50 divisions for example, moves along M as the screw is rotated by H. As with the micrometer screw gauge, the readings on the scale M and the circular scale D enable the distance moved by the screw to be calculated to three places of decimals.

The spherometer is first placed on a flat glass plate and the screw is moved until it just touches the plate. The readings on M and D are then noted. The spherometer is now placed with its three legs on the curved surface whose radius of curvature is required, and the screw is then turned until it just touches this surface, Fig. 117 (ii). Suppose h is the distance moved by the screw, a is the distance from S to any of the three legs A, B, C, and r is the radius of curvature; Fig. 117 (ii) represents a section of the surface taken through one leg A and the screw. Then, from the geometrical property of chords intersecting in a circle, we have, if S is the tip of the screw,

$$SO \cdot OD = AO \cdot OP.$$
$$\therefore h\,(2r - h) = a \cdot a = a^2,$$

since SD = diameter of circle = $2r$.

$$\therefore r = \frac{a^2 + h^2}{2h} = \frac{a^2}{2h} + \frac{h}{2}$$

Thus by measuring h and a the radius of curvature r can be calculated. The spherometer can also be used to measure the radius of curvature of a concave surface, as well as a convex surface; in the former case h is the distance which the screw advances to make contact with the concave surface, having first placed the spherometer on a flat glass plate.

APPENDIX I

FURTHER TOPICS (SCHOLARSHIP-LEVEL)

1. M.K.S. (METRE—KILOGRAM—SECOND) UNITS.

The M.K.S. system of units uses the *metre* as the unit of length, the *kilogram* as the unit of mass, and the *second* as the unit of time. This system has displaced the C.G.S. (centimetre-gram-second) system of units in advanced Electricity because electrical formulæ are simplified when measurements are made in M.K.S. units.

On the M.K.S. system, "velocity" is measured in "metres per second"; "acceleration" is measured in "metres per sec.^{2}" The unit of "force" in this system is called the **newton**; it is that force which gives a mass of 1 kilogram an acceleration of 1 metre per sec.^{2} The unit of force on the C.G.S. system, the dyne, is that force which gives a mass of 1 gram an acceleration of 1 cm. per sec.^{2} Since $P = mf$, with the usual notation,

$$1 \text{ newton} = 1 \text{ kilogram} \times 1 \text{ metre per sec.}^2$$
$$= 1000 \text{ grams} \times 100 \text{ cm. per sec.}^2$$
$$= 100{,}000 \ (10^5) \text{ dynes.}$$

As a simple illustration, suppose an object of mass 40,000 gm. is given an acceleration of 30 cm. per sec.^{2} by a force P. Then $m = 40{,}000$ gm. $= 40$ kgm., $f = 30$ cm./sec.^{2} $= 0.3$ m./sec.^{2}

$$\therefore P = mf = 40 \times 0.3 = 12 \text{ newtons.}$$

The unit of "work" or "energy" on the M.K.S. system is the work done when a force of 1 newton moves through 1 metre in its own direction. Thus   work done = force × distance
$$= 100{,}000 \text{ dynes} \times 100 \text{ cm.} = 10^7 \text{ ergs,}$$
since, by definition, an erg is the work done when 1 dyne moves 1 cm. in its own direction. Now 10^7 ergs = 1 joule, by definition. Thus the unit of energy on the M.K.S. system is the *joule*, the practical unit of energy. The unit of "power" on the M.K.S. system is hence "1 joule per sec.", or the *watt*. As an illustration, suppose a force of 10^6 dynes moves through a distance of 2000 cm. Then $P = 10^6/10^5$ newtons = 10 newtons, and the distance $s = 2000/100 = 20$ metres.

$$\therefore \text{ work done, } W, = P \times s = 10 \times 20 = 200 \text{ joules.}$$

It is not the place here to deal with the electrical and magnetic units and formulæ on the M.K.S. system. The interested reader is recommended to *Electromagnetism*, by Goodier and Ghey (Murray) and to the author's work, *Electricity and Magnetism* (Arnold).

2. GRAVITATION.

Potential Values. The *potential*, V, at a point due to the gravitational field of the earth is defined as numerically equal to the work done in taking a unit mass from infinity to that point. This is analogous to "electric potential".

(i) *Outside the earth.* For a point outside the earth, assumed spherical, we can imagine the whole mass M of the earth concentrated at its centre. The force of attraction on a unit mass outside the earth is thus GM/r^2, where r is the distance from the centre. The work done in moving a distance $(-\delta r)$ towards the earth = force × distance = $-GM . \delta r/r^2$. Hence the potential at a point distant a from the centre is given by

$$V_a = \int_\infty^a -\frac{GM}{r^2}\, dr = \frac{GM}{a} \quad \cdot \quad \cdot \quad \cdot \quad \cdot \quad (1)$$

(ii) *On the earth's surface*, of radius R, we have

$$V = \frac{GM}{R} \quad \cdot \quad \cdot \quad \cdot \quad \cdot \quad \cdot \quad \cdot \quad (2)$$

(iii) *Inside the earth.* At a point distant b from the centre, where b is less than R, the "effective mass" of the earth, M', is that contained in a sphere of radius b. Now the mass of a sphere of given density $\propto$ radius³, since the volume $\propto$ radius³.

$$\therefore M' = \frac{b^3}{R^3} M$$

$$\therefore \text{ potential at point, } V_b, = \frac{GM'}{b} = \frac{GMb^2}{R^3} \quad \cdot \quad \cdot \quad \cdot \quad (3)$$

Velocity of Escape. Suppose a rocket of mass m is fired from the earth's surface Q so that it just escapes from the gravitational influence of the earth. Then work done = m × potential difference between Q and infinity

$$= m \times \frac{GM}{R}.$$

$$\therefore \text{ kinetic energy of rocket} = \tfrac{1}{2} mv^2 = m \times \frac{GM}{R}.$$

$$\therefore v = \sqrt{\frac{2GM}{R}} = \text{velocity of escape.}$$

Magnitude of acceleration due to gravity.

(i) *Above the earth's surface.* Consider an object of mass m at a point distant a from the centre, where $a > R$. Then, if g' is the acceleration due to gravity at this point,

$$mg' = \frac{GmM}{a^2} \qquad . \quad . \quad . \quad . \quad . \quad . \quad \text{(i)}$$

But, if g is the acceleration due to gravity at the earth's surface,

$$mg = \frac{GmM}{R^2} \quad . \quad . \quad . \quad . \quad . \quad . \quad . \quad \text{(ii)}$$

Dividing (i) by (ii), $\therefore \dfrac{g'}{g} = \dfrac{R^2}{a^2}$, or $g' = \dfrac{R^2}{a^2} \cdot g$.

For a height h above the earth, $a = R + h$.

$$\therefore g' = \frac{R^2}{(R+h)^2} \cdot g = \frac{1}{\left(1 + \dfrac{h}{R}\right)^2} \cdot g.$$

$$= \left(1 + \frac{h}{R}\right)^{-2} \cdot g = \left(1 - \frac{2h}{R}\right) g,$$

since powers of $(h/R)^2$ and higher can be neglected when h is small compared with R.

(ii) *Below the earth's surface.* Consider an object of mass m at a point distant b from the centre, where $b < R$. Then, if g'' is the acceleration due to gravity at this point and M' is the "effective mass" of the earth (see p. 182), then

$$mg'' = \frac{GmM'}{b^2} = \frac{GmMb}{R^3},$$

substituting for M' from our result on p. 182. Since $mg = GmM/R^2$, it follows by division that

$$\frac{g''}{g} = \frac{b}{R}, \text{ or } g'' = \frac{b}{R} g.$$

Simple harmonic motion due to gravitation.

(i) *Along diameter of earth.* Suppose a body of mass m is imagined thrown into the earth along a tunnel passing through its centre. At a point distant x from the centre, the force of attraction, P, is given by $P = GmM'/x^2$, where M' is the "effective mass" of the earth. Hence, since $M' = x^3M/R^3$, where M is the mass of the earth and R its radius,

$$P = \frac{GmM'}{x^2} = \frac{GmMx}{R^3}.$$

Now force, P, = mass $\times$ accn. = $m \times$ accn. Since the force and x are in opposite directions, it follows that

$$m \times \text{accn.} = -\frac{GmM}{R^3}.x$$

$$\therefore \text{accn.} = -\frac{GM}{R^3}.x.$$

This is the condition for S.H.M. about the centre of the earth, and the period of oscillation, T, is given by

$$T = \frac{2\pi}{\omega} = 2\pi\sqrt{\frac{R^3}{GM}}. \quad . \quad . \quad . \quad \text{(i)}$$

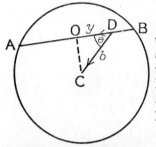

FIG. 118. S.H.M. along chord.

(ii) *Along chord of earth.* Suppose now that a body is thrown into the earth along a tunnel AB which is a "chord" of the earth's circle. Fig. 118. At a point D distant b from the centre C, the force F of attraction towards C is given, from p. 183, by

$$F = \frac{GmM'}{b^2} = \frac{GmMb}{R^3}.$$

$\therefore$ force along AB, P, = $F \cos \theta = \dfrac{GmMb \cos \theta}{R^3}.$

But $b \cos \theta = y$ where OD = y and O is the mid-point of AB.

$$\therefore P = \frac{GmMy}{R^3}.$$

$$\therefore m \times \text{accn. towards O} = -\frac{GmM}{R^3}.y$$

$$\therefore \text{accn. towards O} = -\frac{GM}{R^3}.y$$

$\therefore$ motion is S.H.M. about O, and the period T is given by

$$T = \frac{2\pi}{\omega} = 2\pi\sqrt{\frac{R^3}{GM}} \quad . \quad . \quad . \quad . \quad . \quad \text{(ii)}$$

The period of oscillation is thus the same along the chord and a diameter, from equation (i).

Variation of g with latitude. The acceleration due to gravity, g, varies over the earth's surface. This is due to two main causes. Firstly, the earth is elliptical, with the polar radius, b, 6.357×10^6 metres and the equatorial radius, a, 6.378×10^6 metres, and hence g is greater at the poles than at the equator, where the body is further away from the centre of the earth. Secondly, the earth rotates about the polar axis, AB. Fig. 119. We shall consider this effect in more detail, and suppose the earth is a perfect sphere.

In general, an object of mass m suspended by a spring-balance at a point on the earth would be acted on by an upward force $T = mg'$, where g' is the observed or apparent acceleration due to gravity. There would also be a downward attractive force mg towards the centre of the earth, where g is the acceleration in the absence of rotation.

(1) *At the poles*, A or B, there is no rotation. Hence $mg - T = 0$, or $mg = T = mg'$. Thus $g' = g$.

(2) *At the equator*, C or D, there is a resultant force $mr\omega^2$ towards the centre where r is the earth's radius. Since OD is the vertical, we have

$$mg - T = mr\omega^2.$$

$$\therefore T = mg - mr\omega^2 = mg'$$

$$\therefore g' = g - r\omega^2$$

The radius r of the earth is about 6.37×10^8 cm., and $\omega = [(2\pi/(24 \times 3600)]$ radians per sec.

$$\therefore g - g' = r\omega^2 = \frac{6.37 \times 10^8 \times (2\pi)^2}{(24 \times 3600)^2} = 3.4.$$

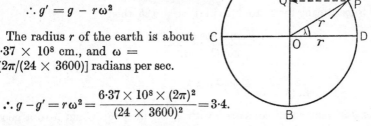

FIG. 119. Variation of g.

Latest figures give g, at the pole, 983.2 cm. per sec.^{2}, and g', at the equator, 978.05 cm./sec.^{2}, a difference of 5.2 cm./sec.^{2} The earth's rotation accounts for 3.4 cm./sec.^{2}

(3) *At latitude λ*. Consider an object suspended by a string at P on the earth, where the latitude is λ. Fig. 119. The resultant force is directed along PQ, and is equal to $m.r \cos \lambda.\omega^2$, since $PQ = r \cos \lambda$. The string suspending the object is now inclined at a very small angle θ to the vertical OP. For motion in a circle of radius PQ, we have

$$mg \cos \lambda - T \cos (\lambda + \theta) = mr\omega^2 \cos \lambda, \qquad \text{(i)}$$

and for no motion in a perpendicular direction,

$$mg \sin \lambda - T \sin (\lambda + \theta) = 0 \qquad \cdots \qquad \text{(ii)}$$

From (i), $T \cos (\lambda + \theta) = mg \cos \lambda - mr\omega^2 \cos \lambda$

From (ii), $T \sin (\lambda + \theta) = mg \sin \lambda.$

G

Squaring and adding,

$$\therefore\ T^2 = (mg\cos\lambda - mr\,\omega^2\cos\lambda)^2 + (mg\sin\lambda)^2 = (mg')^2$$

$$\therefore\ g'^2 = g^2 - 2gr\,\omega^2\cos{}^2\lambda + r^2\,\omega^4\cos{}^2\lambda$$

$$\therefore\ g' = [g^2 - 2gr\,\omega^2\cos{}^2\lambda + r^2\,\omega^4\cos^2\lambda]^{1/2}$$

$$= g\left[1 - \frac{2r\,\omega^2\cos{}^2\lambda}{g} + \frac{r^2\,\omega^4\cos{}^2\lambda}{g^2}\right]^{1/2}$$

Neglecting $r^2\,\omega^4\cos{}^2\lambda/g^2$, which is very small, and expanding by the binomial theorem, we have

$$g' = g\left(1 - \frac{r\,\omega^2\cos{}^2\lambda}{g}\right) = g - r\,\omega^2\cos{}^2\lambda.$$

$\therefore\ g - g' =$ reduction in acceleration of gravity $= r\,\omega^2\cos^2\lambda.$ An accurate formula for the variation of g' with latitude, recommended by an international meeting at Stockholm in 1930, is

$$g' = 980{\cdot}6294 - 2{\cdot}5862\cos 2\lambda + 0{\cdot}0058\cos^2 2\lambda\ \ (\text{cm. per sec}^2.)$$

Substituting for T from (ii) in (i) on p. 185, then

$$mg\cos\lambda - \frac{mg\sin\lambda\cos(\lambda + \theta)}{\sin(\lambda + \theta)} = mr\,\omega^2\cos\lambda.$$

$$\therefore\ \frac{g\sin\theta}{\sin(\lambda + \theta)} = r\,\omega^2\cos\lambda.$$

As θ is very small compared with λ, $\sin(\lambda + \theta) = \sin\lambda$ to a good approximation.

$$\therefore\ \sin\theta = \frac{r\,\omega^2\cos\lambda.\sin\lambda}{g} = \frac{r\,\omega^2}{2g}\sin 2\lambda.$$

Thus θ is greatest when $\lambda = 45°$; in this case θ is about $1/10°$. This is the angle which a plumbline would make with the vertical owing to the earth's rotation.

Kater's Pendulum. The acceleration due to gravity was first measured by the simple pendulum method, and calculated from the relation $g = 4\pi^2 l/T^2$, with the usual notation. The length l, the distance from the point of suspension to the centre of gravity of the bob, however, cannot be determined with very great accuracy.

In 1817 Captain Kater designed a reversible pendulum, with knife-edges for the suspension; it was a compound pendulum. Now it was shown on p. 70 that the same period is obtained between two non-symmetrical points on a compound pendulum when their distance apart is l, the length of the equivalent simple pendulum. Thus if T is the period about either knife-edge when this occurs, $g = 4\pi^2 l/T^2$, where l is now the distance between the knife-edges. The pendulum is made geometrically symmetrical about the mid-point, with a brass bob at one end and a wooden bob of the same size at the other. A movable large and small weight are placed between the knife-edges, which are about one metre apart. The period is then slightly greater than 2 seconds.

To find g, the pendulum is set up in front of an accurate seconds clock, with the bob of the clock and that of the Kater pendulum in line with each other, and both sighted through a telescope. The large weight on the pendulum is moved until the period is nearly the same about either knife-edge, and the small weight is used as a fine adjustment. When the periods are the same, the distance l between the knife-edges is measured very accurately by a comparator method with a microscope and standard metre.

The period T varies when the weights are moved, since the position of the centre of gravity alters. The period is measured by first observing when the two bobs swing exactly in phase through their centres of oscillation. The bob of the clock moves slightly faster, and after a time it has made one more complete oscillation than the pendulum and the two bobs are then again exactly in phase. Suppose the clock has made n oscillations and the pendulum $(n - 1)$ in this time. Then, if T_0 is the period, 2 seconds, of the clock pendulum,

$$(n - 1) T = nT_0.$$

$$\therefore T = T_0 \cdot \frac{n}{n - 1} = T_0 \cdot \frac{1}{1 - \frac{1}{n}} = T_0\left(1 - \frac{1}{n}\right)^{-1}$$

$$= T_0\left(1 + \frac{1}{n} - \frac{1}{n^2} \ldots\right), \text{ by binomial theorem.}$$

Now T and T_0 are so very close that n is large, for example 500. Thus $1/n^2$ and higher powers can be neglected, and hence

$$T = T_0\left(1 + \frac{1}{n}\right) = 2\left(1 + \frac{1}{n}\right).$$

T can be found very accurately by this method, which is called the *method of coincidences*. Thus knowing T and l, g can be calculated from $g = 4\pi^2 l/T^2$. Details of determining g by Kater's pendulum will be found in *Advanced Practical Physics* by Worsnop and Flint (Methuen).

Bessel's formula for g. Bessel showed that it was not necessary to wait until the periods were exactly equal, a very tedious operation.

Suppose the periods are T_1, T_2 when they are nearly equal. Then if h_1, h_2 are the respective C.G. positions from the axis in each case,

$$T_1 = 2\pi\sqrt{\frac{k^2 + h_1{}^2}{h_1 g}}, \; T_2 = 2\pi\sqrt{\frac{k^2 + h_2{}^2}{h_2 g}} \text{ (p. 70)}.$$

Squaring, and subtracting to eliminate k^2 after simplifying, we obtain

$$\frac{8\pi^2}{g} = \frac{T_1{}^2 + T_2{}^2}{h_1 + h_2} + \frac{T_1{}^2 - T_2{}^2}{h_1 - h_2}.$$

The distance $h_1 + h_2$ is the distance between the knife-edges, and can be accurately found. When T_1 and T_2 are very close, the term $(T_1{}^2 - T_2{}^2)/(h_1 - h_2)$ is very small compared with the first term, and little error is therefore made in the whole of the expression on the right-hand side by balancing the pendulum on another knife-edge to find the C.G. and then measuring h_1, h_2. On substituting for T_1, T_2, h_1, h_2 in the above equation, g can be evaluated.

3. VARIATION OF ATMOSPHERIC PRESSURE WITH HEIGHT.

Suppose the air has a uniform density ρ and a pressure p at a height h above the earth's surface. Then, over a further small height δh, the change δp in pressure is given by $\delta p = - \delta h . \rho . g$, the minus indicating that the pressure decreases as the height increases.

$$\therefore \frac{dp}{dh} = - g\rho.$$

Now for a perfect gas of mass m and gas-constant per gram R, $pV = mRT$, with the usual notation, or $p = \rho RT$. Thus $\rho = p/RT$. Substituting for ρ,

$$\therefore \frac{dp}{dh} = - \frac{gp}{RT}$$

$$\therefore \int_{p_0}^{p} \frac{dp}{p} = - \frac{g}{RT} \int_0^h dh,$$

where p_0 is the pressure at the earth's surface, at $h = 0$.

$$\therefore \log_e\left(\frac{p}{p_0}\right) = - \frac{gh}{RT}$$

$$\therefore p = p_0 e^{-gh/RT} \quad . \quad . \quad . \quad . \quad (i)$$

At heights h_1, h_2 above the earth's surface, corresponding to pressures p_1, p_2 respectively, it follows from above that

$$\int_{p_1}^{p_2} \frac{dp}{p} = - \frac{g}{RT} \int_{h_1}^{h_2} dh.$$

$$\therefore \log_e\left(\frac{p_2}{p_1}\right) = -\frac{g}{RT}(h_2 - h_1)$$

$$\therefore p_2 = p_1 e^{-g(h_2-h_1)/RT} \quad . \quad . \quad . \quad . \quad \text{(ii)}$$

Example. Assuming the temperature of the atmosphere to be constant, calculate the height at which the barometer stands at 75 cm., if its reading at sea-level is 76 cm. Density of air $= 1\cdot3 \times 10^{-3}$ gm./ cm.^{3}, density of mercury $= 13\cdot6$ gm./cm.^{3} (*Camb. Schol.*)

Since the density of air $= 1\cdot3 \times 10^{-3}$ gm./cm.^{3} at N.T.P., 1 gram of air occupies a volume of $10^3/1\cdot3$ cm.^{3} Hence, from $pV = RT$,

$$RT = pV = \frac{(76 \times 13\cdot6 \times 981) \times 10^3}{1\cdot3}$$

$$\therefore \frac{RT}{g} = \frac{76 \times 13\cdot6 \times 10^3}{1\cdot3} \quad . \quad . \quad . \quad . \quad (a).$$

From our previous formula, $p = p_0 e^{-gh/RT}$,

$$\frac{gh}{RT} = \log_e\left(\frac{p_0}{p}\right),$$

or
$$h = \frac{RT}{g}\log_e\left(\frac{p_0}{p}\right).$$

Since $(p_0/p) = (76/75)$, it follows with (a) that

$$h = \frac{76 \times 13\cdot6 \times 10^3}{1\cdot3} \times \log_e\left(\frac{76}{75}\right)$$

$$= 10{,}460 \text{ cm.} = 104\cdot6 \text{ metres.}$$

4. FORMATION OF DROPS.

Vapour Pressure above Curved Surface. The saturation vapour pressure (S.V.P.) above a liquid is usually that associated with the vapour pressure outside a plane liquid surface. If the sphere of molecular attraction (p. 112) is drawn round a molecule in a *convex* surface, and also round a molecule in a plane surface, it can be seen that the number of molecules hindering evaporation is less with the convex surface than with the plane surface. Fig. 120. We should therefore expect that the vapour pressure outside a convex surface is greater than outside a plane surface. By similar reasoning, Fig. 120 (i), the vapour pressure outside a concave surface is less than that outside a plane surface.

Lord Kelvin first pointed out the pressure change outside a curved liquid surface, and he derived a formula for it by considering a capillary of radius r dipping into a liquid of obtuse angle of contact completely enclosed. Fig. 120 (ii). For simplicity, suppose the angle of contact is 180°, let the depression of the liquid be h below the plane surface L, and let ρ, σ be the densities of the liquid and vapour respectively. Then,

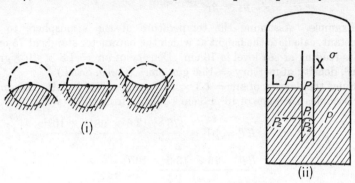

(i)

(ii)

FIG. 120. S.V.P. above curved surface.

with the notation in the figure, using p and p_1 as the pressures outside the plane surface L and convex surface respectively,

for the convex surface, $p_2 - p_1 = \dfrac{2T}{r}$.   .   .   .   (i),

for the vapour column, $p_1 = p + h\sigma g$.   .   .   (ii),

for the liquid column, $p_2 = p + h\rho g$.   .   .   (iii).

From (ii) and (iii), $p_2 - p_1 = (\rho - \sigma)hg$

Hence, with (i), $(\rho - \sigma)hg = \dfrac{2T}{r}$, or $hg = \dfrac{2T}{r(\rho - \sigma)}$.

Thus, from (ii),

$$p_1 - p = h\sigma g = \frac{2T\sigma}{r(\rho - \sigma)}   .   .   \text{(iv)}$$

This formula gives the pressure excess, $\triangle p$, above that outside a plane surface.

Since σ is small compared with ρ, then, to a good approximation,

$$\triangle p = \frac{2T\sigma}{r\rho}.$$

If the vapour obeys the perfect gas laws, $pV = R\theta$, where θ is the absolute temperature and R is the gas constant per gram. Thus $\sigma = 1/V = p/R\theta$.

$$\therefore \triangle p = \frac{2Tp}{Rr\rho\theta},$$

or $\dfrac{\Delta p}{p}$ = relative raising of V.P. = $\dfrac{2T}{Rr\rho\theta}$. (v)

If the variation of σ with height is taken into account, as on p. 188 it can be shown that

$$\log_e\left(\frac{p_1}{p}\right) = \frac{2T}{Rr\rho\theta}.$$

Growth of a Drop. We shall now see how the magnitude of the "excess pressure" Δp outside a drop varies with its radius. For water, $\rho = 1$ gm./c.c., $\sigma = 0.8 \times 10^{-3}$ gm./c.c., $T = 72$ dyne/cm. at 15° C. If the drop has a diameter 1 mm., $r = 0.05$ cm.

$$\therefore \quad \Delta p = \frac{2T\sigma}{r\rho} = \frac{2 \times 72 \times 0.8 \times 10^{-3}}{0.05 \times 1} \text{ dynes/sq. cm.}$$

$$= \frac{2 \times 72 \times 0.8 \times 10^{-3}}{0.05 \times 1 \times 981 \times 13.6} \text{ cm. mercury.}$$

$$= 0.00018 \text{ cm. mercury}$$

This is not an unreasonable "excess pressure" for a supersaturated vapour, and hence drops of diameter 1 mm., if they are once formed on a nucleus, can exist and may then grow.

Suppose, however, that a drop has a diameter of one-thousandth mm. Then $\Delta p = 0.18$ cm. mercury. If the drop has a diameter of one-millionth mm., $\Delta p = 180$ cm. mercury; a drop of this diameter cannot therefore exist and hence evaporates. This rough calculation shows that drops cannot begin to grow in dust-free water-vapour, even when it is supersaturated and cooled. If any dust particle is present, however, it acts as a nucleus of diameter large enough for the drop to form, and then to grow.

A similar formula for Δp, $2T\sigma/r(\rho - \sigma)$, is obtained with a *concave* surface, but this time Δp is the "pressure reduction" below that outside a plane surface. *Condensation* will thus occur relatively easily on concave water surfaces. Cotton and linen materials, which have fine pores tending to form concave liquid surfaces, thus become damp in moist air.

Effect of Electric Charge. The *force per unit area* or stress on a surface having a charge density σ_1 e.s.u. per sq. cm. is given by $2\pi\sigma_1{}^2/K$ dynes per sq. cm., where K is the permittivity. This pressure acts *outwards* on the surface, owing to the mutual repulsion of like charges.

Consider a charged water-drop of radius r. Then, dealing with the equilibrium of one half of the drop as was done on p. 122 for the bubble in water, we obtain

$$2\pi r.T + \pi r^2 p_1 = \pi r^2 p_2 + \pi r^2.\frac{2\pi\sigma_1{}^2}{K}.$$

Simplifying,

$$\therefore p_2 - p_1 = \frac{2T}{r} - \frac{2\pi\sigma_1^2}{K}.$$

Thus, for a *charged* water drop, $2T/r - 2\pi\sigma_1^2/K$ can replace $2T/r$ in the formula for "excess pressure", $\triangle p$, derived previously. In this case, therefore, $\triangle p$ is given by

$$\triangle p = \left(\frac{2T}{r} - \frac{2\pi\sigma_1^2}{K}\right)\left(\frac{\sigma}{\rho - \sigma}\right).$$

Since $2\pi\sigma_1^2/K$ is subtracted from $2T/r$ in the formula, it follows that *drops form more easily on charged nuclei than on uncharged nuclei*, even though their radius may be smaller. This has found application in a unique and now famous method of photographing radiations from radioactive substances, such as α- and β-particles, and atomic (nuclear) explosions and reactions. C. T. R. Wilson's *Cloud-Chamber*, as the apparatus is called, contains a quantity of dust-free super-saturated water-vapour, which undergoes a controlled sudden expansion as α- or β-particles, for example, streak across the space. Water droplets form on the ions left in their wake, leaving a vapour trail like that due to high-flying aircraft on a fine day, the chamber is then momentarily illuminated, and the trail of water-droplets are photographed by the light reflected from them. In this way important information has been obtained about nuclear reactions.

5. MODULUS OF RIGIDITY

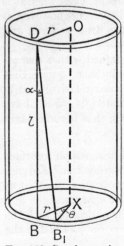

FIG. 121. Couple on wire.

Couple on Torsion Wire. In moving-coil mirror galvanometers, and in determinations of moduli of rigidity, wires are twisted by a couple applied at one end. Consider a wire of radius a, length l, modulus of rigidity n, fixed at the upper end and twisted by a couple of moment C at the other end. If we take a section of the cylindrical wire between radii r and $r + \delta r$, then a "slice" of the material ODBX has been sheared through an angle α to a position ODB_1X, where X is the centre of the lower end of the wire. Fig. 121. From the definition of modulus of rigidity, n, p. 146, n = torsional stress $\div$ torsional strain = $F/A \div \alpha$, where F is the tangential force applied over an area A.

Now A = area of circular annulus at lower end = $2\pi r . \delta r$.

$$\therefore F = nA\alpha = n.2\pi r.\delta r.\alpha.$$

From Fig. 121, it follows that $BB_1 = la$, and $BB_1 = r\theta$.

$$\therefore la = r\theta, \text{ or } a = r\theta/l.$$

$$\therefore F = \frac{n.2\pi r.\delta r.r\theta}{l} = \frac{2\pi n\theta r^2.\delta r}{l}.$$

$\therefore$ moment of F about axis OX of wire $= F.r$

$$= \frac{2\pi n\theta}{l}.r^3.\delta r$$

$\therefore$ total moment, or couple moment, C,

$$= \int_0^a \frac{2\pi n\theta.}{l} r^3\,dr = \frac{2\pi n\theta.}{l}\frac{a^4}{4}$$

$$\therefore C = \frac{\pi na^4\theta}{2l} \qquad . \qquad . \qquad . \qquad . \qquad . \qquad . \qquad (i)$$

If the wire is a hollow cylinder of radii a, b respectively, the limits of integration are altered accordingly, and

$$\text{moment of couple} = \int_a^b \frac{2\pi n\theta.}{l} r^3\,dr = \frac{\pi n(b^4 - a^4)\theta}{2l}$$

Determinations of modulus of rigidity. Dynamical method. One method of measuring the modulus of rigidity of a wire E is to clamp it vertically at one end, attach a horizontal disc D of known moment of inertia, I, at the other end, and then time the horizontal torsional oscillations of D. Fig. 122 (i). On p. 71, it was shown that the period of oscillation, T, $= 2\pi \sqrt{I/c}$, where c is the opposing couple per unit angle of twist. Thus, with our previous notation, as $\theta = 1$,

$$c = \frac{\pi na^4}{2l}.$$

$$\therefore T = 2\pi \sqrt{\frac{2lI}{\pi na^4}}.$$

$$\text{or} \qquad n = \frac{8\pi lI}{a^4 T^2}$$

Hence n can be evaluated from measurements of l, a, I, T.

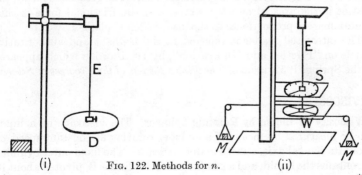

(i)   Fig. 122. Methods for n.   (ii)

Statical method. The modulus of rigidity, n, of the wire E can also be found by measuring the steady deflection θ at the lower end on a scale S graduated in degrees when a couple is applied round a wheel W. Fig. 122 (ii). If M is the mass in each scale-pan, and d is the diameter of W, the moment of the couple on the wire $= Mgd = \pi n a^4 \theta / 2l$. The angle θ in radians, and a, l, are known, and hence n can be evaluated

6. THEORY OF SOLID FRICTION

The laws of solid friction were known hundreds of years ago, but they have been explained only in comparatively recent years, mainly by F. P. Bowden and collaborators. Sensitive methods, based on electrical conductivity measurements, reveal that the true area of contact between two surfaces is extremely small, perhaps one ten-thousandth of the area actually placed together for steel surfaces. This is explained by photographs which show that some of the atoms of a metal project slightly above the surface, making a number of crests or "humps". As Bowden has stated: "The finest mirror, which is flat to a few millionths of an inch, would to anyone of atomic size look rather like the South Downs—valley and rolling hills a hundred or more atoms high." Two metal surfaces thus rest on each others projections when placed one on the other.

Since the area of actual contact is extremely small, the pressures at the points of contact are very high, perhaps 100 tons per square inch for steel surfaces. The projections merge a little under the high pressure, producing adhesion or "welding" at the points, and a force which opposes motion is therefore obtained. This explains Law I of the laws of solid friction (p. 155). When one of the objects is turned over, so that a smaller or larger surface is presented to the other object, measurements show that the small area of actual contact remains constant. Thus the frictional force is independent of the area of the surfaces, which explains Law II. When the load increases the tiny projections are further squeezed by the enormous pressures until the new area of contact becomes big enough to support the load. The greater the load, the greater is the area of actual contact, and the frictional force is thus approximately proportional to the load, which explains Law III.

The interested reader is referred to the brilliant and authoritative article on "Friction and Lubrication", by Dr. Bowden which appeared in the Spring, 1952, issue of *The Times Review of the Progress of Science*.

7. VISCOSITY

Viscosity of Liquid by Rotating Cylinder. The viscosity of a liquid can be measured by means of a cylinder rotating at constant speed ω_0 about its central axis, a method due to Searle. The fixed outer cylinder, A, contains the liquid, and a smaller coaxial cylinder B, pivoted about its central axis, is turned by string round a drum P attached to two equal falling weights, which provide a couple of constant moment G. Fig. 123.

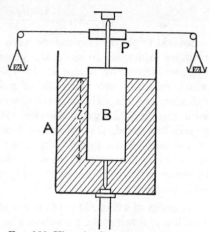

The angular velocity of the liquid between B and the surface of A varies from ω_0 to zero. Since the velocity v at a distance r from the central axis is $r\omega$, the velocity gradient, $dv/dr, = rd\omega/dr$. Consider now a coaxial cylindrical shell of the liquid between radii r and $r + \delta r$. Since the frictional force F acts over a surface area $2\pi rl$, where l is the depth of the bottom of B below the surface,

$$F = \eta \, A \frac{dv}{dr} = \eta . \, 2\pi rl . \, r \, \frac{d\omega}{dr}.$$

Fig. 123. Viscosity by rotating cylinder.

Now moment of F about central axis = couple $G = F.r$.

$$\therefore \; G = \eta . \, 2\pi r^3 l . \, \frac{d\omega}{dr}$$

$$\therefore \; \frac{G}{2\pi\eta l} \int_a^b \frac{dr}{r^3} = \int_0^{\omega_0} d\omega,$$

where a, b are the radii of the inner and outer cylinders respectively.

$$\therefore \; \frac{G}{2\pi\eta l} \left(\frac{1}{2a^2} - \frac{1}{2b^2} \right) = \omega_0$$

$$\therefore \; G = \frac{4\pi\eta la^2 b^2 \omega_0}{b^2 - a^2},$$

or $$\eta = \frac{G(b^2 - a^2)}{4\pi la^2 b^2 \omega_0}.$$

Since the couple, $G, = mgd$, where m is the total mass on each scale-pan and d is the diameter of the wheel P, η can be found when ω_0 is determined and the other quantities are measured.

This calculation has assumed stream-line motion at the lower end of B, and omitted the viscous and other forces at the bottom of the inner cylinder. If the total effect on B is equivalent to a couple of moment $c\omega_0$, where c is some constant, then, more accurately,

$$G = \left(\frac{4\pi\eta la^2 b^2}{b^2 - a^2} + c \right) \omega_0.$$

The effect of c can be eliminated by using two different depths l_1, l_2 of liquid, and arranging the weights on the scale-pans for equilibrium when the angular velocity is ω_0 in each case. Then, by subtraction,

$$G_1 - G_2 = \frac{4\pi\eta(l_1 - l_2)a^2b^2\omega_0}{b^2 - a^2}.$$

Several types of viscometers have been developed on the rotating cylinder principle. In some, the inner cylinder is fixed and the outer cylinder driven by a motor. In 1951 Boyle designed a viscometer which basically uses the rotor of a small motor as a rotating inner cylinder, and the field or rotor assembly as the fixed outer cylinder, with the liquid between the two. When the motor is working at a steady low speed, the power developed is a function of the coefficient of viscosity of the liquid, which can thus be read from a calibrated electrical meter in the circuit. The Boyle viscometer is used to investigate the variation of viscosity of liquid at high pressure such as oil in pipe-lines.

Viscosity of a Gas. On p. 162 it was shown that the volume per second, v, of liquid flowing along a tube under stream-line motion was given by

$$v = \frac{\pi p a^4}{8\eta l}.$$

In deriving the formula it was assumed that the volume per second crossing each section of the tube was constant, which is true for an incompressible substance and hence fairly true for a liquid. When a *gas* flows along a tube, however, the volume increases as the pressure decreases, and hence Poiseuille's formula above must be modified to take this into account.

For a short length δl of the tube, the velocity can be considered constant. The small change of pressure across this length is δp, and the pressure gradient is thus $-dp/dl$, the minus indicating that the pressure diminishes as l increases. Poiseuille's formula now becomes

$$v = \frac{-\pi a^4}{8\eta} \cdot \frac{dp}{dl} \qquad \cdot \quad \cdot \quad \cdot \quad \cdot \quad \cdot \qquad \text{(i)}$$

But from Boyle's law, $pv = P_1V_1 = P_2V_2$, where P_1, P_2 are the respective pressures at the inlet and outlet of the tube, and V_1, V_2 are the corresponding volumes per second. Thus $v = P_1V_1/p$. Substituting in (i),

$$\therefore \quad \frac{P_1V_1}{p} = -\frac{\pi a^4}{8\eta} \cdot \frac{dp}{dl}$$

$$\therefore \quad P_1V_1 \int_0^l dl = -\frac{\pi a^4}{8\eta} \int_{P_1}^{P_2} p \cdot dp$$

$$\therefore \quad P_1V_1 = \frac{\pi a^4}{16\eta l}(P_1{}^2 - P_2{}^2) = P_2V_2 \qquad \cdot \quad \cdot \quad \cdot \qquad \text{(ii)}$$

A simple method of measuring the *viscosity of air* is illustrated in Fig. 124. A tube HL of a few millimetres diameter is joined to a fine capillary tube T, and a mercury pellet M is introduced at the top, as shown. The time taken for M to fall a measured height HL is noted. During this time a volume of air equal to that between H, L is driven through T, and hence the volume per second V_1 is known if the diameter of HL is measured. The pressure P_2 at the open end of T is atmospheric pressure, A; the pressure P_1 at the other end is $(A + p)$, where p is the pressure due to the pellet of mercury. Since $p = mg/b$, where m is the mass of the pellet and b the cross-sectional area of HL, p can be evaluated. Thus knowing the length l and radius a of the capillary tube T, the viscosity η can be found by substituting in equation (ii). A correction is necessary as the mercury sticks to the side of the tube.

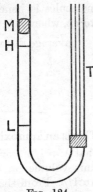

Fig. 124.
Viscosity of air.

Formula for Viscosity on Kinetic Theory. On the kinetic theory of gases, the viscosity or frictional force is accounted for by the transfer of momentum across layers of the gas while it is flowing. Fast moving layers lose molecules to slower-moving layers, and vice-versa, so that changes of momentum take place continually across a given layer, and a corresponding force is produced on it.

Viscosity formula. As a simple example, suppose a gas is moving in a given direction Oz. Then $n/6$ is the number of molecules per unit volume moving normally across this direction, along Ox say, where n is the number of molecules per unit volume. If the average velocity of a molecule is v, the number crossing an area A per second $= nAv/6$. On the average, the molecules crossing a given plane come from two planes on either side each a distance λ away, where λ is the mean free path of the molecules. The molecules in one plane have a velocity $v + \lambda dv/dx$, and the molecules in the other plane have a velocity $v - \lambda dv/dx$, where dv/dx represents the velocity gradient in the direction Ox perpendicular to Oz.

$$\therefore \text{ momentum change per sec.} = \frac{nmAv}{6}\left[\left(v + \lambda\frac{dv}{dx}\right) - \left(v - \lambda\frac{dv}{dx}\right)\right]$$

$$\therefore \text{ frictional force, } F, = \tfrac{1}{3}nm\lambda vA\frac{dv}{dx}.$$

But
$$F = \eta A\frac{dv}{dx}$$

$$\therefore \eta = \tfrac{1}{3}nm\lambda v = \tfrac{1}{3}\rho\lambda v \qquad . \qquad . \qquad . \qquad . \qquad \text{(i)}$$

where ρ is the density of the gas.

Mean free path formula. If σ is the effective diameter of a molecule moving with a velocity c in a constant direction, it will make collisions with all molecules whose distance on either side of its centre is σ or less. In one second, the volume of the cylinder containing these molecules is hence $\pi\sigma^2 c$, and thus the number of collisions made is $\pi\sigma^2 cn$, where n is the number of molecules per unit volume.

∴ average distance between collisions = mean free path λ

$$= \frac{\text{distance moved per second}}{\text{number of collisions}}$$

$$= \frac{c}{\pi\sigma^2 cn} = \frac{1}{\pi\sigma^2 n} \quad \cdots \cdots \quad \text{(ii)}$$

This is an approximate formula for λ; more accurately, Maxwell showed that $\lambda = 1/\sqrt{2}\pi\sigma^2 n$. Thus $\lambda \propto 1/n$. Now the number of molecules per unit volume, n, is proportional to the pressure of the gas. Hence $\lambda \propto 1/p$. From the expression for η in (i), it can now be seen that η *is independent of the pressure*, since ρ, the density, is proportional to pressure. This surprising result was verified by Maxwell by experiment, and it helps to confirm the general truth of the kinetic theory of gases.

8. BROWNIAN MOVEMENT. PERRIN'S DETERMINATION OF N

In 1827 Brown, a botanist, observed through a microscope that pollen particles in suspension were moving about constantly in an irregular manner. It became known later that this was due to the ceaseless bombardment of the particles by the molecules of the liquid, the resultant force being unbalanced and random, and the phenomenon is known as *Brownian movement* or *motion*. Perrin, a French scientist, performed a series of brilliant researches on Brownian motion in 1910. He considered that particles in suspension were moving about like the molecules of the liquid but much slower. Van't Hoff had shown (p. 169) that the associated osmotic pressure obeyed the gas laws, and from his experiments, one of which will now be described, Perrin deduced the magnitude of N, the number of molecules in the gram-molecular weight of a gas, which is known as Avogadro's number.

Theory of Perrin's Determination. Consider a number of similar particles of density ρ suspended in a liquid of density σ. If the volume of a particle is v its weight is $v\rho g$ and the upthrust on it is $v\sigma g$. In a volume of height dh and unit area of cross-section, the number of particles is $n.dh$, where n is the number per c.c. The osmotic pressure dp due to these particles is thus given by

$$dp = -v(\rho - \sigma)gn.dh, \quad \cdots \cdots \quad \text{(i)}$$

where h is measured positively vertically upwards.

Assuming the osmotic pressure p obeys the gas laws, then generally $pV = KT$, where K is the gas constant for the particles. If we consider a volume of l.c.c., then $V = 1$. And if n is the number of particles per c.c. and k is the gas constant per molecule, then $K = nk = nR/N$, where N is the number of molecules in a gram-molecular weight and R is the corresponding (universal) gas constant.

Thus
$$p = nkT = n\,\frac{RT}{N} \qquad . \qquad . \qquad . \qquad . \qquad \text{(ii)}$$

$$\therefore dp = dn\,\frac{RT}{N}$$

From (i), it follows that

$$dn\,\frac{RT}{N} = -v(\rho - \sigma)gn.dh$$

$$\therefore \int_{n_1}^{n_2}\frac{dn}{n} = -\frac{Nvg}{RT}\,(\rho - \sigma)\int_{h_1}^{h_2} dh$$

$$\therefore \log_e\left(\frac{n_2}{n_1}\right) = \frac{Nvg}{RT}\,(\rho - \sigma)\,(h_1 - h_2), \qquad . \qquad . \qquad \text{(iii)}$$

where n_1, n_2 are the respective number of particles per c.c. at heights h_1, h_2.

Perrin's Experiment. Perrin used gamboge particles of uniform size of the order of 10^{-3}mm. diameter; these were obtained by a process of centrifuging, which took several months of patient work. The emulsion was placed on a microscope slide with a cover glass to form a vertical column about 0·1mm. deep, and observed through a powerful microscope mounted vertically. When the suspension had settled down, a count was made continually of the number n_1 of the particles visible at a depth corresponding to h_1. The microscope was then raised slightly, and a new number of particles n_2 was observed corresponding to a depth h_2. The shift of the microscope was $(h_1 - h_2)$. To find the volume v of a particle, the terminal velocity v_0 of the particles was measured as they were dropped through the liquid, and from Stokes' law, $4\pi a^3(\rho - \sigma)g/3 = 6\pi\eta a v_0$. The radius a of the particle can thus be found, and the volume v determined from $4\pi a^3/3$.

On substituting his results in equation (iii), Perrin found N to be of the order $6·8 \times 10^{23}$. This is in good agreement with the value of N found from the kinetic theory of gases, and is very striking evidence in support of the kinetic theory applied to liquids. Before Perrin's experiments many scientists of the day had doubted the existence of molecules and hence the validity of the kinetic theory.

9. SURFACE ENERGY. THE CYLINDRICAL SURFACE

Surface Energy. When the surface area of a liquid is increased, molecules from the interior rise to the surface. They do so against the force of attraction of neighbouring molecules, and hence some mechanical work or energy is always required to increase the surface area. The surface also tends to become cooled, as molecules arriving there from the interior have then fewer degrees of freedom, and thus heat flows into it from the surroundings. It can therefore be said that the total increase in surface energy is the sum of the mechanical energy expended and the heat energy absorbed from the surroundings. Now on p. 118, it was shown that if the surface area increases by unit amount under isothermal conditions, the mechanical work done is numerically equal to T, the surface tension. If H is the quantity of heat flowing into the surface in this case, it follows that

$$\frac{\text{increase in surface energy}}{\text{per unit area}} = T + H.$$

It is shown below that $H = -\theta\, dT/d\theta$, where θ is the absolute temperature of the liquid, and hence, generally,

$$\frac{\text{increase in surface energy}}{\text{per unit area}} = T - \theta\frac{dT}{d\theta} \qquad . \qquad . \qquad \text{(i)}$$

Proof of $H = -T\dfrac{d\theta}{dT}$. Suppose the surface is taken round a Carnot cycle, the axes corresponding to pressure and volume for the case of a gas being replaced respectively by T and A, where A is the surface area. Thus (1) let the area increase by unit amount isothermally at an absolute temperature θ under reversible conditions, when a quantity of heat Q_1 is absorbed and the work done is T; (2) then let the area expand adiabatically until the temperature reaches $\theta - d\theta$, when no heat is absorbed or rejected; (3) then reduce the area isothermally by unit amount at $\theta - d\theta$ under reversible conditions, when a quantity of heat Q_2 is rejected and the work done on the film is $T + dT$; (4) finally, reduce the area adiabatically until the temperature θ is again reached, when the cycle is completed.

From the well-known formula for the Carnot cycle,

$$\frac{Q_1 - Q_2}{Q_1} = \frac{\theta - (\theta - d\theta)}{\theta} = \frac{d\theta}{\theta},$$

or

$$\frac{\text{net work done}}{Q_1} = \frac{d\theta}{\theta}.$$

Now $Q = H =$ heat absorbed when the area is extended isothermally by unit amount, and the net work done $= T - (T + dT) = -dT$.

$$\therefore \quad -\frac{dT}{H} = \frac{d\theta}{\theta},$$

$$\therefore \quad H = -\theta\frac{dT}{d\theta} \qquad \qquad \text{. . . . .} \qquad \text{(ii)}$$

Free Surface Energy. The surface tension T is often called the 'free surface energy' per unit area of a surface, and it must not be confused with the total surface energy, which is given in equation (i). This is greater than T because $dT/d\theta$ is negative, T decreasing when θ increases. Thus at 15°C., $T = 74$ dyne cm.$^{-1}$, $dT/d\theta = -0.15$ dyne °K^{-1}, and $\theta = 288$°K; hence the increase in surface energy per unit area

$$= T - \theta\frac{dT}{d\theta} = 74 + 288 \times 0.15 = 117 \text{ dyne cm.}^{-1}$$

The free surface energy is a measure of the potential energy of the surface; and since an object is in stable equilibrium when its potential energy is a minimum, the shape of a liquid surface will tend to that which makes the surface have a minimum potential energy. The shape of a drop under surface tension forces only will thus be a sphere.

Under gravitational as well as surface tension forces, a liquid will assume a shape in which its total potential energy is a minimum. If the liquid has a high density, such as mercury, the gravitational potential energy will be much greater than the surface tension potential energy, and thus the centre of gravity of the liquid will tend to be as low as possible. On this account a large drop of mercury is flattened at the top. On the other hand, a small drop of liquid of low density will tend to assume a spherical shape, since the surface tension energy is then greater than the gravitational energy; and when gravitational forces are completely excluded, as in Plateau's spherical experiment, p. 113, the shape of the liquid is a perfect sphere.

Rise in Capillary Tube. The height h to which a liquid rises in a capillary tube can be found from energy considerations. Thus suppose the liquid rises a small height x up the tube from its equilibrium position. The additional surface area of the tube covered by the liquid is then $2\pi r x$, where r is the capillary tube radius, and this is also the area by which the air-glass surface has been diminished. Hence

gain in potential energy due to surface tension forces $= 2\pi r x \, (T_2 - T_3)$,

where T_2, T_3 are the respective surface tensions of liquid-solid and air-solid boundaries. Further, the gain in potential energy due to the gravitational force = the work done in raising a volume $\pi r^2 h$ of liquid a distance $x = \pi r^2 h \rho g \, x$, where ρ is the density of the liquid.

By the Principle of Virtual Work, the total gain in potential energy is zero.

$$\therefore \quad 2\pi rx\,(T_2 - T_3) + \pi r^2 h\rho gx = 0$$

$$\therefore \quad T_3 - T_2 = \frac{rh\rho g}{2}$$

But, from p. 117, $T_3 - T_2 = T_1 \cos\theta$,

where T_1 is the surface tension of the air-liquid boundary and θ is the angle of contact between the liquid and solid.

$$\therefore \quad T_1 \cos\theta = \frac{rh\rho g}{2},$$

or, if the angle of contact is zero,

$$T_1 = \frac{rh\rho g}{2}.$$

This formula was deduced on p. 120.

Excess Pressure in Cylindrical Surface. In the most general treatment of curved liquid surfaces, it can be shown that the excess pressure p is given, for one surface, by

$$p = T\left(\frac{1}{r_1} + \frac{1}{r_2}\right), \quad \cdots \quad \text{(iii)}$$

where r_1, r_2 are the respective radii of curvature of the 'principal sections' of the surface. The principal sections are the two sections which have respectively the maximum and minimum radii of curvature. For a spherical surface such as a bubble, the principal sections are in two planes perpendicular to each other, each having a radius of curvature r. Thus $r_1 = r_2 = r$, and hence $p = 2T/r$ for a bubble in water. On the other hand, a cylindrical surface has a curvature in one direction only, in a plane perpendicular to its axis; the other principal section, in the plane containing the axis, has an infinitely large radius. Thus, for a cylindrical surface,

$$p = \frac{T}{r} \quad \cdots \quad \cdots \quad \text{(iv)}$$

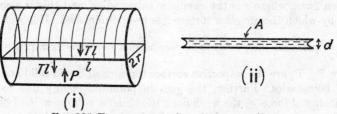

FIG. 125. Excess pressure for cylindrical surfaces.

The excess pressure formula for a cylindrical surface, $p = T/r$, can be deduced by a method similar to that given for the spherical bubble on p. 122. Thus consider the equilibrium of one half of a cylindrical surface, obtained by drawing a plane passing through the axis of the cylinder. Fig. 125 (i). Then, if l is the length of the cylinder and r the radius, the excess pressure p acts over a rectangle of area $l \times 2r$; the surface tension T acts along sides of length l of the film. Hence, for equilibrium,

$$p \times l \times 2r = T \times 2l,$$

$$\therefore \qquad p = \frac{T}{r}.$$

Liquid Between Two Plates. When a small drop of water is squeezed between two plates so that a thin film of liquid is formed between them, a considerable force is required to pull the plates apart.

The magnitude of the force depends on the surface tension T and the thickness d of the film. With a zero angle of contact, Fig. 125 (ii), the radius of curvature r of the film is $d/2$. Thus the atmospheric pressure is greater than the pressure inside the liquid by T/r, or $2T/d$, assuming that the radius of the liquid in contact with the plate is very large compared with d. The plates are therefore squeezed together by a force F given by

$$F = \frac{2TA}{d}, \qquad \cdots \qquad \cdots \qquad \text{(v)}$$

where A is the area of the liquid in contact with the plates. As the thickness of the film contracts, d diminishes; the plates are hence squeezed further together, from (v). If $d = 0 \cdot 0002$ cm., $T = 70$ dyne cm.,$^{-1}$ and $A = 10$ cm^2, then

$$F = \frac{2 \times 70 \times 10}{0 \cdot 0002} = 7 \times 10^6 \, \text{dynes} = 7 \text{ kgm. wt. approx.}$$

Falling Drop. When a drop is formed at the bottom of a vertical circular tube, it can be shown that the drop becomes unstable and breaks away when the radius of the bubble is about equal to the external radius of the tube. At this stage, approximately,

upward force due to surface tension = weight of drop + downward force due to excess pressure:

$$\therefore \quad T.2\pi r = mg + \frac{T}{r}. \pi r^2,$$

as T/r is the excess pressure in a cylindrical film. Thus if m is the mass of a drop,

$$T = \frac{mg}{\pi r} \qquad \cdots \qquad \cdots \qquad \cdots \qquad \text{(vi)}$$

This simplified formula does not hold in practice, and Lord Rayleigh has given an approximate formula, $T = mg/3\cdot8r$, for drops formed on tubes of radii 3–5 mm. Later work showed that $mg = 2\pi rTf(r/V^{1/3})$, where $f(r/V^{1/3})$ is a function of the radius r and the volume V of the drop. The weight of the drop also depends on the rate at which it is formed. The falling drop method has been used to investigate the surface tension of molten metals, as other methods are impractical.

APPENDIX II

MECHANICS

SUMMARY OF DEFINITIONS

Vector quantity. A vector quantity is one which has magnitude and direction (e.g., force, velocity, momentum).

Scalar quantity. A scalar quantity is one which has only magnitude (e.g., density, volume, mass).

DYNAMICS.

Velocity. Displacement/time. 60 m.p.h. = 88 ft. per sec.

Acceleration (f). Change in velocity/time. $g = 32$ ft. per sec.^{2} or 980 cm. per sec.^{2}

Dyne. The force which gives a mass of 1 gram an acceleration of 1 cm. per sec.^{2}

Poundal. The force which gives a mass of 1 lb. an acceleration of 1 ft. per sec. ^{2}

Pound wt. The force due to gravity on a mass of 1 lb.

Gram wt. The force due to gravity on a mass of 1 gram.

Work. Work done = force × distance moved in the direction of the force.

Erg. Work done when a force of 1 dyne moves 1 cm. in the direction of the force.

Joule. 1 joule = 10 million (10^7) ergs.

Foot-pound wt (ft. lb. wt.). Work done when a force of 1 lb. wt. moves 1 foot in the direction of the force.

Kinetic Energy. The energy posessed by an object by virtue of its motion.

Potential Energy. The energy possessed by an object by virtue of its level or position.

Momentum. The product of the mass and the velocity of an object.

Power. The energy expended, or work done, per second.

Watt. 1 joule per second rate of working.

Angular velocity is the angle described per second by a rotating object

Simple harmonic motion is the motion of a particle when its acceleration is directed towards a fixed point and is always proportional to its distance from that point.

Conservation of Energy. The Principle of the Conservation of Energy states that the total energy in a given system is always conserved, although energy may be changed from one form to another.

Conservation of Momentum. The Principle of the Conservation of Momentum states that, if no external forces act on a system of colliding objects, the total momentum of the objects remains constant.

STATICS.

Resolved Component $= P \cos \theta$, where P is the force and θ is the angle between the force and the direction concerned.

Moment. Moment of force about a point = force $\times$ perpendicular distance from point to line of action of force.

Couple. Two equal and opposite forces whose lines of action do not coincide.

Moment of Couple. = one force $\times$ perpendicular distance between forces.

Work done by couple. = moment of couple $\times$ angle of rotation in radians.

Conditions of equilibrium of three forces. (1) The three forces must pass through a point. (2) The algebraic sum of the moments about any point is zero. (3) The algebraic sum of the resolved components in two perpendicular directions is respectively zero.

Conditions of equilibrium of any number of forces. (1) The algebraic sum of the moments about any point is zero. (2) The algebraic sum of the resolved components in any two perpendicular directions is respectively zero.

HYDROSTATICS.

Density (ρ) = mass /volume. (Water has a density of 1 gm./c.c. at 4°C. or $62\frac{1}{2}$ lb./cu. ft.)

Specific gravity (s) = wt. of substance/wt. of equal volume of water.

Archimedes' Principle. The upthrust of a liquid on an object immersed in it = the weight of liquid displaced.

Principle of Flotation. When an object floats, the weight of liquid displaced (upthrust) = the weight of the object.

Pressure. Pressure = average force/area, = $h \rho g$ dynes per sq. cm. when h is in cm., ρ is the density in gm. per c.c. and $g = 980$.

SUMMARY OF FORMULÆ

1.
$$v = u + ft$$
$$s = ut + \tfrac{1}{2}ft^2$$
$$v^2 = u^2 + 2fs$$

u = initial velocity
v = final velocity
f = acceleration
t = time
s = distance.

2. $P = mf$ (P = force, m = mass, f = acceleration.) When m is in lb., f is in ft./sec.^{2}, then P is in *poundals*. When m is in grams, f is in cm./sec.^{2}, then P is in *dynes*.

3. 980 dynes = 1 gram wt. 32 poundals = 1 lb. wt.

4. *Momentum* = mv. (m = mass, v = velocity).

5. *Kinetic energy* = $\tfrac{1}{2}mv^2$. When m is in grams and v is in cm. per sec., then $\tfrac{1}{2}mv^2$ is in *ergs*. When m is in lbs. and v is in ft. per sec., then $\tfrac{1}{2} mv^2$ is in *foot-poundals* (32 foot-poundals = 1 ft. lb. wt.).

6. *Potential energy* = *weight* × *height above ground*. When the weight is in lb. wt. and the height is in feet, the potential energy is in *ft. lb. wt.* When the weight is in gram wt. and the height is in centimetres, the potential energy is in *cm. gm. wt.* When the weight is in dynes and the height is in centimetres, the potential energy is in *ergs*.

7. *Acceleration in circular motion* = v^2/r = $\omega^2 r$, where ω is the angular velocity, and $v(= r\omega)$ is the uniform velocity.

8. *For simple harmonic motion*, acceleration = $-\omega^2 y$, where y is the distance from the centre of oscillation and ω is a constant.

Period of motion, T, = $2\pi/\omega$.

Velocity = $\omega\sqrt{r^2 - y^2}$, where r is the amplitude; maximum velocity = ωr.

9. *Period of simple pendulum*, T, = $2\pi\sqrt{l/g}$. Thus $g = 4\pi^2 l/T^2$.

10. *Force between two small masses* m, M = $G\dfrac{mM}{r^2}$, where r is the distance between the masses and G is the gravitational constant.

11. *Moment of inertia*, I, = $\Sigma\, mr^2$.
    M.I. of uniform rod of length l about axis through centre perpendicular to length = $Ml^2/12$.
    M.I. of uniform rod about axis through one end perpendicular to length = $Ml^2/3$.
    M.I. of ring of radius a about axis through centre perpendicular to plane = Ma^2.
    M.I. of disc about axis through centre perpendicular to plane of disc = $Ma^2/2$.

M.I. of disc about axis through centre in plane of disc $= Ma^2/4$.

M.I. of sphere about axis through centre $= \dfrac{2}{5}Ma^2$.

12. *Kinetic energy of rotation of rigid body* $= \frac{1}{2}I\omega^2$, where ω is the angular velocity.

Total kinetic energy of moving body $= \frac{1}{2}I\omega^2 + \frac{1}{2}Mv^2$, where M is the mass, v is the velocity of the C.G., I is the moment of inertia about the C.G. and ω is the angular velocity about the C.G.

13. Period of oscillation of rigid body $= 2\pi\sqrt{I/mgh}$, where I is the moment of inertia about the point of suspension and h is the distance of the C.G. from the point of suspension.

APPENDIX III

PROPERTIES OF MATTER

SUMMARY OF DEFINITIONS

Surface Tension (T). This is the force in the surface acting at right angles to one side of a line 1 centimetre long drawn in the surface. The units of T are "dynes per cm." Dimensions: $[M][T]^{-2}$

Angle of Contact. This is defined as the angle between the solid surface and the tangent to the liquid surface where it meets the solid surface, the angle being measured through the liquid.

Hooke's law. Provided the elastic limit is not exceeded, the extension of a wire is directly proportional to the tension or load applied.

Elastic limit. The elastic limit is the point first reached when the extension is no longer proportional to the load.

Yield point. The yield point is the point past the elastic limit when the extension of the wire increases rapidly as the load is increased and the wire becomes plastic.

Elastic. A material is said to be elastic if it returns to its original length when the load on it is removed.

Young's Modulus, E, = tensile stress/tensile strain = (force per unit area) ÷ (extension/original length). The units of E are "dynes per sq. cm." Dimensions: $[M][L]^{-1}[T]^{-2}$.

Bulk modulus = pressure ÷ (volume change/original volume).

Rigidity modulus, n, = torsional stress/torsional strain.

Poisson's ratio = (lateral contraction/original diameter) ÷ (longitudinal extension/original length).

Coefficient of Static Friction, μ, = static frictional force F/reaction R, when object is on point of slipping.

Coefficient of Kinetic Friction μ', = kinetic frictional force F'/reaction R.

Coefficient of Viscosity, $\bar{\eta}$ = frictional force exerted on unit area of a liquid in a region of unit velocity gradient. Dimensions: $[M][L]^{-1}[T]^{-1}$.

Osmosis. The name given to the spontaneous flow of solvent through a semi-permeable membrane when there is a difference in concentration on opposite sides of the membrane.

Osmotic pressure may be defined as that pressure required to stop the passage of the solvent through a semi-permeable membrane when there is a difference of concentration on opposite sides of the membrane.

Fick's law of diffusion states that the quantity per second of a solute flowing between two liquids is proportional to the area, to the time, and to the gradient of the concentration.

Graham's law of effusion. The rate of effusion of a gas is inversely proportional to the square root of its density.

SUMMARY OF FORMULÆ.

Excess pressure, p, in a soap-bubble over that inside $= 4T/r$, where T is the surface tension and r is the radius; in the case of a *bubble in a liquid*, $p = 2T/r$.

Excess pressure p on one side of a curved liquid surface over that on the other side $= 2T \cos \theta/r$, where θ is the angle of contact.

Rise in a capillary tube. For an angle of contact of zero, the height h is given by $T = rh\rho g/2$, with the usual notation; for an acute angle of contact θ, h is given by $T \cos \theta = rh\rho g/2$.

Depression in a capillary tube. For an obtuse angle of contact a, the depression h is given by $T \cos (180 - a) = rh\rho g/2$.

Young's modulus, $E = \dfrac{F/A}{e/l}$. Thus $F = EA\dfrac{e}{l}$.

Force in a wire prevented from expanding $= EA\,at$, where a is the linear coefficient of the wire and t is the temperature change.

Energy per c.c. stored in a wire $= \frac{1}{2}$ stress $\times$ strain.

Isothermal bulk modulus of gas $= p$, the pressure of the gas.

Adiabatic bulk modulus for a gas $= \gamma p$, where γ is the ratio of the principal specific heats of the gas and p is the pressure.

Coefficient of friction, μ, $= \tan \theta$, where θ is the angle of friction.

Coefficient of viscosity, η, $= F/(A \times$ velocity gradient$)$. Frictional force $= \eta A \times$ velocity gradient.

Poiseuille's formula. Volume per second of liquid issuing from a pipe in orderly flow $= \pi p a^4/8\eta l$.

Stokes' formula. Frictional force on a sphere moving through a liquid $= 6\pi a\eta v$, where a is the radius and v is the velocity.

Osmosis. $pV = RT$, where p is the osmotic pressure, V is the volume of the solution, T is the absolute temperature and R is a constant analogous to the gas constant.

ANSWERS TO EXERCISES

EXERCISES I (p. 29)

1. (i) 11 sec., (ii) 605 ft., (iii) 56 ft. per sec. **2.** (i) $5\frac{1}{2}$ sec., (ii) 121 ft., (iii) $15\frac{1}{8}$, $15\frac{1}{8}$ ft. lb. wt. **3.** 19·8 m.p.h., N. 30·5° W. **4.** (i) 500 ft. lb. wt. (ii) 10^9 ergs., (iii) 4·9 × 10^9 ergs., (iv) 605 ft. lb. wt. **5.** (i) 5·2 ft. per sec., 57·6 ft. pdls., (ii) 1·2 ft. per sec., 313·6 ft. pdls. **6.** 26·5 m.p.h., S. 41° W.; 7·56 mls. **7.** (i) $2\frac{2}{7}$ ft. per sec., (ii) $4\frac{4}{7}$ ft. per sec.², (iii) 250·8 ft. pdls. **8.** $5\frac{1}{3}$ ft. per sec., 0·95 lb. ° C. **10A.** 13·0 gm. wt. **10B.** 576 ft. **11.** (a) 60, (b) 50, (c) 30 pdls.; (a) $7\frac{1}{2}$ lb. wt., (b) zero. **12.** 172 kgm. wt., 20,080 calories (J = 4·2 joules/cal.). **13.** 14·4 min., 8 naut. mls., 37° S. of E. **14.** $5\frac{1}{2}$ ins. **15.** 83·5%, 0·05. **16.** 10·5° from vertical. **17.** 4871 lb. wt. per sq. ft. **18.** 36·1 m.p.h., 55·4 yds.; 46, 31 yds. from crossing. **19.** 3388 lb. wt.; 39·8 h.p. **20.** (a) 34·3 ft., (b) 128 ft., (c) 82·3 ft.

EXERCISES II (p. 56)

1. (i) 5 radians per sec., (ii) 600 pdls. **2.** (i) 32·8 lb. wt., (ii) 17° 45'. **3.** 69·8°, 43·4 cwt. **4.** 33, 17 lb. wt. **5.** 0·0268 dynes. **6.** 5·99 × 10^{27} gm. **7.** 988 cm. per sec.² **8.** 104·2 ft. per sec. **9.** 43·2 ft. per sec. **10.** 5° 14'. **11.** 93·3 : 1. **12.** 977 cm. per sec.² **13.** 5·5 gm. per c.c. **14.** (i) $\frac{1}{20}$ sec., (ii) 0, 2631 ft. per sec.², (iii) 20·9 ft. per sec., 0. **15.** 99·3 cm. (i) 0, 1·64 ft. per sec.², (ii) 0·52 ft. per sec., 0, (iii) 0·45 ft. per sec., 0·82 ft. per sec.² **16.** 0·32 sec. **17.** 1·57 sec. **18.** 999 cm. per sec.², 446 cm. **19.** (a) 251 cm. per sec., (b) 78,940 cm. per sec.² **20.** (a) $\frac{9}{16}l$ nearer floor, (b) $\frac{7}{16}l$ further from floor. **22.** $v = \frac{2\pi}{T}\sqrt{a^2 - x^2}$, acceleration = $- 4\pi^2 x/T^2$; 210·1, 189·9, 200 gm. wt. **23.** $\frac{1}{2}m\omega^2(a^2 - x^2)$. **25.** 4·9 cm. **26.** 100·7 cm. **27.** $T = 2\pi\sqrt{b/g}$; 2/3 ft. per sec. **28.** 0·45 secs· **29.** 16 cm.; 80 gm.

EXERCISES III (p. 75)

1. (i) 2000, (ii) 8000 gm. cm.² **2.** (i) 72, (ii) 216 lb. ft.² **3.** (i) 40,000, (ii) 80,000, (iii) 20,000 gm. cm.². **4.** 375 ft. pdls. **5.** 11·4 ft./sec.²; 19·1 ft./sec. **6.** (i) 1·98, (ii) 2·31 radians per sec. **7.** 3·85 sec. **8.** 9315 gm. cm.² **10.** 1 : 14. **11.** 256 cm. per sec. **12.** 101·4 cm., 4·29 × 10^5 gm. cm.². **13.** 6,200 gm. cm.² **14.** 50 cm.

EXERCISES IV (p. 93)

1. 2·26 in. **2.** 69·3, 138·6 lb. **3.** 50 lb. ft., $16\frac{2}{3}$ lb. **4.** 0·54, 0·52 ft. **5.** $4\frac{1}{8}$, $4\frac{1}{8}$ lb. **6.** 30°. **8.** 171·4 lb. wt. **9.** 34, 16 lb. **11.** 36, $31\frac{3}{4}$ lb. **12.** 9·837 gm., 1·0005· **13.** 0·037 cm., 0·1°.

211

EXERCISES V (p. 109)

1. Iron : alum., (i) 3 : 2, (ii) 40 : 9. **2.** 162 gm. **4.** 5·1 cm. **6.** 2 : 3. **7.** (a) 75·04 cm., (b) 1003·3 cm. **9.** 1·25. **10.** 40 gm., 240 c.c. **11.** 20·8 gm. **12.** 14·9 cm. **14.** 594·4 gm.; 0·29 gm. **15.** 1·1. **16.** $W\rho/\sigma$; (a) 0·95, (b) 1·19.

EXERCISES VI (p. 132)

1. 1400, 868 dynes. **2.** (i) 6·63, (ii) 5·52 cm. **3.** 2·7 cm. **4** (i) 1·00056 × 10⁶ dynes per sq. cm., (ii) 0·14 cm. **7.** $8\pi T(b^2 - a^2)$, **8.** 7·35 cm.; liquid makes acute angle of contact. **10.** 0·8. **11.** 740 dynes. **12.** (a) decrease, (b) increase. **13.** 0·44 cm. **15.** 5·1 cm. **16.** 10,050 ergs; 8 : 1. **17.** 43·4 dynes per cm. **20.** 19·8 cm. **21.** $\sqrt{r_1^2 + r_2^2}$. **22.** 30·6 dynes/cm.

EXERCISES VII (p. 150)

1. 6·24 × 10⁷ dynes per sq. cm.; 6 × 10⁻⁵; 1·04 × 10¹² dynes per sq. cm. **2.** 6·84 kgm. **3.** 0·076 mm. **5.** 1·1 × 10⁹ dynes. **6.** 7·8 × 10¹¹ dynes per sq. cm. **7.** 22·7 tons. **8.** (a) 0·00022 cm. (b) 546 ergs. **9.** 0·5. **10.** 144·3° C., 3360 kg. **11.** 1·3 × 10⁴. **12.** 0·17 cm. **13.** 4 × 10⁶ dynes, 7·4 × 10⁶ dynes. **14.** 4·95 × 10⁹ dynes per sq. cm. **15.** 28·6 kgm. **16.** 12 ×10⁸ dynes per sq. cm., 3·02 kgm. **17.** 1·27 × 10⁴ gm. **18.** (a) 2 × 10¹² dynes/sq.cm. (b) 4·7 × 10⁵ ergs. **19.** 16 gm., 39,250 ergs.

EXERCISES VIII (p. 173)

2. 222 watts. **5.** 15·3°. **7.** 0·58. **8.** (a) 0·0004 cms., (b) 0·175 cm. per sec. **9.** 1·64 × 10⁹ ergs.; 0·16. **10.** 15 h. 36 m. **11.** 23·2°. **13.** $2\pi\dot{\eta}a_2^3l\omega/(a_1 - a_2)$. **19.** 49·8 cm. **20.** 5·5 gm. per litre.

INDEX

Acceleration, 1
  angular, 33
  of gravity, 3, 42
  uniform, 2
  units of, 2
Adhesion, 116
Adiabatic modulus, 145
Altimeter, 106
Amplitude, 39
Aneroid barometer, 106
Angle of contact, 115-17
Angular momentum, 61
  velocity, 32
ARCHIMEDES' principle, 97
Atmolysis, 173
Atmospheric pressure, 104, 188

Balance, ballistic, 23
  common, 88
Banking of track, 35-37
Bar, 105
Barometer, FORTIN, 105
  corrections to, 105
Boys' C.V., 52
Breaking stress, 137
Brownian movement, 198
Bulk modulus, 144
  of gases, 144
Buoyancy correction, 90

Capillarity, 115, 124
CAVENDISH, 52
Centre of gravity, 84-86
  of mass, 84
Centrifugal force, 34
Centrifuge, 34
Circle, motion in, 32-37
Coefficient of kinetic friction, 155
  of static friction, 154
  of viscosity, 158
Cohesion, 116
Colloids, 171
Common balance, 88
Components of force, 77-78
  of velocity, 7
  resolved, 7
Compound pendulum, 70, 186-8
Conical pendulum, 37
Conservation of energy, 20
  of momentum, 23
Constant of gravitation, 52
Couples, 81, 61
  work done by, 82

Critical velocity, 161
Crystalloids, 171

Density, 95
  determinations of, 95-99, 102-103
  of earth, 54
Diffusion, 171
Dimensions, 24
  applications of, 25, 145, 160, 165
Distance-time curve, 4
Drops and formation, 189-192
Dyne, 13

Earth, density of, 54
  mass of, 54
Efficiency of machines, 87
Effusion of gases, 172
  separation by, 173
EINSTEIN's law, 21
Elastic limit, 137
Elasticity, 136
  adiabatic, 145
  isothermal, 145
Energy in wire, 142-3
  kinetic, 18
  potential, 19
  rotational, 60, 67
Equilibrium, conditions of, 78, 80, 83
Erg, 17
Errors of balance, 88, 90
Excess pressure in bubble, 122, 191

Falling sphere, viscosity by, 165
FICK's law, 171
FLETCHER's trolley, 14
Floating body, 99
Flow, orderly, 161
  turbulent, 160
Foot-pound wt., 17
Force, 13-15
  units of, 13
Friction, coefficient of static, 154
  kinetic (dynamic), 154
  laws of, 155
  limiting, 153

GALILEO, 42
Gases, diffusion of, 172
  effusion of, 172
GRAHAM's law, 172
Gravitation, NEWTON's law of, 51, 182
Gravitational constant, 52

213

214 INDEX

Gravity, acceleration of, 42–3, 183–6
motion under, 3
Gyration, radius of, 65

HARE's apparatus, 103
HICKS' ballistic balance, 23
HOOKE's law, 137
Horse-power, 18
Hydrometer, common, 99
NICHOLSON, 100

Impulse, 22
Inertia, 12
moments of, 60–73

JAEGER's method, 129
Joule, the, 18

KEPLER's laws, 50
Kinetic energy, 18

Levers, 87–8
Limit, elastic, 137

Machines, 86
Manometer, 106
M.K.S. Units, 181
Mean free path, 172
Mechanical advantage, 87
Micrometer screw gauge, 179
Modulus of elasticity, adiabatic, 145
bulk, 144
isothermal, 145
of gases, 144
of rigidity, 146, 192–4
YOUNG's modulus, 139
Molecular sphere of attraction, 112
Moment of couple, 81, 61
of force, 79
Moment of inertia, 60
of cylinder, 63
of disc, 63
of flywheel, 72
of plate, 71
of ring, 62
of rod, 62
of sphere, 64
theorems of, 65, 66
Momentum, 13
conservation of angular, 61
conservation of linear, 21
Moon, motion of, 51
Motion, NEWTON's laws of, 12
in circle, 32
in straight line, 1–6
of projectile, 8
simple harmonic, 38–46
under gravity, 3

NEWTON, 12, 51, 158
NICHOLSON's hydrometer, 100

Orderly flow, 161
Oscillation of liquid, 47
Osmosis, 167
laws of, 168
Osmotic pressure, 168–9
OSTWALD viscometer, 164

Parallel axes, theorem of, 65
forces, 79, 83
Parallelogram of forces, 77
of velocities, 7
Pendulum, ballistic, 23
compound, 70
simple, 41
Period, 39
PFEFFER, 168
Pipe, flow through, 160
Planetary motion, 50
PLATEAU's spherule, 113
Poise, 159
POISEUILLE, 160
POISSON's ratio, 147
Potential energy, 19
Poundal, 13
Power, 18
Pressure, atmospheric, 104
of liquid, 101
Projectiles, 8

Radius of gyration, 65
Range, horizontal, 9
Relative velocity, 10
Resolution of forces, 77–8
Retardation, 3
REYNOLDS, O., 161
Rigidity, modulus of, 146
Rod, moment of inertia of, 62
Rope brake, 155
Rotation about axis, 60–1

Scalars, 6
Semi-permeable membrane, 167
Sensitivity of balance, 89
Shearing strain, 146
stress, 146
Simple harmonic motion, 38–46
pendulum, 41
Soap film, 121, 124
Specific gravity, 95
methods for, 95–9, 102–3
Speed in circle, 32–7
Spherometer, 179
Spring, spiral, 45–6
STOKES' law, 165
Strain, bulk, 144
tensile, 138
torsional, 146
Stress, bulk, 144
tensile, 138
torsional, 146
Stretched wire, energy in, 142
Surface energy, 117, 200